Robert Easton

BLACK TIDE

THE SANTA BARBARA OIL SPILL AND ITS CONSEQUENCES

INTRODUCTION BY ROSS MACDONALD

"I hope that Mr. Easton's book will quicken a sense of urgency within the government to protect our coastlines from oil drilling accidents. I am deeply concerned that effective legislation be provided to protect our oceans and coastlines from oil damage. Mr. Easton's book, I believe, assists the task of public education on these issues both in and out of the government."

SENATOR EDMUND S. MUSKIE

BLACK TIDE:

**The Santa Barbara Oil Spill
and Its Consequences**

BY THE SAME AUTHOR

HISTORY

*Black Tide: The Santa Barbara Oil Spill
and Its Consequences*
The Book of the American West
(WITH JAY MONAGHAN AND OTHERS)

BIOGRAPHY

Max Brand: The Big Westerner
Lord of Beasts: The Saga of Buffalo Jones
(WITH MACKENZIE BROWN)

NOVELS

The Happy Man
The Hearing

NATURAL HISTORY

California Condor: Vanishing American
(WITH DICK SMITH)

EDITINGS

Max Brand's Best Stories
*Bullying the Moqui: Charles F. Lummis' Defense
of the Hopi Indians*
(WITH MACKENZIE BROWN)

Dell

DELACORTE PRESS / NEW YORK

[c 1972]

BLACK TIDE;

THE SANTA BARBARA OIL SPILL AND ITS CONSEQUENCES

Robert Easton

With an Introduction by Ross Macdonald

Designed by Ann Spinelli

Library of Congress Cataloging in Publication Data

Easton, Robert Olney.
  Black tide.

  Bibliography: p.
  1. Oil pollution of rivers, harbors, etc.—Santa
Barbara Channel. I. Title.
GC1556.E2   301.3'1   70-178719

CONTENTS

Part II. The First Year

Part III. Consequences

Appendix

INTRODUCTION

Ross Macdonald

THIS IS THE FIRST full account of an ecological crime—a crime without criminals but with many victims—and a community's response to it. The eruption of the oil well on Union Platform A off Santa Barbara on January 28, 1969, has had profound effects, and could be described as the blowout heard around the world.

The blowout shook the industry and the federal bureaucracy, whose rules and safeguards had failed to prevent it, and is gradually forcing the reform of those rules and safeguards. It triggered a social movement and helped to create a new politics, the politics of ecology, which is likely to exert a decisive influence on future elections and on our lives. It brought to a head our moral and economic doubts about the American uses of energy and raised the question of whether we really have to go on polluting the sea and land and air in order to support our freeway philosophy of one man, one car.

The book begins with basic physical events: the rupture of the well under the sea floor, its running wild for ten days, and the attempts of industry and government to get it stopped. Perhaps the central figure of the early chapters is a young Coast Guard officer, Lieutenant George H. Brown, III, who found himself to be the responsible authority at the scene of the spill, and the human fulcrum of almost incredible weights and pressures. Gradually, the threatened Santa Barbara community becomes the main protagonist, and its life intensifies like that of a city under siege. The drama mounts and expands onto the national stage. There are congressional investigations and debates, and repercussions in senatorial and presidential politics. The book as a whole asks whether and how the American people can control what government and industry, oil and accident, may do to them, and suggests some intelligent answers to these questions.

It was no accident that Robert Easton wrote this book. He is a third-generation Californian and a grandson of Warren Olney, one of the founders of the Sierra Club. His father was a nature-loving cattle rancher, and conservation was a second religion in his household. Bob was raised near Santa Barbara in Santa Maria, which already in the early years of the century had been the scene of a major oil strike, and a major spill.

When I first met Bob in the years just after the war, he was a young ex-infantry officer with a successful first novel and a mass of serious journalism already behind him. The war novel he was writing at night was related to his personal experiences—so closely related, indeed, that he found it difficult to finish: too many men of his company had died. The daytime work with which he supported his wife and family had been chosen as if in unconscious preparation for the present book. He was employed as a foreman by the Richfield Oil Company, helping to build an artificial island on the Rincon, some twenty miles east of Santa Barbara, from which underwater oil wells could be drilled.

The oil operations on the Rincon were not pretty, in spite of the palm trees that were brought in to decorate the artificial island. Still, few Santa Barbarans realized that such operations might some day constitute a threat to the city itself. There had been an oil strike just east of Santa Barbara some fifty years before, and the Summerland shore was still a wasteland being cleaned up at state expense. But such enormities seemed a thing of the past.

In those early postwar years, Santa Barbara was a quiet seaport facing south across white public beaches to blue waters reflecting a clear sky. A boat trip to the Channel Islands was like a voyage to Eden. The channel was alive with fish and dolphins, sea lions, whales in season, birds on the water and in the air. There was so little traffic in town that traffic lights were unnecessary and I could ride my bicycle down the main street with my black dog Skipper carelessly trailing me. There was a sense of freedom and ease in the untainted atmosphere. The city had so many trees and gardens that it seemed to be interfused with live green nature.

Santa Barbara's tradition of living at respectful ease with nature went back a long way. For a thousand years before the white man came, the Indians had built their villages on the coastal slope. They lived on acorns and fish, and decorated their ceremonial caves with some of the finest primitive art in the world. The Santa Barbara pueblo was founded by the Spanish in 1782, the year after Los Angeles. A gradual immigration from the east changed the graceful Spanish character of the city without destroying it, and strengthened it with rigor and independence of thought.

Santa Barbara became a center of West Coast civilization, a place that leading American writers knew and referred to in their books. Naturalists, impressed by the equable climate, transplanted flowers and trees from other continents. Santa Barbara's Museum of Natural History was founded by William L. Dawson, whose *Birds of California* is still the classic on that subject. The Museum, the Botanic Garden, and the nearby branch of the University of California have made the city a center for the study of natural history, and attracted nature-loving residents from all over the country and the world. The local branch of the Audubon Society, in this city of 70,000, has over 750 members.

The Audubon emblem, the common egret, is a reminder that the national society was founded to save that bird from extinction. Similarly, the Santa Barbara Audubon Society has a special interest in preserving the California condor. It is not too much to say that in Southern California that great threatened bird is a symbol of survival, and of warning. The condor is our canary in the mine— the mine slowly filling with pollutants which is a possible image of our world—and if the condor survives, perhaps we may too.

This was one of the central ideas of the book about the condor which Bob Easton wrote with Dick Smith in the mid-1960s. This slim book marked a milestone in Bob's life, pointing toward his future as a historian of Santa Barbara's ecological disaster, and grounded in his personal and family past. When Bob was a small boy, his father had taken him into the wilderness near his ranch and shown him condors. In the 1930s, the elder Easton led a successful national campaign to set up the Sisquoc Condor Sanctuary in that wilderness. But in the 1960s, the condor was still in trouble, having declined to a population of forty or so. Now it was Bob who took the lead in trying to save it.

The issue was not only the survival of the condor, but the preservation of the wilderness over which the condor flew. Both were threatened by Forest Service plans to build a paved road along the Sierra Madre Ridge, which marks the northern rim of the Sisquoc wilderness and is itself part of the condor flyway. Bob fought mightily for the endangered wilderness and its birds.

During this time I came to know Bob Easton well and saw him grow into first a community and ultimately a national leader. Our little "wilderness campaign" group was largely made up of leaders: Fred Eissler of the Sierra Club, Dick Smith of the *Santa Barbara News-Press,* Jim Mills, now president of the Santa Barbara Audubon Society, and our gray eminence Ian McMillan of Shandon, perhaps California's most effective conservationist. Over a period of several years we met irregularly. The Sierra Madre Ridge road was put to sleep, only to be replaced by a larger but related issue.

This was the establishment of the San Rafael Wilderness Area, the first under the Wilderness Act of 1964. In its final dimensions, on which our group insisted and held firm, this national wilderness covers some 140,000 acres in the Santa Barbara back country. After many months of educational and political activity, Fred Eissler and Bob went to Washington to see the expanded wilderness bill through Congress. They came back proud, feeling that Santa Barbara had established itself as a center of conservation in the west. This wilderness campaign helped to determine the strategy and tactics of the massive and continuing campaign against oil in our channel.

Santa Barbara had had to fight continually to preserve both her amenities and her reputation as a conservation center. Like most other Southern California cities, it had more than doubled in size since the war. It was faced with serious traffic problems and accompanying air and noise pollution. The overhead freeway proposed by the State Highway Division threatened to broadcast this pollution further, and to cut the downtown business section in two. Visible decay in the central part of the city called for rehabilitation and restoration.

The city resisted many threats. The wild growth that overran San Jose and other cities in this period was checked in Santa Barbara by the city's refusal to accept any but smokeless industry. The overhead freeway has been stalled for years, and plans for it are being gradually and reluctantly altered by the Highway Division. An enlightened citizen force led by Miss Pearl Chase prevented the building of high-rise apartments in the city, and has held back a later plan which would lead to suburban sprawl.

It was an ecologically aware citizen force that held the city together during the oil crisis. Though the city is quite conservative politically, and backed Nixon and Reagan in recent elections, it is far from devoid of intellectual activism. This activism can be reminiscent of a New England town meeting, where citizens are a functioning and vocal part of government. The civic life of Santa Barbara has been punctuated, loudly, by such meetings.

The oil crisis crept up on us in near silence. Concentrating on protecting the city and the surrounding lands, we didn't fully realize that the sea could be in danger. In my early years in Santa Barbara, I had made the narrator of a novel say: "I turned on my back and floated, looking up at the sky, nothing around me but cool clear Pacific, nothing in my eyes but long blue space. It was as close as I ever got to cleanliness and freedom, as far as I ever got from all the people. They had jerrybuilt the beaches from San Diego to the Golden Gate, bulldozed super-highways through the mountains, cut down a thousand years of redwood growth, and built an urban wilderness in the desert. They couldn't touch the ocean. They poured their sewage into it, but it couldn't be tainted."

My narrator and I were wrong. A series of oil drilling platforms had been erected in the state tidelands southeast of Santa Barbara. Now there was pressure for further platforms in the deeper and more treacherous federal waters outside the three-mile limit. The pressure was intensified by the federal government's need for money to finance the war in Indochina, and local government was unable to withstand it. A number of citizens, including Fred Eissler and Bob Easton, tried to open public discussion on the matter, but the decision had already been made in Washington, based on Interior Department findings which were rather loosely related to local reality. Without a public hearing, or any serious examination of the dangers of deep-water drilling in the earthquake-prone channel, oil rights in large sections of the channel were auctioned off to the oil companies. After the damage was done, we learned why there had been no public hearings: a permanent official in the Interior Department had vetoed it on the grounds that it might "stir up the natives."

At this time, Bob was employed as a senior writer in the U.S. Naval Laboratory at Port Hueneme. By a neat twist of fate, he was putting together a massive anonymous tome on underwater construction which gave him further preparation for writing the present book. At the same time, he was researching and writing a biography of Max Brand, his father-in-law and literary mentor. His working life was relieved by long walks in the wilderness he had helped to preserve. When he had a moral or intellectual or political problem—and more and more the conservation problems of the community tended to migrate to him—he would carry it into the back country for a day or two and come out with a solution or at least a fresh approach.

The walks Bob took with me and my dog Brandy were shorter. During those walks, we talked about the things that men in their fifties are ordinarily concerned with—our past lives, children and grandchildren, our work, and how to preserve the country we were walking through.

The great oil spill that began on January 28, 1969, failed to interrupt our walks, but it displaced other topics of conversation. I remember a day, about two weeks after the eruption, when we stopped on Mountain Drive and looked out over the contaminated sea. The flowing oil had been partly choked off, but it was still leaking up through the ruptured sea floor. Thousands of diving birds had died, and the quality of human life in the area was being threatened. The beaches were black for forty miles along the coast, and reblackened every day as the tides came in. The odor of crude oil reached us like the whiff of a decaying future.

It seemed to us that if the spill was to have a meaning, that meaning would have to be created by the men on the scene. Somehow the black disaster of Santa Barbara must be converted into a turning point in our history, a signpost marking the end of such ruinous environmental carelessness. This view was presented in an article for the *New York Times Magazine* which Bob Easton and I collaborated on. Then I turned back to my fiction. Bob went on by himself to traverse a wilderness of fact and write this book about the blow to Santa Barbara's life and her historic response— the book his entire life had prepared him to write.

Like those ancient Greek historians who fought in the wars they later chronicled, the author is a witness as well as a recorder. He shared with the other residents of Santa Barbara, and shares with the reader, the sickening uncertainties of the early days of the spill, when it appeared that this beautiful city would be degraded into an industrial slum. He shared the months of conflict and doubt, as it became clear that the lessons of the spill were being lost on the federal government and its favored industry, and that the sell-out of the Santa Barbara Channel would be allowed to proceed. He shared, and contributed to, the realization that our fate was in our own hands, that only the people on the spot could hope to counter and change a self-destructive national policy. He describes from firsthand knowledge the organization and use of citizen movements like GOO (Get Oil Out!) without whose advice and dissent both big government and big industry seem to be one-eyed giants. He is one of the citizen-litigants who are still seeking in the federal courts a full disclosure from the government of the uncertain physical situation in the channel.

Yet the reader will be pleasantly surprised to find that this book is in no sense a work of special pleading. It was written after laborious and detailed research by a trained historian who does not let his personal views distort the record. The scientific evidence was derived from and checked by competent biologists and ecologists, and other experts. The clear and detailed explanation of how the spill came to occur and how it was eventually checked is based on all available reports, including those of the U.S. Geological Survey, and on the testimony of eyewitnesses and participants. Weeks and months of interviewing underlie the day-to-day account. For example, before writing the story of Lieutenant Brown's activities, the author spent some days talking to the young Coast Guard lieutenant and recording everything he said.

Since then, Lieutenant Brown has been detached from his Santa

Barbara command and has begun work, under Coast Guard auspices, toward an advanced degree in the ecological field. The people of Santa Barbara had hoped that a similarly enlightened response to the city's near tragedy would be made by other agencies of the federal government. But the Department of the Interior, staffed by many of the same permanent officials whose recommendations and decisions precipitated the disaster, is persisting in its determination to convert the Santa Barbara Channel into an oil field.

The issue, as it appears to local residents, is whether their environment can be bought and sold over their objections, or whether there is an inalienable right to the use and enjoyment of air and water. It is a test case, between a pervasive new form of tyranny and an ancient freedom, which will help to determine the future conditions of life throughout the United States.

Santa Barbara, September 8, 1971

I

THE FIRST
TEN DAYS

1

BLOWOUT

THE DAY BEGAN with patches of blue sky and some sun, but the tops of the mountains that rose abruptly behind Santa Barbara, California, were covered with clouds, following heavy rains, and so were the tops of the mountains on the islands twenty miles off shore. The islands—Anacapa, Santa Cruz, Santa Rosa, San Miguel —lay in an east-west line paralleling the mainland for more than sixty miles. They looked like foreign lands, blue and mysterious in the rainwashed air. As rain squalls passed over the Santa Barbara Channel, they hid the islands from onshore observers. They also hid offshore drilling Platforms A and B, recently emplaced by the Union Oil Company five and a half miles from the city's waterfront.

The city, famous for its beauty and charm, lay on a slope between low foothills facing the sea. From harbor and palm-tree-lined beaches, its one main thoroughfare, State Street, ran up three miles to a crest near the old Spanish mission. Its downtown buildings were low-rise. Many, such as the City Hall and *News-Press* buildings in the central square, were of stucco and tile, as were many of the houses set in the trees and gardens of the hillsides.

About seventy-five thousand people lived in Santa Barbara and as many more lived in the adjacent coastal communities of Montecito, Summerland, and Carpinteria on the east and Goleta and Isla Vista on the west. Most of them depended on their natural environment in some way for a living.

Tourism was the area's economic base. More than four million people came every year to enjoy mountains, beaches, oceans, and islands, and their gentle climate. But there were also research and development industries, residential and retirement facilities, medical centers, a campus of the University of California, commercial and sport fishing, some lemon and avocado groves, and, lately, offshore oil.

At 7:25 A.M. William R. (Bill) Robinson arrived at the Union Oil Company dock at the Navy Pier near the foot of the breakwater ready to board the work boat that would take him and some forty other building-trades workers—pipe fitters, electricians, sheet metal workers—to Platform A, where they were completing piping and wiring of the huge structure. Like others assembling in the gray cool morning, Robinson was middle-aged. He had a wife, three children in school, and had chosen Santa Barbara for his home because he liked the climate and atmosphere. He disliked channel oil development, which seemed a threat to the city's natural surroundings, but the money to be made on the platforms— as much as $1,200 weekly including overtime—overcame his objections. He wore work boots and Windbreaker jacket and carried a lunch pail. His hard hat and his tools were waiting for him on Platform A.

As the work boat was leaving the harbor, Lieutenant George H. Brown, III, entered his office in U.S. Coast Guard Group Headquarters on the waterfront, a stone's throw from Union's dock. The one-story cinder-block building was the same size and had the same appearance as the public rest room nearby. The city had built both buildings and leased one to the Coast Guard. Brown's office occupied nearly half its usable interior. The other half was crammed with teletype, radio equipment, lockers, a desk, and a head. Brown, a stocky, bright-eyed young man of twenty-seven, a former Sea Scout from Braintree, Massachusetts, had recently commanded a cutter in Vietnam coastal waters. As Commander Coast Guard Group, Santa Barbara, his responsibilities included 150 miles of coastline from Point Dume, south of Oxnard, northward around the continental corner at Point Conception to the mouth of the Santa Maria River. In this area he was responsible for search and rescue missions; enforcement of federal laws; safety standards for yachts, motorboats, and other noncommercial vessels; supervision of Coast Guard installations at Conception, Arguello, Anacapa Island, and Port Hueneme; and pollution control.

Lieutenant Brown was wearing a blue winter uniform this morning which exactly resembled that of the Navy except for the buttons. For the past three days he had been tramping rain-swept beaches and telephoning oil companies to determine the source of oil that had come ashore at Rincon, eighteen miles southeast of Santa Barbara. It was low-gravity crude in moderate amounts. After talking with State Fish and Game Department representatives concerned with pollution in state waters, Brown had concluded that the oil came from pipes and sumps on the mainland broken open by recent floods and not from offshore platforms.

There were twelve drilling platforms scattered along the coast for fifty miles. Eight stood in state water, within three miles from shore. Four, including Union's two new ones, stood in so-called federal water, between the three- and twelve-mile limits. Union was operating Platforms A and B for a group that included Gulf Oil Corporation, Mobil Oil Corporation, and Texaco Incorporated. The federal government had leased the consortium the right to drill on the 5,400 ocean-floor acres of Federal Lease Tract 402, in return for $61,418,000 in cash, plus a royalty of one-sixth market price per barrel of oil produced, and an annual rental of $16,200 for the tract.

With its even larger partners, Union hoped to develop an oil field under Platforms A and B that would improve its tenuous position in or near the top "big ten" of a fiercely competitive industry. Conglomerates were the order of the day, but Union did not want to be conglomerated. With assets of $2.4 billion, the Union Oil Company of California was struggling for its independence. It was the eleventh largest oil company in the United States.

It had been founded in the Santa Barbara Channel area, but its operations now extended from Alaska to Indonesia, to Hong Kong, to Louisiana, to Chicago, and to many other parts of the world. It operated petrochemical companies and huge tankers. It manufactured fireplace briquets and agricultural fertilizers. It was a modern industrial giant.

Union's two controversial new platforms lay opposite a community that had been founded as a Spanish settlement in the late 1700s and peopled later largely by New Englanders. Ironically in the light of what was to happen, Santa Barbara had been named for Saint Barbara of Nicomedia, the patron saint of petroleum.

The community's psychic life, as well as its economic life, was largely centered in its natural surroundings including the great oaks and sycamores that grew down its canyons to the water's edge. For forty years Santa Barbarans had had an architectural board of review to see that downtown buildings harmonized with good taste. They had banned billboards, high-rise buildings, and urban sprawl, and had fought off an elevated freeway that would have risen like a technological spite fence between them and their seascape. They had bought and beautified five miles of beach front as a public park, and they had resisted oil development, onshore and offshore, as their Puritan forefathers had resisted the devil.

Present-day Santa Barbarans, against offshore oil drilling in general, had particularly opposed Union's two new platforms as an immediate threat to the city's tourist and recreation industries and to the area's ecology. With their drilling towers, Platforms A and B rose as high above the water as twenty-story buildings and their potential for environmental disruption loomed as large as their silhouettes on a clear day. A virtual forest of seventy similar platforms and about four thousand wells was the appalling prospect for the channel's federal water. In response to citizen protests, government and industry spokesmen had given assurances that this vast development would be managed without adverse effect. Modern technology would provide the answers. "You have nothing to fear," Secretary of the Interior Stewart L. Udall had promised Santa Barbarans two years earlier, when the federal leases were proposed, "no leases will be granted except under conditions that will protect your environment."

On Platform A, Well A-21 had been drilled to its maximum depth of 3,479 feet and the crew was removing the drill pipe from the hole. The platform stood in 188 feet of water. The top of its vertical drilling rig reached 210 feet above the surface of the sea. Its structural framework of steel pipes weighed about 3,000 tons. Steel pilings inside its hollow legs had been driven into the ocean floor to stabilize it against wind, wave, and earthquake. Its super-structure supported two 115- by 134-foot decks, drilling slots for 56 wells, a galley and lounge, sleeping quarters for a dozen men, workshops, and a helipad. There was in addition a slant-drilling rig, protruding at an angle of about 30 degrees, for tapping oil sands that lay too near the ocean floor to be tapped by the vertical rig. A 34,000-volt submarine cable brought power to the platform from shore, and a submarine pipeline was ready to carry its petroleum to onshore processing plants. Platform A had cost about $5 million. Each of its 56 wells would cost about a quarter million more.

Under the vertical rig, the crew was pulling up the drill pipe so that electrical recordings of the geological formations penetrated by the hole could be made. Then the entire hole would be protected with steel casing, as the upper 239 feet already were. Well A-21 had been drilled in only fourteen days. Penetrating rapidly through shallow oil-bearing sands and shales, a $12\frac{1}{4}$-inch-diameter steel-alloy bit rotating at the end of the $4\frac{1}{2}$-inch-diameter drill pipe had reached a deeper oil horizon. Drilling mud—a viscous grayish-colored chemical fluid of high specific gravity—circulating down through the pipe, out through apertures in the bit, and up through the annulus—the space between the drill pipe and the sides of the hole—had prevented the bit from overheating under the tremendous pressure of pipe from above and the resistance of earth from below. The drilling mud had plastered the walls of the hole and prevented them from caving, and it had carried the bit's cuttings to the surface. But the most important thing it had done was to balance the pressure of oil or gas encountered during drilling.

Oil-well drilling requires a balancing act: man-made (mud-made) pressures from above versus earth-made pressures from below.

Sometimes this balance is upset by the use of a drilling mud that is too light in weight. Sometimes it is upset by pulling up the drill pipe too fast. The result is a blowout: an uncontrolled eruption of gas or oil.

By 10:45 A.M. on January 28 the crew employed by Union's drilling contractor, Peter Bawden Drilling Incorporated, had removed seven "stands"—seven 90-foot lengths of drill pipe—from the hole and set them in racks at the side of the rig. The first five stands had "pulled tight," indicating that mud and debris might be clogging the hole, but the next two pulled freely. As each successive stand was hauled up into the derrick by the traveling block, the drilling crew unscrewed it at the rotary table at deck level. They were in the act of disconnecting the eighth stand when Bill Robinson, working nearby, heard a loud hissing roar that filled him with instant alarm. He looked up and saw dark gray mud mixed with gas shoot out the top of stand number eight, ninety feet above the deck, and cascade down upon men and equipment. The crew hastily finished disconnecting the eighth stand and set it in the racks. As they did so, mud and gas shot with a deafening roar from the open pipe at their feet and rose twenty feet or more into the derrick. Well A-21 had blown out, and the largest disaster of its kind in U.S. history had begun.

Oil-well blowouts are not extreme rarities. They happen at a rate of about 2.5 per thousand wells drilled. Some are never heard of. Others are memorable.

In 1901, the famous Lucas Gusher at the Spindletop Field in East Texas blew for nine days at the rate of 100,000 barrels per day. In 1904, Union's Hartnell Number 1, known as "Old Maud," blew out on land near Santa Maria in northern Santa Barbara County, about sixty miles from the site of Well A-21.

Old Maud gushed 12,000 barrels per day. Oil began pouring down creeks and gullies. In an attempt to stop it, somebody closed a valve. Oil began spouting up through gopher holes and cracks in the earth for hundreds of feet roundabout. The surrounding fields were full of miniature geysers, until finally the valve was opened, the underlying pressures were released, and the oil started flowing up through the well again instead of up through the earth.

The event was to recur in a modified form in the case of Well A-21. What made it remarkably unusual was the fact that four previous Platform A wells had been successfully drilled through similar formations and were waiting to be placed in production.

Despite the mud showering down on them and darkening the drill deck, three crewmen picked up the inside blowout preventer, an emergency check valve standing about two feet high and weighing about seventy-five pounds, and tried to screw it into the open end of the drill pipe. It was like trying to screw something into the mouth of a hurricane. The three made little headway against a pressure that was soon to reach an estimated 1,150 to 1,660 pounds per square inch. Their hats were blown off. Verbal communication became almost impossible. They slipped on the muddy steel floor, and were beaten back, plastered and drenched with falling mud.

All at once the mud flow ceased and was followed by gaseous mist that roared out in a dark cloud, enveloping the deck and reducing visibility almost to zero. The hydrocarbon mist billowed up to the top of the derrick in a column resembling a cloud of steam. Explosion and fire were uppermost thoughts in everyone's mind.

Choking, eyes watering, the crew put down the inside blowout preventer and hooked the traveling block onto the kelly, a pipe about thirty feet long, with the intention of stabbing it into the open drill pipe and forcing drilling mud through it into the well, to stop the flow of gas. The kelly is used to turn the drill string and conduct mud into the well during normal drilling operations. When not in use it rests in a hole near the rotary table called the "rathole." As the traveling block was lifting it out of the rathole, the hose connecting it to the mud pumps caught on a plug projecting from the standpipe, a containment pipe through which highly pressurized mud flows into the well once all connections are made. The plug ripped out, opening the standpipe, and destroying the possibility of well control via the kelly.

The crew then moved to the final means of well control: the blind rams. The two rams were contained in opposite sides of a large steel valve located in the well column immediately below the rotary table. The valve weighed about four tons. Activating it would bring the rams together over the open hole, like two giant fists meeting face to face. To clear the way, the drill pipe— all 2,759 feet of it remaining in Well A-21—was dropped to the bottom of the hole.

Then the blind rams were activated by pushbutton control. Their 20-inch-wide, 4-inch-thick faces, surfaced with bonded rubber to prevent even a molecule of gas or oil from escaping, met.

Well A-21 was sealed at the surface, according to official reports. The automatic time-indicator chart on the rig floor showed that the interval between the disconnecting of the eighth stand and the dropping of the drill pipe into the hole was approximately thirteen minutes.

Except for drilling crew and key supervisory personnel, everybody had been evacuated from the platform. The crewmen stood in a drenched daze, shaking from exertion and shock, not quite sure what had happened or what was happening.

Bill Robinson and his fellow building-trades workers were being taken by boat to uncompleted Platform B, half a mile distant. Workmen there had stopped what they were doing to watch the blowout. When Robinson joined them, he looked back. Gas resembling smoke was still roaring out of Well A-21 and reaching nearly to the top of the vertical rig. It kept on roaring and billowing. Soon, in the water beyond, its watchers saw the surface lifting ominously in what they called the "big boil."

Nearer at hand, approximately halfway between the two platforms, a smaller eruption appeared. Perhaps attracted by its bubbles and noise, two gray whales, en route between their winter breeding grounds in the lagoons of Baja California and their summer feeding grounds in the Arctic, made their way toward the smaller boil.

Back at Platform A, the crew had been laboring to pump heavy mud into the well via a small-diameter pipe connecting with the bore below the blind rams. Their efforts were of no avail. Well A-21 was wild.

Between ten and fifteen minutes after the dropping of the drill pipe, according to the Interior Department record, the first bubbles of gas were observed in the ocean around the platform. Soon large boils appeared about 800 feet east of the platform. There were several of them, and they seemed to be on a line with the geologic fault over which Platform A was located.

"Control was apparently lost through a shallow oil sand that intersected a shallow fault," the record said.

The record would be disputed later.

Having worked most of the weekend and late into Monday evening and having missed a Saturday shopping expedition with his wife, Lieutenant Brown was planning to take the afternoon off and meet her at Sears' store in the new La Cumbre Plaza Shopping Center. At 12:50 he was on the point of leaving his office when he received a telephone call from Don Craggs, Union Oil's offshore production superintendent for the Santa Barbara area. According to Brown's record of the conversation, Craggs said that a well being drilled from Platform A had blown out and gas was escaping into the ocean. "Is any oil escaping?" Brown asked. Craggs said there was no oil escaping. He said he had reported the blowout to the Los Angeles district office of the U.S. Geological Survey's Oil and Gas Division, the Interior Department agency responsible for supervising drilling in the channel's federal water, and that he was reporting it to Brown in order to alert the Coast Guard in case of accident. Craggs did not mention the escape of gas and hydrocarbon mist onto the platform and the existence of explosion and fire hazard. Brown asked him if he wanted a cutter to stand by. Craggs said not now. He added that efforts were underway to connect with the dropped drill pipe, regain circulation of drilling mud, and control the well, and expressed confidence that these efforts would be successful soon.

Brown absorbed these details and then said that he was concerned about oil pollution and that the Coast Guard was prepared to assist immediately if need be. He asked Craggs to call him if oil appeared with the gas. Craggs agreed to do so.

After Craggs hung up, Brown notified the Coast Guard cutter *Point Judith,* berthed in Santa Barbara Harbor. He asked the *Judith* to be prepared to move to the vicinity of the platform if need be. Then Brown left to meet his wife in the long-delayed shopping venture, telling the yeoman on duty he would be checking by phone during the afternoon to see if there was further word from Craggs. When asked later why he did not alert local officials, or go himself to Platform A, Brown replied that Craggs' presentation was low-keyed, that he specifically declined help, mentioned no oil pollution or fire hazard, and gave the impression of a situation which would soon be controlled.

Brown checked with his yeoman twice during the afternoon, but there was no further word from Craggs.

By 4:30 P.M. County Supervisor Daniel G. Grant had completed a tour of areas near Carpinteria which had been devastated by the recent floods. In company with Governor Ronald Reagan and county officials, he had returned to the Supervisors' Conference Room in the county's new administration building across the street from the courthouse. There Grant was participating in a discussion of what could be done to aid the flood victims, some of whom were homeless. A note was handed him: there was a long-distance call. Grant sent back word he couldn't take the call. Back came the word: the call was urgent. Grant felt he couldn't walk out on the Governor. He sent word asking that the call be placed later or a message left. No message was left. No long-distance call reached Grant after he returned to his home about 5:30.

So Union Oil's attempt to tell Grant what had happened on Platform A, nearly six hours before, failed; and county and city remained uninformed of what was happening just off their shores.

At 5:45 P.M. Lieutenant Brown was preparing to sit down to supper at home when the telephone rang. It was an official of the State Department of Fish and Game, speaking from Ventura thirty miles down the coast. He said he had just received a call from Fish and Game's regional office at San Pedro, seventy miles farther down the coast. Someone had telephoned the San Pedro office and reported seeing an oil gusher on a platform off Santa Barbara at about 11 A.M. that morning. Did Brown know anything about such a gusher? Brown described the situation at Platform A. Then the Ventura man said that Fish and Game's downtown Los Angeles office had received a call from the Union Oil Company, a few minutes before five o'clock, stating that a well located in Tract

402 off Santa Barbara had blown out and was losing oil into adjacent waters.

It was the first word Brown had heard about escaping oil. He said he would investigate and call back. From Craggs' office, he learned Craggs had gone to Platform A by boat. Brown left word for Craggs to call him.

It was dark now. Brown had pulled up his chair to a baked chicken supper when Craggs called, at 6:10. Craggs said he had just returned from the platform, that the gas rising to the surface contained oil, and that a pollution situation was developing.

After informing Ventura, Brown went to his office on the waterfront. No one was on duty, office hours being from 8:00 A.M. to 4:30 P.M. Brown telephoned Eleventh Coast Guard District Headquarters at Long Beach, near Los Angeles, and reported the situation at Platform A to the duty officer. He asked for a heli-copter so that he could make an aerial inspection at first light next morning, and he asked that a State Fish and Game Department representative be included in the flight.

Brown wondered what the flight would reveal. The thought of Santa Barbara's beaches blackened with oil crossed his mind. He was tempted to call local officials but hesitated to alarm them at a late hour of night. Suppose the blowout was controlled by morn-ing? He decided to wait until he knew more about the situation.

As the minutes ticked by, Brown wrote for the record, in long-hand, in customary message form, an account of his conversations with Craggs and with the Ventura Fish and Game official and his telephone report to district headquarters, and sent the lengthy message via teletype to Coast Guard Headquarters, Long Beach.

Knowing he was faced with a problem of growing seriousness, he went to his desk and reviewed plans developed for use in case of offshore oil spills. First there was the National Multiagency Oil and Hazardous Materials Contingency Plan. Signed two months earlier by President Lyndon B. Johnson, the National Plan, as it was called, had been prepared in haste following the wreck of Union Oil's tanker *Torrey Canyon,* which polluted beaches in England and France in the spring of 1967. The plan established response teams at national and regional level. The teams were composed of representatives from the departments of Interior;

Defense; Transportation (of which the Coast Guard was a part); Health, Education, and Welfare; and the Office of Emergency Planning. They were instructed to develop systems for discovering, reporting, and controlling pollution of U.S. waters. Development of cooperative plans by state and local governments was encouraged. But the National Plan had been operative only since the preceding November 13, and little had been done to implement it at local level.

Far more compelling for Brown was the Eleventh Coast Guard District's Marine Chemical Disaster Plan, also an outgrowth of the *Torrey Canyon* accident. This plan had been effective for more than a year and was part of a nationwide network of similar plans designed to protect U.S. waters pending development of the more comprehensive National Plan. Under it Brown had conducted meetings with state and local officials, inventoried equipment, created a communications net, and established a skeletal structure for handling a massive oil spill.

He knew, for example, that at the Naval Construction Battalion Center at Port Hueneme, forty miles southeast, there were pontoons that might be effective for containing oil in rough water if a submarine pipeline burst. He knew that Eleventh Naval District Headquarters, San Diego, two hundred miles distant, had salvage equipment, in case a tanker ran aground in the channel. He knew the names and telephone numbers of key officials in Santa Barbara and Ventura counties and of key personnel in the U.S. Army Corps of Engineers office in Los Angeles. In the event of an oil spill, if the responsible party refused to clear it up the Corps of Engineers was empowered to make a contract with a private contractor to clean up the spill. Later, the responsible party would be billed by the government. Brown knew there were modest stockpiles of chemical dispersants in Los Angeles, Long Beach, and Santa Barbara, and that oil company work boats in the channel carried a few drums of dispersants for use in case of small or "normal" spills.

But he did not know how any or all of this could be translated into an effective plan of action in a real situation. None of it had been prepared with the thought of a blowout in mind: a well literally gushing oil into the sea. Such an eventuality had not been seriously considered in contingency planning—perhaps because, as some people were to say, mention of it would have caused violent public reaction against the Santa Barbara Channel drilling program; perhaps because, as others were to say, although twenty-four blowouts had been officially reported as occurring in the federal waters of the United States, only five, all of them in the Gulf of Mexico, had released oil, and the oil had not reached shore in significant quantity.

There were additional grounds for serious thought. Under both the national and interim plans, a ranking Coast Guard officer became on-scene commander in case of a massive oil spill. If the situation at Platform A continued to develop adversely, Brown might find himself presiding over a disaster such as had never happened before in the United States or anywhere else.

At 10 P.M. Craggs called, saying he planned to station an oil company boat in the vicinity of Platform A at about 3 A.M. next morning to spray chemical dispersants on the spilling oil, if it became necessary.

Brown advised him to notify the Federal Water Pollution Control Administration's regional office in San Francisco, since FWPCA and not the Coast Guard had jurisdiction over use of chemical dispersants.

Brown's office light burned until after midnight. Most of the town was asleep. During the day the weather had turned cold and blustery. As the night wore on, the slick grew steadily larger.

2

A BOILING OCEAN

BY WEDNESDAY MORNING the oil had surged up through the fissures from the rocks and sands where it had lain undisturbed for thousands of centuries. Most authorities believe that oil is formed from decayed remains of tiny plants and animals that settled to the bottom of the sea millions of years ago. Sediments settled on top of them. The weight of the sediments, heat, bacterial action, and other natural forces changed the tiny plants and animals into what we call oil.

Under Platform A, the oil was contained in geologic formations laid down in the Miocene and Pliocene epochs ten to fifteen million years ago. They had been tilted, faulted, and fractured by seismic activity. Some of the underlying oil, however, was so near the surface that it had leaked into the water when the pilings securing Platform A were emplaced.

The upper oil sands were not highly pressurized by gas; the lower were. Gas and oil from below, later evidence showed, was making its way up the uncased bore of Well A-21 to a point somewhere between 240 and 300 feet below the ocean's floor.

There it entered the upper sands and from there it reached the surface along pores and fissures in faulted and fragmented clay-stone and siltstone rock.

The water around Platform A seethed as if in a boiling cauldron. Gas rose skyward into the starry night which was clear and cold after the rainy weather.

Lights blazed on Platform A as reinforced crews worked to connect with the dropped drill pipe. They still hoped to force heavy drilling mud into the hole and control the well.

By about 2 A.M., Wednesday, nine 30-foot lengths of pipe, 270 feet in all, had been inserted into the well and connected with the lost drill string, or "fish." Fifteen more lengths were needed to connect the string to the platform.

While the men on Platform A continued fishing in the well hole, Lieutenant Brown left home, shortly before 6 A.M., and drove toward the airport at Goleta, ten miles west of Santa Barbara.

At the airport, State Fish and Game Warden Jack Vorhies was waiting. They waited together for a while. They expected the plane at first light, between 6:30 and 7:00. When it didn't come, Brown telephoned the Coast Guard Air Station at Los Angeles International Airport. There was mechanical trouble. The plane would be leaving soon.

About 8 A.M. the Coast Guard helicopter appeared, a boat-hulled Sikorsky turbojet. A few minutes later the two official observers were flying over Santa Barbara Point. As Platform A came into view, Brown saw something he found hard to believe. "My God, what's that?" he exclaimed involuntarily.

"That's what you're going to see!" replied the pilot, who had flown over Platform A on his way up from Los Angeles.

It looked like a world gone wrong. The slick's heaviest concentration, brownish black, reached southward—or seaward—from the platform for a distance of half a mile. There it thinned and continued southerly for about four miles. Then it veered southeast toward the shore for another mile. A rainbow-colored area extended for two miles west and two to four miles east of the main slick. A similar rainbowed area extended eight to ten miles south of the platform.

Brown and Vorhies estimated the size of the slick at between

50 and 75 square miles. Though it was drifting away from shore, its course might change at any time.

While Brown and Vorhies were flying, County Supervisor Grant walked into the lobby of the county's administration building. There he met Walter Healy, a Santa Barbara *News-Press* reporter.

"There's a rumor of a leak at Union's Platform A," Healy said. "Do you know anything?"

Grant said a local radio station had telephoned him with such a report the evening before, and he had referred them to the Coast Guard. Radio KIST spokesmen said later they had tried unsuccessfully to contact the Coast Guard.

As soon as Grant got to his office on the fourth floor, he placed a long-distance call to his friend R. E. Thompson, a public relations official at Union's main office in Los Angeles. Thompson, he was told, was en route to Santa Barbara. Before Grant could find out anything further, Thompson walked in.

"He looked like a beaten man," Grant recalled. "He slumped into a chair and said there'd been a blowout on Platform A. I asked him if it was serious. He said it was."

While Grant and Thompson were talking, the city editor of the *News-Press* received a phone call from a man who declined to give his name. The anonymous caller said he was a worker on Platform A, that a blowout had occurred, causing a large oil slick, and a serious pollution problem was developing.

As a result Bob Sollen, a reporter specializing in oil news, and Tom Kleveland, a veteran columnist, were assigned to the story. Columnist Kleveland promptly put a call through to Union's Los Angeles office and asked to speak to the president. He was told that the president was in a meeting. He asked to speak to the director of public relations. That official too was in a meeting. Finally an assistant confirmed that there had been an accident at Platform A and oil was spilling into the water.

The confirmation came twenty-three hours after the blowout of Well A-21.

While Bob Sollen remained at his desk to act as news central, Tom Kleveland went down to the harbor to find a boat to take

Oil heading toward Miramar Beach, Santa Barbara.
February 14, 1969. DICK SMITH PHOTO.

him to Platform A. He found Union's work boat *Swallow* on the point of leaving and hitchhiked a ride. The *Swallow* had a radio by which he could connect with Union's onshore office, and thence with the newspaper.

In the meantime, *News-Press* editors were telephoning local officials. One of these was George Clyde. Clyde was chairman of the joint county-city Channel Oil Advisory Committee, a watchdog group formed to keep an eye on channel oil development. He was also a county supervisor and had become a political leader in the anti-oil fight. He was furious when he heard the news of the blowout since he had been on the receiving end of what he called the Department of Interior's "hellbent rush" to lease the channel's federal lands for oil. Over and over he had heard the assurances of government and industry spokesmen that the Santa Barbara environment had nothing to fear from channel oil development.

He went storming down the hall to the office of his fellow supervisor, Dan Grant. There he found the Union Oil man, Thompson, in the midst of an apologetic explanation.

Other officials drifted in. Thompson wanted the supervisors to go with him to Union's waterfront office for a briefing. They demurred. The briefing was set for Grant's office at 10:30, only a few minutes away now. Union Vice President John R. Fraser came in. The briefing began.

Fraser and Thompson told the supervisors that trying to connect with a dropped drill pipe, 720 feet down in a hole, "was like trying to put a watch together on the wall across the room from you, using a screwdriver that's real limber and four feet long."

The County Planning Director, arriving late, looked in astonishment for Clyde. When he asked where he was, Grant told him: "He's blown his top. He's down the hall in his office writing the President a telegram."

The Director promptly went down the hall to help Clyde compose the telegram to President Nixon, who had been in office just seven days. The telegram read: "Major oil spill verified in Santa Barbara Channel from drilling operation on platform in federal waters. Department of Interior and oil industry said prior to leasing that safeguards would prevent such major spillage. Since they are not adequate, request immediate cessation of all oil drilling in federal waters in Santa Barbara Channel pending investigation and permanent correction. Request is not limited to platform in question but to all such platforms."

It was the first of many telegrams of its kind, and it was the President's introduction to a situation that was to involve him deeply. Copies went to Walter J. Hickel, who had been confirmed in office as Secretary of the Interior five days earlier, and to Donald W. Solanas, director of the U.S. Geological Survey's Oil and Gas Division's regional office in Los Angeles.

By now calls from the *News-Press,* from radio stations, and from the local television station had alerted most city and county officials. Telephone lines were clogged. Mayor Firestone could not be found. George Clyde called a meeting of city and county officials for the Supervisors' Conference Room at 1:15.

While the media were alerting the city, Lieutenant Brown and his companion, State Fish and Game Warden Jack Vorhies, had completed their overflight and were attending a briefing at Union's waterfront office. With what some were to call wise caution and others deplorable slowness, Brown had determined to find out fully the nature and extent of the problem at Platform A before reporting to his superiors.

He also wanted to know the oil company's plans. From Don Craggs, the production supervisor for Union, and others, he and Vorhies heard that gas was still flowing up the well bore from deep levels and out through faults and fissures to the surface, carrying oil with it. Attempts to reconnect with the drill pipe were continuing. The well should be shut in by late afternoon; if not, by next day. Surface concentrations of gas and oil in the vicinity of Platform A had reached dangerous levels and chemical dispersants were being used to reduce the hazard.

Platform A was in danger of being immolated in a funeral pyre arising from its own oil.

The Federal Water Pollution Control Administration, San Francisco, had been notified, as Brown had advised Craggs the night before, of Union's intention to use chemicals.

Chemicals, however, were a touchy subject. They had done as much or more damage to marine and bird life at the time of the *Torrey Canyon* disaster as had the oil itself. They were said to have eaten through the water hoses used by English beach defenders when the oil came ashore. But new formulas were supposedly less toxic. Brown listened while older men talked, realizing that if he was to be on-scene commander he would have to assert himself. Neither he nor Vorhies liked the idea of using chemicals.

Returning to his office, Brown reported by telephone to the Acting Commander of the Eleventh Coast Guard District. Brown said that the situation, although serious, did not pose an immediate threat to coastal communities in Santa Barbara and Ventura counties. He said he intended to advise the communities of the situation and the action being taken, and he recommended that the cleanup be deferred until the flow of gas and oil had been controlled and the extent of its pollution was known. But if pollution threatened coastal communities, cleanup action should be initiated at once.

Brown advised against the use of chemicals except in the immediate vicinity of the platform and approved their use there only to minimize hazards to life and property. He suggested that regular aerial surveillance continue and that mariners be warned to stay away from a five-square-mile area south and east of Platform A.

These recommendations were accepted by the Coast Guard which would send a fixed-wing aircraft to Santa Barbara that afternoon with Fish and Game personnel aboard, to pick up Brown and take him on a reconnaissance of the channel.

Next, Brown sent Eleventh District Headquarters the customary teletype message establishing, for the record, what he had seen and done that morning, and what he had just reported by telephone.

Then at 1:55, he started to notify local officials, beginning with the Santa Barbara City Administrator, whose secretary tartly informed him that the Administrator was attending a meeting of city and county officials on the subject of the spill, a meeting to which Brown had not been invited.

Brown said afterward that if the oil had been heading for shore, instead of out to sea, he would have notified the local officials, even before informing his commanding officer.

Brown's apparent laxness gave rise to allegations that the Coast Guard was in league with the oil companies and other federal agencies in withholding the truth about the oil spill. It also, for the moment, made Brown persona non grata among local officials.

Mayor Gerald S. Firestone heard the news while waiting on a customer in his State Street women's wear store. His first thought, he said, was not of the economic threat but of the threat to the entire personality of the city. Firestone had been born and raised in Santa Barbara and felt its nature keenly. Like most local businessmen, he believed natural surroundings to be Santa Barbara's chief community asset. Tall, dark, and in his early forties, he had been appointed mayor by his fellow City Council members a month before, to fill a vacancy caused by the election of his predecessor to the State Legislature. He hurriedly contacted city hall for details and made arrangements to fly over the platform next day and see the slick himself.

Columnist Tom Kleveland had radioed to the *News-Press* from the oil boat *Swallow* that the big bubble east of Platform A raised the ocean surface to a height of three feet. It looked like "a big yellow boil bursting with pus." Its appearance was partly caused by the silt being roiled up from the bottom with the rising oil and gas, partly by the emulsion created by the oil-seawater mix. The emulsion modified the natural black color of the oil, resulting in what scientists call "the chocolate mousse effect."

As it spread away from the violently erupting boils, the oil resumed its natural black color, while retaining substantial shades of brown. As it thinned it took on the iridescent, or rainbow, appearance noted earlier by Brown and Vorhies.

Meanwhile, the newspaper's conservation writer, Dick Smith, with his pilot, was approaching the platform from the air in a twin-engine Piper Aztec.

"Looking into the eye of this submarine catastrophe was like looking into the pit of an active volcano," Smith reported.

As they flew over the platform at 2,500 feet, the smell of gas became so strong that Smith shut the window he had opened in order to take photographs. An air current tilted the plane's wings. Smith thought it was a column of rising gas. "Let's get out of here!" both men said.

In their minds was the thought of the engines igniting the rising gas.

The pilot banked the Aztec away sharply and they circled the platform at 1,800 feet.

In the meeting at the County Administration Building, local officials and newsmen were listening to Union's vice president, John Fraser. Fraser evidently intended to minimize the seriousness of what was happening. A tall, lean, man who approximated the Hollywood image of the top executive, he spoke easily about Well A-21 being under control within twenty-four hours. Fraser showed little or none of the agitation he had displayed earlier in Supervisor Grant's office.

Asked how large the area of the spill was, Fraser mentioned diameters of 1,000 and 3,000 feet. The City Public Works Director challenged him; he had talked to Brown on the phone before coming to the meeting. "Brown just told me it covered 75 square miles."

The Director's comment caused alarm; but Fraser stuck to his figures, saying he referred to the heaviest concentrations. He cited the difficulty of estimating the size of an area where oil was drifting in so many different directions, with so many spreading fingers.

Though there was a suspicion that Union was being less than frank, Fraser's authority and presence were compelling. His listeners were reminded that they were laymen; he the expert. They had relied on oil industry assurances that advanced technology would protect their environment, and they tended to continue to rely on it, but not quite so credulously.

The question of the flow rate of the escaping oil came up. Fraser spoke in terms of 3.5 gallons per minute or 5,000 gallons per day. A reporter from the *News-Press* quoted a 5,000-barrel figure he claimed to have received from Union's Los Angeles office. (A barrel was equivalent to 42 gallons.)

"If that's true," Fraser said jokingly, "we've got a bonanza out there."

In retrospect, newsmen and local officials dated the beginning of an information gap from this meeting. Union officials, on their part, saw the meeting as the beginning of news distortion by the media. Whatever the name, such failure of communication was to become a feature of the Santa Barbara Oil Spill.

County Supervisor George Clyde now charged Fraser with causing the twenty-four-hour delay in notifying local officials. Fraser replied that the Coast Guard and U.S. Geological Survey had been notified around noon the day before. It was the Coast Guard's and USGS's job, not Union's, to notify local officials. This confirmed a growing feeling that the Coast Guard and USGS were culpable, if not actually in league with the oil industry. The specter of a government-industry conspiracy in the channel raised its head. Were the policemen in league with the policed?

Clyde was shocked to hear Fraser say that drilling of new wells would proceed at Platform A as soon as the leak was stopped. But Clyde felt impelled by the urgency of the spreading slick to telephone State Senator Robert J. Lagomarsino, representing the Santa Barbara region in the Legislature in Sacramento. He asked Lagomarsino to persuade the Department of Fish and Game to suspend its ban on the use of chemicals in state waters, because chemicals might break up the slick and save Santa Barbara's beaches.

Lagomarsino called back a few minutes later with Fish and Game's grudging acquiescence.

At 4:30 the meeting broke up. The assurances of the oil company seemed to Santa Barbarans to be in conflict with what was happening, and what was happening seemed impossible to determine accurately.

The oil company evidently sensed a rising hostility that seemed emotional and at variance with the facts of life in the channel. Such facts included the rights of sovereign U.S. corporations and individuals to drill for oil and otherwise conduct business, despite occupational mishaps, on leases lawfully acquired from the federal government. Twenty-six companies had paid the U.S. Treasury a record total of $602,719,261.60 for drilling rights in the channel. In addition they would pay the one-sixth-market-price royalty on each of the channel's estimated 4 billion barrels of oil, each barrel now worth about $3.50. The government's royalty might total $2.5 billion. In addition, the oil companies had spent more than $100 million in exploratory and other development. All of this not only established certain rights, it represented a major contribution to the welfare of the nation and the region. As almost everyone knew, oil was vital to national defense and the national economy. From nylons and plastics, to paints and pesticides, from pharmaceuticals to Army trucks, virtually every American was dependent every day on some form of oil. Closer to home, Southern California alone consumed 20 percent of all the gasoline produced in the United States; and Southern California was oil-poor and needed the Santa Barbara Channel supplies.

As oil company spokesmen had pointed out, rich rewards could flow to coastal communities as a result of the development of the channel's oil. There could be fat payrolls, valuable onshore facilities, and a positive development of commerce generally.

In an operation on such a scale, routine accidents were bound to happen; but they would be incidental compared to the benefits derived, and damage could be minimized if everyone cooperated. These were the views of the oil industry.

At 4:30 P.M. Lieutenant Brown was flying over the channel in the fixed-wing aircraft the Coast Guard had provided. It was a Grumman Albatross, a twin-engined, boat-hulled seaplane with wing tanks serving as floats. With him were five Fish and Game officials.

What Brown saw this time was, in his words, "ten times worse than what I saw in the morning." His stomach did a quick flip-flop. On the pad he carried attached to the clipboard on his lap he wrote: "Don't panic!"

The slick, uncoiling like a living thing, had curved around in the shape of a huge horseshoe. It was heading for the beaches southeast of Santa Barbara.

As soon as Brown landed, he telephoned the Coast Guard District Commander again and gave him the six recommendations he had jotted down, with what seemed now surprising coolness, under "Don't panic!": (1) activate the Eleventh Coast Guard District and National Contingency plans and establish an on-scene command post at Coast Guard Group Headquarters, Santa Barbara; (2) continue aerial surveillance; (3) stop use of chemicals because of their ineffectiveness; (4) reinforce Coast Guard Group, Santa Barbara, with two officers and four enlisted men; (5) provide two vehicles for beach monitoring; (6) authorize one additional telephone.

Brown estimated the spill's area at 100 square miles. He waited, half-expecting—half-hoping—to hear the District Commander's voice relieving him, replacing him with a senior officer; but the Commander unhesitatingly said: "Go to it. It's all yours."

It was a large order for a young man of twenty-seven. Activating the never-before-activated National Contingency Plan meant setting in motion more than a dozen state and federal agencies in a costly multi-manpowered effort for which there were no blueprints and in which mistakes were bound to be made. The responsibilities were enormous. Succeed or fail, Brown's effort was sure to be highly publicized and widely criticized. Thoughts of the *Torrey Canyon* disaster and attendant problems had crossed his mind. But the time for hesitating was past.

In his new capacity as on-scene commander, Brown began arranging a meeting for 9 P.M. in the conference room at the County Administration Building. Having been given authority, he must now establish it among those with whom he was to exercise it.

The evening paper brought many people their first word of the spill. Bob Sollen of the *News-Press* had put together information supplied by Kleveland and Smith, under a glaring headline: BIG OFFSHORE OIL LEAK POSING CHANNEL THREAT. The flow of oil was estimated at 5,000 barrels per day. Fraser was quoted as saying the spill "should be under control or completely stopped" within twenty-four hours and that the atmosphere around the platform was being monitored for gas and there was no fire danger.

But many Santa Barbarans went out of doors, or to their windows, and looked seaward apprehensively in the gathering dusk.

It was a critical meeting, that 9 P.M. gathering in the County Administration Building's conference room. The Santa Barbara and Ventura officials came anxious for firm information and firm leadership. The Santa Barbarans were more concerned than the Venturans. Ventura was farther from the scene of the leak and much of its economy was dependent on oil.

Oil company representatives apparently hoped to allay fears and gain time to cope with their problem.

Lieutenant Brown came determined to establish his authority, to place in operation the National Contingency Plan, and, perhaps most important of all, to induce Union to accept responsibility for control and cleanup of the escaping oil. His position was difficult. He knew that most if not all of his hearers would be critical of his authority, capacity, youth, and recent conduct. Some Santa Barbarans would be downright hostile. They would associate him with everything wrong at Platform A. He would be the scapegoat for the federal government's presence in the channel. But the slick, moving shoreward in the darkness, was like a seaborne bomb moving in on the meeting. "Resources belonging to the people of the United States are wasting away at the rate of an undetermined number of gallons per minute," as Brown pointed out.

He began with a summary of the situation at Platform A. He was in full uniform, wearing decorations including the red ribbon of the Bronze Star awarded for performance under fire in Vietnam, and had decided to remain standing while presiding, in order to give himself greater stature in his hearers' eyes. He realized that if he failed to act forcibly now, he might lose control of the entire situation by next day, and that would probably be the worst thing that could happen.

Grant and Clyde were roaring at him, demanding to know why something wasn't being done to stop the oil, and why they hadn't heard about the leak sooner.

Lieutenant Brown, a deft talker with a lawyer's adroitness, held them off, while moving toward his main purpose. This was to induce Union to take responsibility for control and cleanup of the escaping oil. If Union refused, his task would be immeasurably more complicated.

He explained that under the National Contingency Plan, he was in charge of coordinating the pollution control and cleanup effort. As on-scene commander he would procure resources, provide documentation for cost-recovery and law enforcement, determine the amount and location of the spilling oil. But he could not go down to the water and stop the leak, as Grant, Clyde, Firestone, and others seemed to wish him to do.

Thus he came to the crucial question: Who was to do the work of controlling and cleaning up the escaping oil?

Brown had decided to employ the device of the reaffirmative question: "You will accept responsibility for harbor protection, won't you?" he asked Thomas H. Gaines, Union's coordinator of air and water conservation. With all eyes on him, Gaines said yes.

Again, Brown said: "You will accept responsibility for beach cleanup, won't you?" Again Gaines acquiesced.

Finally Brown asked him if he would accept responsibility for abatement and containment of the escaping oil at its source, and Gaines agreed to do so.

Having secured Union's acceptance of responsibility in all three categories, in the presence of officials and newsmen, Brown breathed more easily.

Union was to make much of its voluntary acceptance of responsibility for cleanup and control, an acceptance that would cost millions. The long-term nature of the situation was slowly emerging. The problem was not going to be solved in twenty-four hours, perhaps not in forty-eight.

Gaines reported that the dropped drill pipe had been reconnected with the platform but that circulation of drilling mud could not be established because of an obstruction in the pipe. A valve was stuck. Efforts were being made to remove the obstruction. Heavy equipment was being rushed from Los Angeles. The Red Adair blowout-control experts from Houston, Texas, were arriving next day to help if need be. Arrangements were being made to provide oil containment booms for harbor and slough entrances. Chemical dispersants were being employed to break up the slick.

The local officials were not reassured and neither was Brown. Not only had fail-safe devices failed; so had mechanical correctives. A stuck valve was permitting the disaster to multiply.

At 11:30 word came that Union was evacuating all personnel from Platform A because of hazardous gas conditions.

The meeting broke up around midnight. Most of the officials had been convinced of Brown's ability to lead. And if they didn't understand exactly how the National Contingency Plan worked, they knew it existed. But, deeply, they felt that they had been betrayed by the federal government's oil and gas people, and by the oil industry, and that the extent of their betrayal was just beginning to unfold.

Brown went back to his office to prepare for the rush of activity he knew would come with morning. He felt more confident, having survived his first test as on-scene commander.

Newsmen went home feeling that the credibility gap between oil company statements and other statements was wider than ever. Brown had mentioned 100 square miles of slick; Gaines, 5 miles. There had been further disagreement about the flow rate of escaping oil.

3

OIL OFF SHORE

BY MORNING the slick extended over 150 square miles from near Santa Barbara to near Ventura. To newsmen and Union Oil officials flying over it, it looked like a pair of jaws threatening the shore. The lower jaw thrust toward the beaches at Rincon near the Santa Barbara-Ventura County line. The upper curved seaward and then shoreward to threaten Ventura's beaches and marina. The bite between was 15 miles, and the jaws were slowly closing under the influence of a 5- to 10-knot onshore wind and a 1- to 2-knot current.

Within the main body of the slick, there was an area about 5 miles square, near Platform A, almost totally covered with black oil. This was surrounded by a much larger area of predominantly black oil mixed with some iridescence. The mixed area was bordered with iridescent patches. Ugly black streaks ran here and there. Separate from the slick's main body, a mass of iridescent oil about 5 miles long and 2 miles wide was floating toward the channel islands.

The slick had become a phenomenon with a life and character of its own. As it moved over the surface of the water, at thicknesses ranging from about one inch near the platform to a few millionths of an inch in distant iridescent areas, its more volatile components evaporated. The denser tarry remnant tended to coagulate and sink. Grains of silt floating in the seawater hastened the sinking process by providing nuclei around which the droplets of oil could coagulate. But as the older oil became degraded and sank, new oil was added from the eruptions at Platform A. Pushing out on the surface at varying rates and in varying directions—depending on waves, winds, and currents—the new oil mingled with the old; and thus there was constant motion, renewal, and decay within the body of the slick.

Among Santa Barbarans who had trouble sleeping after the first news of the spill on Wednesday night was James A. (Bud) Bottoms, graphic arts director at General Electric's Center for Advanced Studies of Scientific and Social Problems, one of Santa Barbara's "think factories." Bottoms had opposed channel oil development virtually from the day in 1947 when he moved north from Los Angeles to escape crowding, smog, and noise. Now aged forty-two and father of four children, he sat up in bed thinking about the slick. He jotted down some notes: "We never wanted the oil here. We couldn't stop it. Now we're going to get it out."

In the morning when he reached his office on State Street, Bottoms said to his colleague Marvin Stuart: "We've got to get oil out!"

Stuart, a public relations expert, immediately exclaimed: "That's it! GOO! We'll call it 'GOO,' for 'Get Oil Out!'"

Bottoms and Stuart planned a citizens movement that they hoped would spread widely and deeply enough to sweep oil out of the channel. Bottoms went across the street to the *News-Press* building to talk to the newspaper about it; while Stuart telephoned Alvin C. Weingand, a Santa Barbara hotel man and former state senator, and asked him to head the new movement. Weingand, who had fought oil development since the 1930s when he had purchased San Ysidro Ranch Hotel and Cottages in association with the movie actor Ronald Colman, immediately accepted.

Sightseers in increasing numbers were going down to the shoreline to watch the expected arrival of the oil. Favorable winds and currents had held the slick off shore during the night. Now it was only 50 yards from the beaches at Rincon.

With a kind of morbid curiosity, like helpless victims about to be exposed to a contagious disease, people waited for the first touch of the oil on the sand.

Up in the town, officials waited for word from Union. At 10 A.M. word reached them that Union considered it safe to re-occupy Platform A. The evacuation had lasted approximately twelve hours. During this time, the platform had stood like an unlit fuse attached to a giant powder magazine. But the Coast Guard cutter *Point Judith,* standing by to warn vessels away from the area, reported no incidents, although her own white hull was turning black at the waterline.

Coastal defenses were mustering. At 10:20, lightweight plastic booms provided by Union were ready for positioning at the Ventura Marina. Similar booms were ready for placement at the Southern California Edison Company's electrical generating plant at Mandalay, five miles south of Ventura, where circulating sea-water was used as a coolant in a steam-generating system. A 1600-foot boom was being trucked in segments toward Santa Barbara Harbor. Hopefully the booms would repel the surface-moving oil.

Three crop-dusting aircraft, old Grumman biplanes, were spray-ing the slick with the chemical dispersants Corexit, manufactured by the Standard Oil Company of New Jersey, and Polycomplex A-11, manufactured by the Guardian Chemical Corporation of New York. If applied properly these chemicals were said to be low in toxicity to marine or bird life. When combined with agitation from the planes' propellers, from surface vessels, and from wave action, they were supposed to break up the slick into microsized droplets of oil which would more readily be consumed by bacteria and degraded by atmospheric forces. Flying from Parsons Airfield in the lemon groves near Carpinteria, the three old Grummans emptied eighty 55-gallon drums on the water. The pilots claimed good results, when they talked to reporter Gary Clark of Radio Station KDB, but other observers found the treatment less effec-tive.

The slick continued to move south and east, threatening Ven-tura and Los Angeles counties, while pushing fingers out toward the channel islands. At 11:15 a containment boom was in place across the mouth of Channel Islands Harbor on the mainland five miles south of Mandalay. As yet there was no oil ashore, though Lieutenant Brown and other air observers could see it creeping through the kelp beds and gathering at the edge of the breakers at Rincon. Perhaps it would go away; but at 4:30 it was ashore in the Rincon area, alongside U.S. Highway 101, midway between Santa Barbara and Ventura. It came in as light brown scum that remained on the sand as the waves receded and made a rainbow film in their backwash. It touched shore for about a thousand yards. Here and there it left gobs of tarlike material, and its odor penetrated inland to dwellings and business structures along the highway. Motorists stopped to look. Some of them cursed the oil industry and federal government. Others were heard to comment: "You can't fight city hall!"

Sea birds were beginning to be affected, too. Fred Sibley, ornithologist with the U.S. Bureau of Sport Fisheries and Wildlife, found several colonies of western grebes and a colony of California murres in serious trouble. Grebes and murres are diving birds. Diving repeatedly through the surface film of oil coated their feathers. As they preened themselves, they ingested the oil. The oil soaked into the interstices of their feathers and destroyed their natural insulation. It also seriously reduced their ability to fly, swim, and feed.

Where the oil was heaviest, Sibley found a number of dead grebes as well as a number sick enough to keep them from running when he approached. "Not all the birds with oil on their feathers will die soon," he said, "but attempts to save the most severely affected will probably prove fruitless." His prophecy proved true.

In addition to grebes and murres, Sibley found sanderlings, plovers, gulls, godwits, curlews, willets, surf scoters and several other species of ducks with oil on them.

Other forms of life were being threatened. At the Pacific Missile Range at Point Mugu, on the coast 45 miles southeast from Santa Barbara, the U.S. Navy evacuated its trained porpoises from their pens in the ocean and placed them in tanks on land. If the oil reached the area, a spokesman said, it could be deadly to animals used in various kinds of research.

At 1:30 P.M., the California Regional Operating Team, established by the National Contingency Plan, had met in San Francisco. It declared the situation at Santa Barbara to be a pollution incident within the meaning of the National Plan. It confirmed the actions authorized by the Coast Guard and taken by Lieutenant Brown and suggested the use of floating equipment and pumps for removal of concentrated surface oil in the vicinity of Platform A.

In Sacramento, Governor Reagan urged that the federal government give the State of California supervisory control of federal leases off its shores. The implication was that Washington was not adequately regulating offshore drilling and thus was endangering the state's coastal environment.

The people of the state were waiting for Governor Reagan to announce his position on the oil spill. Reagan, a conservative Republican, was known to be friendly toward the oil industry, many of whose members had contributed substantially to his election. Reagan's leading backer, Henry Salvatori, was head of a petroleum exploration company. Besides, the State of California had a substantial stake in the channel. Its offshore leases there yielded about $5 million annually in royalties. This was small change compared to revenues in prospect for the national treasury from federal leases, but it was enough to involve the state government deeply and to render any anti-oil move by Reagan or the Republican-dominated State Legislature highly problematical.

But concern about the spill was being voiced in Washington by Republican Congressman Charles M. Teague. Teague, recently elected to his eighth term, represented all of Santa Barbara and Ventura counties and a coastal portion of Los Angeles County. After conferring with Secretary of the Interior Hickel, Teague reported to his constituents that Hickel thought federal offshore oil drilling regulations deficient. They were being reviewed. Hickel informed Teague that a team of Interior Department pollution experts was emplaning for Santa Barbara to help with the pollution defense effort. The team was headed by Kenneth Biglane, who had participated in the *Torrey Canyon* episode and in the cleanup of oil spilled from the tanker *Ocean Eagle* at San Juan, Puerto Rico, in March, 1968.

When Santa Barbarans heard this, they felt somewhat reassured. Help was coming from the highest source.

The evening edition of the Santa Barbara *News-Press* told of the efforts of Bottoms, Stuart, and Weingand to form a popular anti-oil movement called "Get Oil Out!" It seemed almost a futile gesture compared with the enormity of what was happening.

A public rally was announced for Saturday morning at the beach at the foot of Stearns Wharf, and the following Monday was proclaimed "Black Monday" when motorists were urged not to buy gasoline or motor oil.

GOO's program of action included letters of protest to representatives and officials in Washington and Sacramento; a public burning of oil company credit cards; boycotting of gas stations connected with companies involved in channel drilling; formation of car pools; and walking, riding, or taking the bus whenever possible rather than driving a car.

Despite its seeming futility, all of this struck a new note. Historically Santa Barbara's resistance to oil had taken conventional forms—letters, petitions, meetings, hearings. But this time some of its people were too impatient to wait. Perhaps a new chapter in local history was going to be written.

Union continued to assemble heavy equipment at the platform to drill through the stuck valve and open Well A-21 to control by mud and cement. The valve was located in the first length of pipe snubbed onto the lost "fish," or drill string. It was a one-way safety valve designed to permit mud to flow down the drill pipe but not up. It had served its purpose in that it had permitted mud to flow down, as Union attempted to kill the well after reconnecting the drill string to the platform; but the openings in the bit had proved to be clogged. No mud flowed out into the annulus and circulated to the surface. And when an attempt was made to unscrew the pipe containing the valve and remove it so that a perforating gun could be lowered to force holes in the drill pipe similar to those in the clogged bit, the pipe stuck fast. Now the only solution was to mill through the valve.

Work was expected to begin at dawn next morning. Spraying of chemicals from aircraft had meanwhile been suspended. Instead, Union planned to use a 170-foot vessel equipped with a boom and spray arms to apply chemicals to the shoreward side of the slick. Beginning to make good its cleanup promise, Union had arranged for standby crews to remove oil that might collect on the booms guarding harbors and marinas during the night.

The Red Adair wild-well experts, heroes of the film *Hellfighters,* had arrived from Houston and were predicting early success in controlling the well. Ranging over the world, the Adair men had just controlled a month-long blowout in Australian waters. Three of them, dressed in red worksuits and brand-new golden-brown riggers' boots, landed from a helicopter at Parsons Airstrip following a flight over Platform A. One *News-Press* reporter estimated the size of the smallest at 6 feet 3 inches and 240 pounds. They looked like professional football linemen as they brushed by him, and he heard them say that they had made their decisions and ordered necessary equipment from the helicopter as they were flying above the slick.

By Thursday evening, the slick was off Ventura, creeping steadily down the coast. Port Hueneme Harbor and the Point Mugu Lagoon were boomed for protection. Santa Barbara had been saved by a combination of winds and currents. Its citizens dared to hope that this good fortune would continue. The slick had begun to play a major role in the lives of thousands of people and a significant role in the national life. Where it was going, what it was threatening, became the central question locally; and its progress was reported in newspapers in New York, St. Louis, and Los Angeles, as well as on national television.

4

LINES OF DEFENSE

BY FRIDAY, January 31, oil covered nearly 200 square miles of ocean. In its denser concentrations it was shutting out vital light required by tiny marine organisms. As it came ashore, it was beginning to affect barnacles and other forms of life in the inter-tidal zone. A pilot flying over the channel saw a school of gray whales moving northward through the slick, blowing as they went, and wondered if they would be affected by the oil.

The slick had changed direction during the night and was creeping back up the coast. Its leading edge was now at Carpinteria. A light film touched beaches continuously from Carpinteria to Rincon. From Rincon, brown fingers touched at various points for fourteen miles south and east. But it was a light touch. It might still be prevented from reaching Santa Barbara.

Chemicals seemed the prime defensive weapon of the moment, perhaps because there was no other. A small fleet of work boats, hired by Union, was spraying and churning up the shoreward side of the slick between Santa Barbara's beaches and Platform A, while crop-dusting Grummans, back in action, "dive-bombed" with Corexit and Polycomplex A-11.

But the on-scene commander was dubious of the weapons being used. So were his two advisors. The head of the Interior Department's team, Kenneth Biglane, had arrived from Washington. With him was Paul De Falco, regional director for the Federal Water Pollution Control Administration, who had flown down from San Francisco.

Lieutenant Brown, De Falco, and Biglane made some computations. During a two-day period, January 30–31, Union reported using 8,085 gallons of Corexit alone. At the manufacturer's recommended ratio of 2 to 10 parts chemical per 100 parts oil, this implied an oil-flow rate as high as 404,250 or as low as 80,850 gallons for the two-day period.

But Union insisted the flow rate was approximately 21,000 gallons per day. Either Union was using more chemicals than it should, or more oil was escaping than Union estimated. In either case, sea birds and marine life were threatened with injury from the chemicals.

Others besides Brown, De Falco, and Biglane were questioning Union's estimates. At General Research Corporation, a Santa Barbara firm, a young scientist who flew over the slick daily, Alan A. Allen, had become convinced that Union's estimates of the escaping oil were about ten times too low. Allen's estimates of oil-film thickness were based largely on the appearance of the slick from the air. Oil that had the characteristic dark color of crude oil was, he felt confident from studying records of other slicks, on the order of one thousandth of an inch or greater in thickness. Thinner oil would take on a dull gray or brown appearance, becoming iridescent around one hundred thousandth of an inch. Allen analyzed the slick in terms of thickness, area, and rate of growth. By comparing his data with previous slicks of known spillage, and considering the many factors that control the ultimate fate of oil on seawater, he estimated that leakage during the first days of the Santa Barbara spill could be conservatively estimated to be at least 5,000 barrels (210,000 gallons) per day.

Meanwhile, Kenneth Biglane, flying over the slick as he arrived from Washington, had given Allen's figures some support by estimating the slick to represent a total spillage of about 500,000 gallons, or about 170,000 gallons daily.

Young volunteers bathe a Western grebe at bird-rescue center. SANTA BARBARA NEWS-PRESS.

Allen's findings and Biglane's estimate sharpened for the public the question of the amount of oil escaping and the amount of chemicals that could safely be applied.

An on-scene spokesman for the 69,000-member Sierra Club telegraphed Secretary Hickel, reminding him of damage done to birds and marine life by chemicals following the *Torrey Canyon* disaster and urging that their use at Santa Barbara be stopped. The chemicals used to help disperse the 30,000,000 gallons of Kuwait crude released by the *Torrey Canyon* had included twelve varieties of commercially manufactured detergents. Like many of their U.S. counterparts, they were mixtures of three compounds: a surfactant (surface active agent), an organic solvent, and a stabilizer. The surfactant, usually an ethylene oxide condensate, was the primary oil emulsifier. The solvent, containing a substantial proportion of toxic aromatics, enabled the surfactant to mix with oil and form an emulsion. Such substances as coconut oil diethanolamide stabilized the emulsion. The *Torrey Canyon* detergents had proved lethal to a variety of intertidal organisms, particularly barnacles and limpets. They had also proved harmful to plankton in the open sea. True, they had at times been applied indiscriminately by untrained personnel. But in combination with floating oil, they had proved fatal to an estimated 25,000 sea birds, chiefly of the diving varieties: guillemots, cormorants, razorbills, and shags.

Now rising bird casualties on the Santa Barbara coast increased the popular feeling against chemicals. Fish and Game officials had reported 150 grebes and a number of seagulls doomed by contamination. But citizens charged this was a gross underestimate and smacked of official concealment of unpleasant facts. A Santa Barbara Audubon Society spokesman claimed that more than a thousand grebes had been trapped in the slick off Rincon and that oil and chemical emulsion were coating the beaches there.

Bird treatment stations had been established at the Santa Barbara Humane Society in the Goleta area; at the Child's Estate, a public zoo on the Santa Barbara waterfront; and at Carpinteria State Beach Park where experts and equipment provided by Union were stationed in a trailer.

Treatment varied. In a typical procedure each oil-soaked bird was bathed in a solution of Polycomplex A-11, to dissolve the petroleum. Then it was rinsed in fresh water, dried, and put in a warm place to ward off pneumonia. Some beach residents were using baby oil, butter, or soap and water on the distressed victims. The danger in all cases was that the treatment would remove the bird's body oil, thus denying it natural protection against the elements, or that oil and chemicals ingested during preening would prove fatal.

Birds were the first visible victims of the disaster and became a symbol of what was happening.

But Union went on spraying chemicals, at a cost of $75,000 a day, because there was nothing much else to do.

For the on-scene command trio, this touchy situation was complicated by lack of firsthand knowledge. They depended on Union for their information. Union in turn depended on its plane and boat operators to report the amounts of chemicals used. Later, FWPCA observers rode boats applying chemicals and kept accurate records. For the present things were simply happening as best they could.

Political reaction was spreading. Mayor Firestone had flown over the channel and wired California's senators in Washington: "The United States government must take immediate steps to prevent the possibility of a recurrence of the gas and oil spillage now uncontrolled on the Southern California coastline."

Failure to act on the part of the federal government, Firestone said, would lead to a recommendation by him that the Santa Barbara City Council appeal to Congress.

Senator Alan Cranston, a Democrat, had already called for a cessation of drilling "in the problem area." There had been silence, on the other hand, from Republican Senator George Murphy, the former movie star.

As Mayor Firestone was sending his telegrams, two other politicians were making an aerial inspection of the channel. They were State Senator Lagomarsino and Santa Barbara's representative in the State Assembly, W. Don MacGillivray, both Republicans. Despite their flight, and what it revealed, neither would support the drilling ban proposed by George Clyde or the approach to Congress suggested by Firestone. Instead they called for stronger drilling regulations and a strong move by the state to take over supervisory control of federal offshore drilling. Thus there was cleavage on the political front.

County Supervisor Clyde, nevertheless, announced Friday afternoon that he was going to ask the Board of Supervisors on Monday morning for a formal resolution proposing a ban on drilling. Perhaps Clyde was encouraged by the anti-oil high school students who picketed the county's Administration Building during the afternoon.

Clyde as yet had had no reply from President Nixon to his telegram sent earlier in the week. But, as chairman of the Channel Oil Advisory Committee, he had wired Secretary Hickel asking for a cessation of drilling, and Hickel had replied, merely, that he "shared Clyde's concern"—and was sending additional experts.

"Our point is," said Clyde, publicly criticizing Hickel's response, "that we do not want additional well holes punched in the faulty, weak structures in the channel until we have guarantees against a repetition of this tragic occurrence."

The idea of further drilling was as abhorrent to most Santa Barbarans as kicking a helpless victim, already prostrate and in danger of suffocation.

Uncertainties continued into Saturday morning, and then one of them was quickly settled. Brown, De Falco, and Biglane cracked down on Union's use of chemicals. They had become convinced that Union's estimate of the escaping oil was about ten times too low. Besides, chemicals were not dispersing the slick or controlling its spread.

Chemical use was henceforth confined—with one exception—to the immediate vicinity of the platform and there only to reduce hazard to life or property.

It was a difficult decision to make. Suppose the oil company sued the federal government, claiming it had been denied extensive use of chemicals and was thus unable to control the spill?

But after obtaining legal advice, Lieutenant Brown and his advisors went ahead with the limitation.

The command trio was also finding the company's efforts at mechanical control and containment ineffectual. Containment booms for use in the vicinity of Platform A were not yet in place. Union was preparing 1,000 feet of 30-inch-diameter weighted-skirt plastic boom to be placed in U-shape, like a gaping mouth, across the main drift of the slick. Suction apparatus would transfer captive oil from inside the mouth to waiting boats. The Navy was sending a yard oiler, a vessel of 250,000 gallons capacity, from San Diego for possible use as a storage tank for the sucked-up oil. But none of this equipment was operational yet, and oil gushed out of the sea bottom and floated away unchecked.

Union had had to suspend operations on Platform A for an hour, at midday Friday, due to a buildup of gas in Well A-21. Crews were attempting to bleed off the rising gas pressure through an unused waterline running to shore. Then they could begin work with special equipment designed to remove or drill through the troublesome valve. They would need a $2\frac{1}{8}$-inch-diameter mill for cutting and penetrating, operating at the end of a $2\frac{3}{8}$-inch-diameter tubing driven by a heavy power swivel.

Lieutenant Brown urged Union to speed containment measures in the vicinity of the platform by making a boom of telephone poles and emplacing it at once. He contacted the telephone company, and Union began fabricating the boom on the beach near the harbor mouth. Brown also urged the use of straw in beach and near-shore cleanup. Straw had proved effective at the time of the *Torrey Canyon* disaster. It absorbed oil to the amount of five times its own weight. To help further, Brown arranged with the Navy for surface craft at Point Mugu Naval Station to be sent to Santa Barbara with pontoons, barges, air compressors, suction pumps, tugs, and Navy personnel to man them.

Brown, along with Paul De Falco, regional director for the Federal Water Pollution Control Administration, and Kenneth Biglane, head of the team of Interior Department experts, was debating taking control of the entire abatement and cleanup operation, but it would probably have meant hiring the same crews Union was hiring, on platform, sea, and shore; and he had no available funds.

Complicating a takeover decision was the fact that another triumvirate—Hickel's new set of experts—had appeared on-scene, set up headquarters, and begun exercising power. It was composed of Eugene W. Standley, the Interior Department's chief petroleum engineer; Dewey Acuff, an official of the U.S. Geological Survey in Washington; and D. W. Solanas, regional oil and gas supervisor for the USGS in Los Angeles.

The newly arrived trio shared offices with Union in the Marine Center Building on the breakwater, three minutes' walk from Brown's headquarters; but they had established no working contact with Brown, Biglane, or De Falco. Yet Standley, Acuff, and Solanas were supervisors of all offshore oil operations in the channel's federal water, including Union's at Platform A. They were technical experts, empowered to talk nuts and bolts with oil people. Taking over Platform A operations would involve taking the experts over. And by statute (the Outer Continental Shelf Lands Act of 1953) and by departmental directive, they were in charge of operations at the platform.

For Santa Barbarans as for Brown's command group, the new arrivals raised questions. It was Standley, Acuff, and Solanas who, according to knowledgeable observers, had been chiefly responsible for opening the channel's federal lands to drilling. It was they who had advised former Secretary Udall as they were now advising Hickel. If Standley, Acuff, and Solanas had been chiefly responsible for initiating channel drilling, why, people asked, were they not implicated with Union in what had happened? Why did they share offices with the people they were supposed to regulate? Could they be trusted to regard the present situation objectively? Why weren't they cooperating with the on-scene command group? Solanas had allowed Union to place casing to only 239 feet below the ocean floor. Lack of adequate casing was the most important factor in the blowout, many people were saying.

Government integrity and competence were called into question by the presence of the new trio, as oil company integrity and competence had been by the failure of the all-out chemical attack and the failure to control the leaking oil. Public opinion was further inflamed.

Citizen resistance was given direction Saturday morning by the first meeting of GOO. It was held appropriately at the waterfront facing the troubled channel. Present were Democrats and Republicans, shaven and unshaven, rich and poor, young and old. Mounting a low platform, wearing blue jeans, and speaking in characteristic drawl from under a broad-brimmed hat, Bud Bottoms introduced GOO's new leader, Alvin Weingand.

The former State Senator, now nearing sixty, had opposed channel oil development for many years. He had been an early advocate of birth control as a mean of decreasing social and environmental problems. Weingand's nose was pugilistically flattened, as if from championing underdog causes. He was colorful in checked sport coat and yellow shirt; and his words rang with conviction as he urged immediate cessation of channel oil operations, immediate end to channel leasing, and removal of oil platforms and rigs at the earliest possible date.

The three hundred persons present heard these sweeping statements with some amazement. Weingand drove them home. "Any notion that chemicals or any other kind of technology can save us is nonsense," he reiterated, gesturing at the channel behind him. "Only we can get oil out!"

His hearers had the feeling that something was going to happen despite the enormous disparity of the opposing forces: a handful of people vs. the U.S. government and oil industry. An essential voice had been raised.

Mrs. George M. Sidenberg, an energetic and articulate widow, had prepared petitions and began circulating them through the crowd. The petitions were in effect a bill of particulars, beginning: "The Citizens of the South Coastal Area of Santa Barbara County HAVE HAD IT! State and federally owned leased areas have marred the beauty of the channel's waters with ugly rigs and platforms . . . Continual small breaks have caused visible oil slicks weekly, and one large break a few months ago defiled the sea for a number of days. . . . Now, what we have feared has happened. Vast quantities of oil are being released into the sea, heading for our harbors and beaches, destroying our most valuable economic and aesthetic assets. . . ."

Like an overture, Mrs. Sidenberg's petitions touched notes that were to be heard often. People began signing with enthusiasm. They volunteered to circulate additional petitions. GOO began to move.

It was high time. The oil was in the surf at Summerland at the city's limits.

5

ACTION IN WASHINGTON

THERE WAS HOPE among South Coast residents that President Nixon might intervene personally to save Santa Barbara and its environment from the invading oil. In his inaugural address Nixon had said: "In protecting our environment we will and must press urgently forward."

Despite strong support from the oil industry during his campaign, Nixon was reportedly anxious to show that he was pro-conservation and anti-pollution and was not to be outdone by the ambitious programs in these areas initiated by the Johnson Administration. The channel oil leases had been the work of his Democratic predecessors. A Republican President might repudiate them.

The new President's special environmental task force, headed by Russell E. Train, president of the Conservation Foundation, had recommended the appointment of a Special Assistant for Environmental Affairs who would "evidence dramatically the new Administration's concern for a better environment." The President was known to be sensitive to attacks by conservationists and Democratic members of Congress on his new Secretary of

the Interior and might wish to let Hickel shine as an environmental savior. As Governor of Alaska, Hickel had been charged
with favoring oilmen to the detriment of natural resources. He
had spent five grueling days before a U.S. Senate committee before winning confirmation to his Cabinet post; and a substantial
portion of the time had been spent defending a remark made
earlier: "I think we have had a policy of conservation just for
conservation's sake." The unfortunate remark was being identified as Administration policy.

Finally, the President was a Californian. With Southern California's shoreline threatened by a massive oil slick, a native son,
ten days in the White House, might be expected to act in his
administration's first big test in a newly sensitive area of the
national life: environment.

Evidently some of these thoughts were going through the President's mind.

At 10 A.M. on Sunday, February 2, Secretary Hickel was preparing to go to church, when a White House aide informed him
he was going to Santa Barbara instead.

While Hickel's Air Force transport was winging toward California, the winds and waves seemed to respond to the President's
action by driving the oil out to sea. They forced the slick into
a circular motion centering on Platform A. As it milled on its
black center, as if uncertain which way to go next, its perimeter
swelled until it reached completely across the channel and was
touching Anacapa Island as well as the beaches at Carpinteria and
Rincon.

By early Sunday afternoon, there was a traffic jam twenty miles
long on U.S. Highway 101 between Santa Barbara and Ventura,
as motorists lined up bumper to bumper to see the encroaching
oil.

A recent article in *Sports Illustrated* suggested that Victor J.
Yannacone, Jr., a New York lawyer, had found a way to bring
environmental issues into court. Yannacone had won a milestone
case in New York State curtailing the use of DDT, and was fighting a similar case in Wisconsin. He was backed by an organization
of scientists calling themselves the Environmental Defense Fund,
meaning a fund of knowledge devoted to environmental defense.

Perhaps something like EDF could be organized in Santa

Barbara, or perhaps Yannacone and EDF could be involved in the Santa Barbara oil fight.

Other words of what seemed wisdom were appearing that Sunday. A science commentator for the *Los Angeles Times* wrote: "The handwriting is on the wall. And the message is clear. Either man controls his exploding population, his crowding into cities, and his industrial activities, or he faces disaster through his pollution and his manipulation of our planetary environment." It was a dire early-warning note in what was to become a chorus.

A professor of physics who was also the vice chancellor for research and graduate affairs at the University of California at Santa Barbara, echoed it: "Up to now science and technology have been used to increase wealth. We now have to use science and technology to preserve our environment."

The *Los Angeles Times* article concluded: "Rachel Carson was wrong. It is not the spring that is silent. It is the scientists and engineers—the one element in our society that really knows what is happening in the pollution of our environment."

It seemed that history was offering the Santa Barbara Oil Spill as an example of what ought not to happen—and, perhaps, of what ought to be done about it.

Out at sea, the discoloration of the oil on the blue water looked like a spreading infection. The winds and rough seas that had turned back the slick and made it into the shape of a giant millwheel were hindering the placement of containment booms near Platform A. The lightweight plastic booms broke up. The heavier telephone-pole booms were not yet ready. Work boats were trying to suck up surface oil from the heaviest concentrations. But it was like trying to bail out a tub with a spoon.

The drilling barge *Wodeco II* had arrived and had begun drilling a relief well, as a backup means of stopping the leak should all other efforts fail. The barge had been towed up from Long Beach and positioned about 1,000 feet east of Platform A. The new well was being drilled at an angle aimed at intersecting Well A-21 at about the 3,000-foot level. The well would be lined with steel casing throughout and would permit delivery of drilling mud in large quantities directly into the bottom of Well A-21.

If such a massive delivery failed to stop the leak, Union would indeed be in trouble. A failure would be indication that the fissures or chimneys conducting the oil upward originated at the 3,000-foot level rather than near the surface.

Another reason for the relief well was the possibility that Platform A might be wholly or partially destroyed by explosion or fire, making the new well the only means of controlling the leak.

But it would take about two weeks to complete. Meanwhile efforts to remove the stuck valve in the dropped drill pipe and regain control of A-21 from the platform continued. And the oil also continued to gush unchecked.

It was too dark at 8:20 P.M. for Secretary of the Interior Hickel to see the spill when his plane flew in.

The moment Hickel's short, solid figure appeared, smiling and confident, a group from GOO picketed him with placards demanding: *Get Oil Out!*

Hickel bypassed them and held a news conference, in which he said that Union had been following federal regulations when the blowout occurred and suggested it was the regulations that were to blame, rather than the oil company.

He concluded with a statement most of his hearers, particularly George Clyde, did not want to hear. "I see no reason to stop off-shore drilling at this time."

At Coast Guard Headquarters he was briefed by federal and state officials as well as by a senior vice president in charge of worldwide production for Union, who had known Hickel in Alaska. Then he went to spend the night at the Santa Barbara Biltmore, on the waterfront facing Platform A and the hovering slick. There he was briefed by his newly arrived experts, Standley, Acuff, and Solanas, the men who had advised former Secretary Udall.

George Clyde went to his telephone to muster support for the resolution he would submit to the Board of Supervisors the following morning, with Hickel present. The resolution would be critical of the federal government and would call for an immediate halt to channel drilling. He would ask Hickel to concur.

Clyde was at his office early next day to continue behind-the-scenes preparations for putting pressure on Hickel. They included a phone call to Senator Edmund Muskie's office in Washington. The Maine Democrat, his party's candidate for Vice President in the election of the preceding November, was a recognized leader in the national anti-pollution fight. Clyde hoped to enlist Muskie's help. He failed to reach Muskie but talked to his assistant. Muskie's assistant listened, and then said: "We're having a hearing here in Washington, Wednesday. Why don't you come and testify?"

Clyde said he would, if the supervisors would send him. By then it was almost time for the Board of Supervisors' meeting. People were crowding into the hearing room on the fourth floor of the County Administration Building. They wanted a look at the new Secretary of the Interior and a piece of the action Clyde hoped to generate.

Hickel was sitting in the front row looking very much like an ordinary citizen, though there seemed a little uncertainty about him now, as if the inexperience of being only ten days in office was telling.

The five supervisors had taken their seats on the dais after greeting the visiting Secretary. The clerk of the board read George Clyde's resolution. It bluntly blamed the Department of the Interior and the Johnson Administration for the blowout and spill and called for a halt to drilling in federal waters.

The resolution passed unanimously. Hickel was invited to concur. Reddening, he leaned over to an aide and asked if it would be proper to give his approval.

Clyde intervened: "We only ask that you prohibit further holes being punched into this faulty, weak, gaseous crust until valid guarantees against recurrence can be given."

Hickel replied: "Yes, that is a reasonable request."

The supervisors took this to mean that a cessation of drilling would be ordered. Minutes later a newsman informed Clyde that it was not what Hickel had meant at all. Nobody, perhaps the Secretary included, was ever sure what the Secretary had actually meant. By now Hickel had left to fly over the channel for a firsthand look at the disaster. There was a chance he would change his mind. He hadn't seen the heart of the matter yet.

What Hickel saw did change his mind. On returning from his flight shortly before noon, he was visibly moved. In his second airport news conference in two days, he called on the oil companies operating the channel's federal leases to "voluntarily suspend" drilling, until there had been a "complete reevaluation and reassessment" of the situation.

There was immediate response from Humble Oil and Refining Company, Phillips, Gulf, Texaco, and Mobil, all of whom shut down drilling operations.

As Hickel flew off toward Washington, Santa Barbarans felt that perhaps the miracle they had hoped for was happening. But next morning, they learned that the drilling halt was over. By what seemed an incredible tour de force—or a bitter joke—oil company and Interior Department officials met in the Biltmore Hotel during Monday afternoon and evening, effected the complete "reevaluation and reassessment" Hickel had promised; and before Hickel's jet landed in Washington late Monday night, the companies that had suspended drilling were ready to resume it.

Santa Barbarans were furious when they heard about the overnight drilling moratorium and its end. The decision makers who had brought the oil upon them were continuing to make decisions that might affect them vitally, and they were not being consulted. And Hickel had flown off to Washington leaving matters in the hands of his underlings.

Black Monday, as it was named by GOO, had proved full of tricks. It seemed that the Nixon Administration had been playing games in a deadly serious context. By contrast, GOO's Monday boycott of oil products, which had once seemed a rather childish trick to many Santa Barbarans, seemed suddenly a necessary gesture of protest.

Brown and his cohorts De Falco and Biglane were almost as astonished as the Santa Barbarans by the brief moratorium. The meeting at the Biltmore had not included them, either. It had been run by the opposition triumvirate of Standley, Acuff, and Solanas, Hickel's oil-drilling experts.

But the oil itself was getting ready to play the biggest trick of all. The wind was veering into the southeast and blowing hard toward shore.

6

OIL ON SHORE

As GEORGE CLYDE and County Planning Director Richard Whitehead overflew the channel at midday Tuesday on their way to Senator Muskie's hearing in Washington, they could see the oil moving before the wind toward Santa Barbara's harbor and beaches.

While changing planes at the Los Angeles airport, Clyde reported by telephone to the *News-Press* what he had seen. A community already angered by what appeared to be the Nixon Administration's cavalier treatment of its predicament braced itself against massive environmental pollution.

As Clyde and Whitehead jetted toward the capital, oil reached the harbor mouth. It was fresh, highly volatile, highly toxic, and perhaps highly inflammable.

By 5 P.M. an inflatable, foam-rubber, plastic-coated boom was in place across the mouth of Santa Barbara Harbor. It stretched diagonally for 1,800 feet from the sandbar at the end of the breakwater to the beach at the foot of Stearns Wharf. The boom was in two sections: the one nearer the breakwater was yellow, 600 feet long, had a diameter of 18 inches, and a skirt extending to a depth of 30 inches; the one nearer the beach was black, had a diameter of about 8 inches, and an 8-inch skirt. The two sections were joined throughout by a wire cable and were tied to the wharf by a Manila rope, or so later evidence showed.

Oil driven by the 15-knot southeast storm wind was backing up heavily against the section of boom nearer the breakwater. Soon it reached an alarming depth of 8 inches on the surface of the water.

At 5:15 P.M. Mayor Firestone was in Lieutenant Brown's office for an on-scene briefing. Barry Meyer, advance man for Senator Muskie, had arrived from Washington and was sitting in a chair in the corner. Meyer, quiet and astute, was preparing the way for Muskie's visit to Santa Barbara the following Friday. What transpired between Firestone and Brown became the property of Meyer and Senator Muskie's Senate Subcommittee on Air and Water Pollution as well as of those present.

Brown and Firestone agreed to evacuate occupants of boats in the harbor, to close off the harbor area, to order the city fire department to patrol the seawall and beaches for potential fire and explosion, and to alert harbor patrolmen and city public works forces for immediate emergency duty at the waterfront.

Then the two men stepped outside to the seawall to look at the harbor. Black oil was lapping at their feet.

"You could smell the gasoline in it," Brown said later.

Whether the oil was coming under the boom, over it, or through it they did not know. Firestone summoned the City Administrator and department heads. They met in a utility room a few yards along the seawall from Brown's office.

While they were meeting, the boom at the harbor entrance broke. A Union Oil spokesman claimed a city-operated dredge-tender nudged it. City officials claimed the Manila rope tying it to the wharf broke or came untied, under the increasing pressure of oil, wind, and waves.

There was no question that oil flooded the harbor to a depth of several inches. The hulls of some eight hundred boats were blackened. The entire area between the breakwater and the waterfront seawall became a kind of oil sump.

The first concern of the defending forces was fire and explosion. Warnings were issued against open flames and the use of spark-producing machinery. City firemen deployed with portable hand-pumps as well as wheeled equipment. Fire Chief Del May, a former oil worker, took a sample of the fresh oil and hurried it to the fire station so that its flash point (the lowest temperature at which the oil would be ignited by an open flame) could be determined. Police Chief Jack Hawe's men, aided by officers of the California State Highway Patrol, restricted traffic on streets adjacent to the harbor and on Stearns Wharf. Because of danger to life and property, Brown, De Falco, and Biglane lifted the ban on the use of chemicals near shore. Union Oil contractors' boats and Coast Guard Auxiliary vessels began spraying the nonflammable Polycomplex A-11 throughout the harbor.

City employees and Union's contract crews reassembled the broken boom and emplaced it in a fall-back position between the breakwater sandbar and the West Beach groin. On Stearns Wharf, a crane worked under floodlights to complete the telephone-pole boom designed to contain the oil escaping from under Platform A.

In the midst of this turmoil, word came that Union—which earlier in the day had successfully milled through the stuck valve, regained circulation of mud in Well A-21, and mounted a massive effort to kill the blowout with 4,000 barrels of mud—had failed in its latest control effort.

Again Brown, De Falco, and Biglane debated taking over control and cleanup operations from Union. Union seemed to them to be moving too slowly, to be doing one thing at a time and awaiting its outcome, instead of taking concurrent measures in an all-out effort to kill the well and control the spill at whatever cost. As the trio debated it began to rain. The rain reduced the fire hazard in the harbor, helped disperse the oil, and helped persuade the on-scene commanders to wait a little longer before taking operations out of Union's hands. A decisive factor was Union's immediate response to their latest ultimatum: if 7 vacuum trucks, 30 tons of straw, and 10 punts with men to operate them were not present in the parking lot adjacent to command headquarters by 7 A.M. next day, they would take charge of the entire control and cleanup effort.

A favorable report from Fire Chief May helped reduce tensions. The oil in the harbor had a comparatively high flash point of 180 degrees. A feeling of fatalism now prevailed. The worst had happened and was still happening, and there was nothing more that anyone could do to prevent it.

The news spread rapidly. A man in Pennsylvania telephoned Santa Barbara's Harbor Master. He offered to come and solve Santa Barbara's problems if the Harbor Master would pay his way. Another man telephoned from London, England. He, too, had the solution. But he was so drunk the Harbor Master could not understand what it was.

Sightseers and concerned citizens gathered at the barricades in the dark and rain. "Get Oil Out!" posters appeared on murky lampposts and seawalls.

Up at the City Hall, the City Council was meeting late. Mayor Firestone was reporting on conditions at the harbor. At 10:30 P.M. the council passed a resolution asking for help from the federal government and calling for an immediate halt to channel oil drilling.

Carried by the southeast wind, the odor of oil permeated to all parts of the city, even to the houses in the foothills. It told Santa Barbarans that what they had dreaded for so long was now a fact, and that the community would never be quite the same again.

In Washington at the Capitol Hill Hotel, County Supervisor Clyde and County Planning Director Whitehead were working hard at testimony they planned to deliver at Senator Muskie's committee hearing next morning. They had brought forty pounds of documents with them. They hoped to boil this material down into sentences that would strike hard on behalf of their city.

7

THE STINKING MESS

EARLY WEDNESDAY MORNING Ian McMillan, author and natu-
ralist, drove over San Marcos Pass in the Santa Ynez Mountains
behind Santa Barbara. Though he was at an elevation of 2,300 feet
and was 15 airline miles from Platform A, McMillan could see the
platform standing up like a gray wart on the face of a dull brown
sea, and he could smell the oil. "The whole channel must be full
of oil," he thought.

Though he is a noted authority on the California condor,
McMillan more closely resembles an eagle. He would sound more
like a screaming eagle when he described smelling oil at the top
of the pass. He was coming to inspect the spill on behalf of the
Defenders of Wildlife, a national conservation organization based
in Washington, D.C.

When McMillan arrived at Santa Barbara Harbor, he saw dozens
of men working at cleaning black carpets of ooze that had once
been beaches. They were raking up oil-soaked straw, which had
been scattered as absorbent, and loading it into trucks. As fast
as they raked up the straw, more came in with each wave. They

had a strange automaton look, as if they could not quite believe what they were doing.

Others, equally strange appearing, were floating around in boats ladling oil-soaked straw out of the water. Many of them wore bright-yellow rain suits, as if to set off the black oil they spilled on themselves.

About a hundred yards off shore, a work boat was spreading straw from a blowing machine of the kind used in freeway landscaping jobs. A similar machine was spreading straw from the beach. Black facsimiles of birds struggled here and there among the men and machinery, or lay dead.

The sun had come out and registered objects in bright focus. It looked as if everyone, and everything, had gone a little crazy.

Most of the people in the crowd at the barricade at the entrance to Stearns Wharf were silent. A few were crying.

The police officer let McMillan pass when he learned of his official mission. As he walked out on the wharf above a sea of oil, McMillan had a shocking sense of premonition, as if he were seeing a preview of man's corporate death as result of his corporate tampering.

At the commercial fishermen's headquarters beyond the restaurants and curio shops he found Gene Hall, in front of the Smoke House which he operated. Wearing boots and jeans, Hall, a blue-eyed, middle-aged man with a weathered, capable look, was standing around a lobster-boiling pot in company with two other fishermen. There was nothing in the pot. The men's faces were long, their message grim.

Because of the oil, they could not get their boats out of the harbor. Even if they got them out, they could not fish. Their gear would become a slimy mess if dropped overboard. If they hauled up the lobster traps they had already emplaced on the ocean floor, the traps would be ruined and the lobsters killed or contaminated.

Hall thought the abalone and lobsters on which he depended for a living would be destroyed by the oil. It was an opinion widely held. At least fifteen fishing boats were trapped in the harbor along with Hall's. One belonged to David Reed, who furnished Hall and other jobbers with fish and shellfish. Reed's $20,000 trawler, *Atomic Girl,* was owned free and clear. He had a backlog of jobber contracts grossing $800 to $1,200 weekly. When

Clean-up crew in skiff. Santa Barbara Harbor.
February 10, 1969. DICK SMITH PHOTO.

Dave Reed left home early Wednesday morning, he had a bright future. Now he was facing ruin. Hall said his own loss would be $3,000 a week, not counting his investment.

Finding no boat available for a channel inspection, McMillan drove to the airport. Soon he was flying over the channel in a twin-engined Cessna, accompanied by Daniel E. Hood, a young Pan American Airways pilot taking a day off.

Hood, a Santa Barbara resident, had observed the slick regularly on his Pan Am flights between Los Angeles and Honolulu during the previous week. He startled McMillan by saying there was oil twenty miles seaward of the islands.

From Goleta, their plane followed the shoreline until it was over the harbor. On the beaches below, the toiling workers looked like figures in Dante's hell. Seaward, the oil spread out in brown or black or rainbowed sheets and fingers. A freshening southeast wind was pushing the mess toward shore.

As the plane circled above Platform A, which had been looming large in McMillan's mind, he saw that the platform was surprisingly dwarfed by its surroundings. Like the men on the beaches, it shrank to its relative size in nature, no larger than what it was: a little device that had caused much trouble.

Most of the oil was coming from the large eruption near the northeast leg. There were smaller eruptions nearby, to east and west. The impression was of the earth being disemboweled and its entrails floating away. The stench was unpleasant and Mc-Millan was glad when the plane turned away toward the islands and a breath of fresh air.

Anacapa, a national monument, was surrounded by oil. A dozen California sea lions were either trapped or resting on rocks in a cove on its seaward side. The brown pelicans who regularly nest on the Anacapa cliffs had not yet arrived; but the golden coreopsis, for which the island's plateau is famous, was just coming into bloom.

After circling Anacapa twice at low level, McMillan flew westward across oil-stained water toward Santa Cruz, the 21-mile-long central member of the island chain. Flying the islands is a memorable experience even without the presence of oil. Deep blue water comes right up to shore. White surf surges into huge caves and natural arches. Acres of empty land rise to mountain peaks.

Though occasional cattle and sheep grazed on the rugged side of Santa Cruz (a privately owned ranch of 62,000 acres), the scene had changed little since the first white men saw it in 1542.

Segments of the main oil slick were staining the shoreline. A solitary sea lion plunged through one of them. In the passage between Santa Cruz and Santa Rosa Island, oil was pouring seaward in a vast metallic-looking sheet that glistened under the sun. Far out there, it seemed to mingle with the oil moving out between Anacapa and Santa Cruz, thus encircling the islands in a huge petroleum embrace.

The National Park Service regarded the Channel Islands as the finest undeveloped natural resource on the Pacific Coast, and bills creating a Channel Islands National Park had been before Congress since 1963. None had been acted upon—perhaps now it was too late.

The plane flew on over the gentle pasture lands of Santa Rosa, another island ranch, toward the sea mammal colonies at the western tip of San Miguel. San Miguel is a patch of sand in a lonely sea. No humans live there. It is controlled by the Navy and is sometimes used as a bombing range and sometimes visited by scientists studying its plant and animal life. As the plane flew along San Miguel's channel coast, Dan Hood pointed to a patch of brownish foam on the surface of the water. There had been similar patches earlier. "That's the residue from the chemical dispersants," he said, and McMillan agreed.

Then they came to the seal and sea lion colonies of Point Bennett, a chief objective of McMillan's inspection. Point Bennett resembles a sandy finger pointed into the deep sea. It is a last outreach of western land, a continent's end. It was densely populated with pelagic mammals that had heaved themselves up on its beaches to bask and breed. There were literally thousands of them, perhaps fifteen thousand, clustered in family groups, dark clots on the white sand. Individuals lay still, or played, or swam in the water near shore. Many were stretched out asleep, or dead; it was impossible to tell which. Bordered by the blue water, they looked like giant slugs in some incredible garden.

The huge two-ton elephant seals were particularly noticeable. As the plane dipped lower, McMillan could make out the Steller sea lions, smaller than the elephants but still huge. Finally there were the California sea lions—the so-called trained seals of circuses. He thought he saw one colony of the rare northern fur seal.

The family and tribal clusters were often only a few feet apart, each centered around dominant males. Members intermingled good-humoredly in the course of moving about.

McMillan and Hood had flown into the heart of a natural sanctuary. They realized they themselves represented the disruptive forces they had come to investigate, as their gasoline engine propelled them along.

Against an inclination not to do so, McMillan had the plane make two low passes, looking for animals dead or distressed because of oil. At 200 miles an hour, it was impossible to make more than a general observation, but he saw no oil on the beaches or on any of the animals. It was a finding other viewers would soon reverse amid much controversy.

In fact, the controversy had already begun. As McMillan's plane was flying, a harbor seal coated with oil and in apparent distress was brought to the treatment station at the Child's Estate on the Santa Barbara waterfront, and a research team from the State Department of Fish and Game was inspecting Santa Cruz Island by boat and finding thirty-five sea lions covered with oil "but in no apparent distress." Was the oil proving harmful to sea mammals or wasn't it?

As McMillan flew toward the mainland, he saw iridescent slicks below him. Now the plane had to climb to avoid low storm clouds. Then Point Conception, the continental corner, rose breathtakingly before him, as he made landfall in the manner of flyers and sailors coming from the outer Pacific.

Along the mainland coast in the direction of Santa Barbara, oil was heavy in the kelp beds near shore. The kelp was acting like a sponge, accumulating oil and releasing it shoreward under the influence of currents and tides.

When McMillan reached the airport he had been airborne an hour and a half. Neither Coast Guard nor Fish and Game representatives, nor newsmen, had made so comprehensive a flight. McMillan estimated the area within the perimeter of the slick to be at least 800 square miles, possibly 1,200; and there were unestimated areas far out to sea. These estimates were confirmed by other observers the following day.

McMillan was appalled at the size of the disaster. He felt its threat to wildlife had been minimized in official reports. This feeling was confirmed a few minutes later during a meeting with a University of California at Santa Barbara biologist. The biologist agreed that the chief threat of the spill was its unknown, long-range effect on marine life. He felt that microorganisms on which the smaller fish depended for food were sure to be affected and that the damage would inevitably run throughout the food chains of the sea.

Five suction-pump trucks with tank capacity of 4,200 gallons each were spotted around the harbor seawall, like giant vacuum cleaners, their nozzles sucking the surface ooze off the water.

Oil was penetrating the breakwater and splashing over it at high tide, as well as entering under the boom at the harbor's mouth.

Mayor Firestone stood near the blackened seashore talking to newsmen. "People are angry. You bet they're angry!" he was saying. "This city is known throughout the world as an attractive community. Look at it now! We have laws which prohibit oil drilling within the city limits. But what can we do about this? This comes from outside."

Paul De Falco, regional director for the Federal Water Pollution Administration, was standing not far away. An irate citizen pushed up to De Falco, apparently mistaking him for an oil company official, and vehemently demanded that he do something. A *Los Angeles Times* reporter overheard what followed.

"I don't know what you want me to do, sir," the portly De Falco replied, mildly.

"Is that what you represent?" the man said, indicating the oily scum on the beach.

"I represent your country," said De Falco.

"That's not my country out there," the citizen snapped. "It's your country."

After high school let out, Kathy Morales had gone down to the sandbar at the end of the breakwater. It was not the sandbar she had known. When Dick Smith of the *News-Press* found her she was crying. Smith saw the reason. Nearby on the sand a dying loon was in convulsions, covered from head to foot with black, sticky crude oil.

Tears ran down the girl's face as she watched the loon die.

"You want to talk about The Establishment?" she asked. "This is my life—out here. I come out here all the time to watch the sea and the birds and animals. I can't think of coming down here for a stroll again. I can't think of some day bringing my children here to watch and to play. I don't know now," she said, with the tears streaming down her cheeks, "if it will ever be the same again, and no one can tell me."

8

A NATIONAL ISSUE

THE HEARING before the Subcommittee on Air and Water Pollution of the Committee on Public Works of the United States Senate began at 10 A.M., Washington time. It could hardly have occurred at a timelier moment for Santa Barbara's cause. The morning newspapers carried headlines telling of the oil ashore, and radio-television networks were featuring the inundation at the moment when lawmakers and witnesses were assembling 2,295 miles away to consider it.

The hearing was held in Room 4420 of the New Senate Office Building, diagonally across the street from the national capitol's main entrance. Senators present included Randolph of West Virginia, Spong of Virginia, Eagleton of Missouri, Boggs of Delaware, Cooper of Kentucky, Baker of Tennessee, Dole of Kansas, Gravel of Alaska, Packwood of Oregon, and Cranston of California. It was an unusually large turnout for a subcommittee hearing. More than fifty newsmen were on hand, including representatives of three major television networks. A Muskie aide said afterward that only the Senate Foreign Relations Committee hearings on Vietnam had attracted more attention.

Tall and Lincolnesque in the chair, the recipient of more than thirty million votes for Vice President of the United States at the election of the preceding November, Muskie presided. Thanks to Barry Meyer, his talented advance man in Santa Barbara, Muskie knew nearly as much about what was happening on-scene as anyone in the room. He opened the proceedings by saying that the hearings on Senate anti-pollution bills S.7 and S.544 had taken on new significance since the disastrous spill at Santa Barbara.

"To the people who live there, the spill is a very real threat. To those of us who have been trying for years to legislate in the area of pollution control, it is another justification for broadened federal responsibility to cope with pollution disasters. Cautious and informed decisions are not an exorbitant price to pay for the protection of our nation's water resources."

George Clyde was the first witness. He had been in telephone contact with Lieutenant Brown in Santa Barbara and learned that oil was in the harbor, and the situation a "stinking mess." Then he lashed out. He told the senators that in his opinion Secretary Hickel's establishing and disestablishing the drilling moratorium smacked of "cynicism and pure hypocrisy." Clyde charged that during the months preceding leasing of the channel's federal lands, "everyone in the Minerals Division of the Interior Department was hellbent to get this drilling underway despite strong opposition from local residents." He did not know what political pressure had been involved in overriding Santa Barbara County's demand for a limited trial area in which drilling would proceed slowly and experimentally. But he alleged that: "The oil industry had great influence in the Interior Department."

He implied that the Johnson Administration had brought strong pressure to bear to have the leases issued. Ripping again into the resumption of drilling, he asked: "I think it is fair to ask two questions: Can new regulations of this magnitude and seriousness be worked out overnight? And are they just merely current techniques of some oil companies, and not true regulations worked out by a supposedly independent government department?"

Clyde said that Santa Barbara was: "A place where people live because they love it. Human rights must have priority over the dollar"; and he concluded: "We need help. We have not gotten this help from the Interior Department."

The senators sat silent. TV cameras whirred. A man does not often have a chance to speak to a national audience on behalf of his community at the moment of its dire distress.

"I suppose I'm Monday-morning quarterbacking," Muskie said, "but given the geological history of the area, I would think some study should have been made before drilling was allowed, if there was any question of structural stability."

Senator Baker wanted to know who in the Interior Department had assured Clyde that technical accidents were unlikely if not impossible.

"Assistant Secretary Cordell Moore," Clyde answered.

Muskie asked who in the oil industry had influenced the Interior Department to grant the channel leases.

Clyde named no names but said that "within a matter of minutes" after "we said anything" to the Department of the Interior, "the oil industry knew exactly what we had said, verbatim."

Senator Cooper of Kentucky introduced a relaxing note. "A week ago, I drove along the coastline between Los Angeles and Santa Barbara, and I found it one of the most beautiful areas in this country."

Muskie said that Santa Barbara was undoubtedly one of the most beautiful areas west of Maine.

The senators appeared sympathetic but gave no indication of what they would do. They kept Clyde on the stand nearly two hours, answering their questions and showing slides of the disaster area.

After lunch it was the Union Oil Company's President's turn. The TV lights glared down on Fred Hartley as they had on Clyde. To some observers, Hartley had the assurance, even the cocksureness, of the self-made man. In thirty years with Union, he had worked his way up to the presidency. He was a Canadian by birth and known as a ruthlessly hard worker and hard driver, with a pinch-penny make-money attitude that had put the company's finances wonderfully in the black. Union's net profit for 1968 had been $151.2 million.

Like Clyde's, Hartley's physical appearance was conventional: middle-size, middle-aged, middle class, indicating, said some, that the issues involved were essentially middle class, white, and of

The Establishment. Hartley's tone was quite different from Clyde's, however.

To many he sounded as if he were in a board meeting where minor stockholders were causing a temporary disruption.

"I would like first to stress that we do have here a federal government-industry partnership involved in the development of offshore oil on the outer continental shelf," he began. "It has to do basically, this partnership, with the desire of all concerned, both those in and out of government, for the development of oil resources for the supply of the energy requirements of this country. It certainly is a long historical relationship."

Hartley seemed to want to turn the hearing into a colloquy among equals: himself and the senators.

"Would I be interrupting too much to ask a question or two at this point?" Muskie put in. "As I understand it, the Union Oil Company has accepted full responsibility for the costs of the cleanup?"

"We don't think that is a matter to be argued at this point," Hartley replied. "We think that there is an overview on this thing that says that the problem has to be solved." Presumably by "problem" Hartley meant the spill itself.

"Are you reserving the legal question of liability at this point?"

"I would say that we are proceeding on the basis of being prudent in our responsibilities."

"I understand, and I don't intend by my questions to try to force a legal opinion out of you that you are not prepared to make."

Hartley then gave an account of the blowout and spill. He described how "oily mud and gas" came roaring up the drill pipe and "poured over the top of the derrick" and how he personally had kept Governor Reagan and Secretary Hickel informed of the situation, and how deeply he regretted the accident.

While claiming Union had used reasonable diligence in drilling Well A-21 and had complied with federal regulations, he admitted he was taking additional precautions in drilling the relief well. At times his apologia assumed philosophical tones: "Mother Nature, if you have had much contact with her, you will find is always teaching us new things."

Muskie asked Hartley if the possibility of a blowout could reasonably have been anticipated.

"Senator, if it had been reasonable for us to anticipate that, I'd be the last fellow in the world to drill that well."

Muskie inquired how it could now be safe, then, to resume drilling elsewhere in the channel.

Hartley said the decision to resume drilling was a cooperative one in which federal officials received the views of oilmen. As for shutting down channel drilling completely, he said he had told Governor Reagan that to halt all drilling would be "like shutting down the whole university system because of a riot at San Francisco."

Hartley went on to describe new efforts Union was making to control Well A-21. Boats, barges, hundreds of men, and new and higher-pressure pumps, designed to force vastly larger and heavier quantities of drilling mud into the well, were to be employed. He stressed the strenuous and dangerous nature of the effort. "I am always tremendously impressed," he said, "at the publicity that death of birds receives versus the loss of people in our country in this day and age."

He found the absence of human fatalities at Santa Barbara significant. "Although it has been referred to as a disaster, it is not a disaster to people. There is no one being killed."

The senators questioned Hartley politely but sharply. He allowed himself to make one more controversial statement. "At least we will [by drilling] be depressurizing this unstable area for future time." Hartley suggested that the drilling might eliminate the possibility "that during an earthquake something will rupture." It seemed to many of his hearers a questionable form of earthquake insurance.

Hartley testified for two hours and forty-five minutes. Afterward, the spill was no longer merely a news story; it was a national issue. The confrontation of Clyde and Hartley before the Muskie committee—and before national radio, television, and newspaper audiences—dramatized the essential conflict at Santa Barbara: the local community on the one hand vs. national government and big industry on the other. It made clear that there was serious conflict of interest on the government's side. The government was involved in a catastrophic event it had helped to cause (by granting the leases), in which it was expected to provide solutions (by legislative or executive action), yet in which it was deeply involved financially.

But perhaps the chief thing the hearing did was to make clear to millions of individual citizens throughout the country that they and their communities might one day be standing where Clyde and Santa Barbara were standing, and for similar reasons.

9

THE POLITICS OF POLLUTION

CONGRESSMAN CHARLES TEAGUE was hand-carrying a letter to Secretary Hickel. As Representative for all of Santa Barbara and Ventura counties and a coastal portion of Los Angeles County, he urged that all drilling for oil in the federal waters of the Santa Barbara Channel be "immediately and permanently stopped," no matter what the cost to the federal government.

It was the first official call for an unconditional, total, and permanent ban on channel drilling—the strongest statement yet made on the subject by anybody except GOO. Coming from a veteran Republican congressman known for his support of business interests, it indicated what the spill was doing to established lines of thought.

Teague urged, further, that the drilling be stopped by an executive order of the Secretary of the Interior, or of the President, because action "might be difficult to achieve" by congressional legislation.

There was growing bipartisan support on Capitol Hill for legislative action. Senator Gaylord Nelson of Wisconsin, a leader in the fight to control the use of DDT and other persistent pesticides, called for a moratorium on channel drilling. Nelson, a Democrat, urged a special tax on oil companies to create an emergency cleanup fund for use against such spills as the one at Santa Barbara. And Representative Paul G. Rogers, a Florida Democrat, said he would introduce a bill to make it a federal crime to pollute waters or beaches with oil. Penalties would include a fine of $5,000 or a year in prison, as well as responsibility for cleanup.

But the growing support had a long way to grow. Secretary Hickel was defending his decision to resume drilling. Hickel said that stricter safety measures for channel wells had been prescribed by Interior Department engineers. The measures included more frequent testing of blowout-prevention devices, more rigid procedures for the application of drilling mud and for the installation of additional casing.

The President supported his secretary by saying he thought Hickel had acted promptly in establishing and disestablishing the voluntary drilling halt; he did not say the "disestablishing" had been done by underlings. "Looking to the future," the President said, "we have to get at the source of the problem, so that such disasters will not occur again."

Apparently he too was settling for stricter regulations and continued drilling.

Later on Thursday, February 6, Congressman Teague called on Nixon at the White House. He repeated the request he had made earlier to Hickel: that drilling in the channel's federal waters be stopped permanently and unconditionally. After a thirty-minute talk with the President, Teague told reporters that economic losses at Santa Barbara might run into hundreds of millions of dollars and equal those of the San Francisco earthquake and fire of 1906. But there was still no indication of White House support for a moratorium on drilling, let alone the permanent ban suggested by Teague.

In Sacramento, Governor Reagan said he saw no reason to discontinue drilling in the Santa Barbara Channel and added that he would not support any campaign to remove offshore wells from the channel area. Asked if he thought the wells should be there at all, he replied: "All of us would be happier if progress didn't require some of the things that take place." Reagan said there must be a "happy medium" between the "needs of progress" and the need to preserve natural beauty.

Reagan's appointment earlier in the week of G. Ray Arnett of Bakersfield, an employee of the Atlantic Richfield Oil Company, to be director of the State Department of Fish and Game, had upset many Santa Barbarans. It seemed to them proof of increased oil company influence at state level. Now the community saw itself confronting state as well as federal government, plus the U.S. oil industry. And all three of its adversaries were indulging in platitudes while oil flooded Santa Barbara's beaches and drilling in the channel continued.

There was one ray of hope at Sacramento. John Mayfield, deputy director of the state's Department of Conservation, said that the blowout would never have occurred if Platform A had been governed by state regulations. State regulations required casing to be set to a depth of 1,200 feet below the ocean floor, rather than the 239 feet permitted Union in Well A-21.

Mayfield's statement touched a sore spot glossed over by Hartley at the Senate hearing the day before. It seemed that Union and the federal government might have been technically, as well as morally, derelict in their conduct toward Santa Barbara and its environment. If the exposure of these facts did no immediate good, it made a growing case against the defendants for some future judgment day.

There were further developments in Sacramento that gave Santa Barbarans momentary encouragement. The State Water Resources Board asked for consultation with federal authorities on new oil-drilling regulations affecting the California coastline. The demand of the State Water Board pleased Santa Barbarans, who were used to being excluded from federal conferences pertaining to their welfare. Fellow sufferers might make future allies.

One of them, Ellen Stern Harris, already was. Mrs. Harris, a member of the Los Angeles Regional Water Quality Control Board, strenuously urged a cessation of channel drilling. She said that the public was distressed by the power of the oil companies to determine public policy. She charged that by making large political contributions, the oil industry was able to dominate key appointments to government agencies, thus preventing necessary regulation of oil company activity by these groups.

Though the Water Resources Board failed, by a split vote, to ask the cessation of drilling urged by Mrs. Harris, her outspokenness attracted attention.

It made Santa Barbarans think of Ian McMillan during the 1950s and his charges of undue closeness between government regulatory bodies and the industrial interests they were supposed to regulate. In the 1950s a program of insect control was initiated along the west side of the San Joaquin Valley near McMillan's home. One hundred and fifty thousand acres of range land were sprayed annually with DDT, accompanied by official leaflets explaining and applauding the spraying. McMillan's voice had been almost alone in publicly questioning the wisdom of such practices.

To prove and extend his point now, he had stopped at El Capitan State Beach, twenty miles west of Santa Barbara. No oil was supposed to be ashore there, according to a map shown him by Lieutenant Brown at Coast Guard Headquarters.

"Any oil reached here yet?" he asked the official in charge at the beach park entrance.

"Haven't seen any."

McMillan went down to the beach where he found oil distributed widely in tarry gobs. He picked up a dead grebe totally covered with oil. Although attempting to step only on clean ground, he came back with oil on his boots.

What Santa Barbarans wanted was a major statement at top level labeling the spill a menace to the entire life of a region, including man. There was no such statement as yet, but an increasing number of voices like McMillan's and Mrs. Harris' were beginning to be raised, and for almost the first time, listened to.

Would this rising opinion become operable in time to save Santa Barbara from being smothered in oil? Perhaps. It had powerful energizers. News media were giving the spill sharp editorial criticism as well as in-depth reportage.

"The burden of proof is now heavily on those who maintain that drilling can take place in this area without inflicting irreparable damage," the *New York Times* said. If drillers could not provide dependable assurance against damage, the government should cancel channel leases and make a financial settlement with the oil companies.

In Chicago, a cartoon by Bill Mauldin in the *Sun-Times*

depicted Hickel at the oars of a rowboat adjacent to a gushing oil platform, where a workman, dripping with oil, explained: "Sorry, Wally. Let's say it was exploitation for exploitation's sake."

The *Los Angeles Times,* one of three daily papers read by the President, asked: "Is the nation so in need of new oil supplies or the U.S. Treasury so anxious for revenue that California's priceless shoreline should be imperiled?"

And the *San Francisco Chronicle* was dismayed to find that, at the very moment disaster struck Santa Barbara, the state was preparing to lease sections of San Francisco Bay for oil drilling.

The *News-Press* was calling for a complete drilling and production shutdown of all oil operations in the channel's federal waters and for increased personal commitment by citizens. "If Santa Barbarans are going to have to fight this oil invasion of their beaches, and the stench of it over their homes, businesses, and hillsides, more of them must be heard from."

More and more of them were. Hundreds of letters, telegrams, and telephone calls were pouring toward Washington. And in Washington, where he was scheduled to meet with the President's science advisor, George Clyde sent word that he would be at hand, next day, to tour the beaches with Senator Muskie.

The tide was rising. Muskie's visit would put pressure on Hickel and Nixon to do something more than they had done. Though vacuum trucks working all night had sucked an estimated 1,200 barrels of oil from the harbor, oil was still thick there. Hopefully Muskie would see it and more. His visit might be a turning point.

Oil was ashore solidly now on a twenty-mile front from near Carpinteria to near Goleta and was touching sporadically at El Capitan and elsewhere. People were dipping Union Oil credit cards in it and mailing them to the company's main office in Los Angeles.

Citizens by the hundreds helped bring birds and oil-stained seals to rescue stations. There were almost no live birds to be seen on the beaches or flying overhead.

By Thursday afternoon, all Santa Barbara beaches were posted with orange-and-black signs, reading: *Danger. Keep Out. Water Contaminated.* Uptown, someone had hung a large hand-lettered sign on a U.S. 101 freeway overpass: *Visit Santa Barbara's Dead Sea. A Project of Your Federal Government.*

City officials had assembled to hear why the voluntary drilling
halt had lasted less than twenty-four hours. Briefing them were
Hickel's experts, Standley, Acuff, and Solanas. Standley explained
that where drilling had not penetrated oil sands, it was stopped.
Where it was at a critical stage of reservoir penetration, it was
allowed to continue, since to stop would be dangerous.

It seemed there was a plausible explanation for everything except why drilling should not be totally stopped and oil operations
in the channel totally discontinued.

And meanwhile oil rolled ashore in steady dark-brown waves.
There was talk of armed resistance and of blowing up Platform A.

Word of some or all of this apparently reached the White House,
or perhaps it was word of Senator Muskie's impending visit to
Santa Barbara that penetrated there. The contest between Nixon
and Muskie for political leadership of the anti-pollution movement had begun.

Late Thursday, the Nixon Administration reversed itself and
suspended all operations on federal oil leases in the Santa Barbara
Channel, with the exception of Union's relief well. The suspension
included both drilling of new wells and production from existing
ones.

Announcing the suspension, Hickel gave as reason the lack of
geological knowledge of the channel's floor.

Santa Barbarans thought they knew a better reason. People had
begun to act in new ways and ask new questions.

10

CRISIS ENDED

WHEN WORD of the suspension of oil operations in the channel's federal waters reached Santa Barbara early Friday morning, it gave a tremendous lift to the anti-oil movement. Apparently all that remained to be done was to make the suspension permanent—and get oil out.

Already GOO had collected more than thirty thousand signatures on its anti-oil petitions. There was further evidence that momentum had swung to Santa Barbara's side. Shortly before noon, a $1.3 billion damage suit was filed in Superior Court against Union and Union's three partners in the ownership of Platform A and the Tract 402 lease: Gulf, Mobil, and Texaco. The suit was a "class" action—a civil procedure where the issue was of common interest to a variety of plaintiffs, and one representative of each of several classes was permitted to file a complaint on behalf of all in his class.

Representing persons allegedly damaged by the oil were Gene Hall for the fishing industry; G. Norman Bacon for boat sellers and boat owners; Dorothy Ferre, a legal secretary, suing for those who enjoyed the amenities of the beach and coastline for aesthetic

*Results of a walk
on a Santa Barbara beach
shortly after the
oil spill began.*
DICK SMITH PHOTO.

purposes; and Mrs. Thomas Kelland and Mrs. Jack Watling, representing owners of beach-front property, some of which was valued at $2,000 per frontage foot.

Perhaps being sued for vast sums would discourage Union and its fellow developers of channel oil. Some observers thought that only economic loss would get the oil companies out of the channel. They pointed to the current decline in the value of Union's stock as significant. On the day of the blowout the stock had sold for $58 per share on the New York Stock Exchange. Today it was selling for 53¾. They also cited Union's cleanup costs, mounting to hundreds of thousands of dollars.

Adding to the weight of such arguments, Union's insurance adjusters, Crawford and Company, had opened an office in a mobile trailer parked near the breakwater. A spokesman announced that Crawford was accepting damage claims against Union resulting from the spill.

Things were looking favorable for GOO and its sympathizers. They did not represent a totality of the community, however. "My husband happens to make a living on one of those so-called unsightly oil rigs in your channel," one woman wrote, "and we are as sorry as anybody about what has happened. Granted there is much damage, and it will take some time before it is cleaned up, but Union is doing everything it can to help now."

Supporting this view were elements of the business community that stood to gain from offshore oil operations, particularly persons or firms engaged in construction or servicing of the platforms. Banks and financial institutions were mostly lukewarm or non-committal. But the Chamber of Commerce prepared to join city and county in a suit for damages, citing "appalling potential economic loss to the community" as the result of the spill.

Adding further weight to the anti-oil position, Mayor Sam Yorty of Los Angeles appointed Deputy Mayor Joseph M. Quinn head of an emergency task force to work with Navy and Coast Guard in protecting that city's beaches and harbor areas. A Los Angeles County supervisor, viewing the approach of Santa Barbara oil with alarm, noted that one million persons per day used the Los Angeles beaches in summer.

A Los Angeles newspaper quoted one of Red Adair's well-control experts as saying that, during the past year, his firm had handled eleven blowouts like Santa Barbara's, in various parts of the world. Blowouts, he said, had become so common in the Louisiana offshore field that they scarcely rated notice in the newspapers. His comments opened large, ugly vistas previously hidden from public view.

Supervisor Dan Grant recalled that the Venezuelan government had been trying for years to get U.S. oil companies to clean up Lake Maracaibo, a center of Venezuelan production. "They lost a whole platform there after a blowout," he said. "It simply disappeared into the lake."

If Washington was as unprepared to handle a major spill as events at Santa Barbara had revealed it to be, the unpreparedness of the Venezuelan government was not difficult to imagine. To Venezuela could be added Australia, Indonesia, and Africa, off whose shores oil development was in progress. The shorelines of the world suddenly appeared at the mercy of the oil companies, or of fate, or both.

Grant thought the companies might welcome a chance to get out of the channel gracefully. Fred Hartley, defending Union's tactics, had told him drilling there was a delicate matter, like breaking eggs.

"What they're particularly afraid of," Grant said, "is that if they're kicked out here it will set a precedent; and they'll be kicked out of other places too."

Senator Muskie's plane was scheduled to arrive at 1 P.M. Several hundred people were waiting at the Goleta airport. Many carried homemade signs: *Get oil out!* or *California: State of the Union Oil Company* or *The South Coast Is Dying! Help Us Muskie!*

Most of those present were middle-aged, middle-class citizens who had never engaged in a public demonstration before; but there were a number of young people, many from the nearby university campus. While they were waiting, a blue-and-orange Union Oil jet landed. Out stepped Fred Hartley. From the crowd's viewpoint, this was too good to be true. The demonstrators sent up boos and catcalls and waved their signs.

Apparently thinking they had assembled to picket him, Hartley stalked angrily over to them.

"What's your name?" he demanded of the first person he came to.

"My name is Kenneth Millar," the man said, "and I happen to be secretary of the Scenic Shoreline Preservation Conference." Luck seemed to be persistently against Union.

"That was quite a speech," Hartley replied huffily and stalked off. Millar also happened to be the well-known mystery novelist Ross Macdonald and was soon turning his pen against Hartley and the oil spill.

A television reporter asked Hartley what he thought of the crowd's reaction, but Hartley pushed the microphone aside.

Muskie's plane arrived a few minutes later. "Drilling should have been stopped immediately until we worked out the dimensions of this problem," Muskie said.

Accompanied by Lieutenant Brown, Coast Guard Admiral Chester Bender, Senator Cranston, and Jesse M. Unruh, Democratic leader of the State Assembly and a prospective candidate for governor against Reagan, Muskie flew over the channel. Shaking his head in concern, and getting his shoes oily, he toured the city's waterfront and watched men raking up oil-soaked straw. A member of GOO stepped up to him with a Get Oil Out! petition. Muskie signed it.

But those looking for a sweeping solution from Senator Muskie were disappointed. The meaning of his visit seemed to be that leading Democrats cared as much or more than leading Republicans about Santa Barbara's plight.

On another level, the Muskie visit separated the exploitive forces of industry and government off shore from the preservative forces of government and people on shore. If the government was ambivalent, it was perhaps not hopelessly so.

Yet the oil went on flowing, and words were not deeds. All the king's horses and all the king's men could not put the ocean's bottom together again.

Out on Platform A, pressures of another kind were running high in the nine powerful pumps that were ready to cram drilling mud down the throat of Well A-21. It was Union's all-out effort to kill the well and stop the leak. If it failed, no one could predict what would happen next.

The nine powerful (5,000 pounds per square inch) HOWCO (Halliburton Oil Well Cementing Company) pumps had begun injecting green dye mixed with seawater into the well at 11:05 A.M. The seawater was intended to keep the well bore clear, to maintain circulation, and to reduce gas pressure while leaky lines were repaired and final arrangements made. The dye was a tracer. As its green stain appeared on the surface, it indicated there was still connection between the well bore and the fissures leading upward through the ocean floor. It also showed where these fissures were located relative to the surface of the water.

At 4 P.M., heavy mud began going into the well. Union executives claimed it was the heaviest they had ever heard of, but in fact mud as heavy or heavier was often used to kill wells. It weighed from 90 to 135 pounds per cubic foot. There were approximately 14,000 barrels of it. There had not been room on Platform A to accommodate all of it in addition to the equipment needed for injecting it, so Platform B had been pressed into service as a staging area. Platform B had been connected to Well A-21 by a 12-inch submarine pipeline three-quarters of a mile long. Barges stood by with additional mud supplies.

The nine HOWCO pumps forced mud down Well A-21's drill pipe, while rig pumps forced it down the annulus. The mud entering the drill pipe emerged through perforations at a depth of between 2,584 and 2,607 feet, and rose up the annulus sealing openings and fissures as it progressed. The mud going down the annulus spread, when it reached the end of the casing at 239 feet below the ocean floor, and sealed off openings and fissures in the well bore nearer the surface.

Pressures delivered by the HOWCOs ranged up to 3,750 pounds per square inch as they consumed 30 barrels of mud per minute. Running for long in company with the rig pumps, they would exhaust the mud available. They must succeed quickly or not at all.

At 4:30 P.M. anxious watchers on Platform A saw mud returning to the surface, indicating it was still leaking out of the well bore. Perhaps 14,000 barrels would not be enough. Well A-21 had gulped down 3,000 barrels on Monday and scarcely shown the effect.

But now 116-pound mud was going in. For an hour, everything hung in the balance. Then, at 5:30 P.M., the oily brown boil located near the platform's northeast leg began to change to clear seawater, indicating that the bore was becoming sealed and only gas was escaping to the surface.

By now, 7,000 barrels, or half the available supply of mud, had been injected. Union, whose people had worked desperately, around the clock at times, for nearly eleven days, was faced with an indefinite future of oil leakage, gigantic expense, monumental loss of face.

By 6:30 P.M. the watchers saw with relief that the boil had diminished to a few small bubbles of gas with only traces of oil. It was high time. Thirteen thousand barrels of mud had been consumed. By 8 P.M., according to the U.S. Geological Survey's report, even the gas bubbles had stopped.

Next came the death stroke. By 12 midnight 1,150 sacks of cement had been forced down the drill pipe, out through the perforations at deep level, and up the annulus to a point near the ocean floor. By midnight February 7, Well A-21 was dead—choked with cement.

A few small bubbles of what was officially called "residual gas" continued to rise, but no oil was reported escaping from the ocean floor.

When the news broke next day, it seemed that the Santa Barbara Oil Spill was over. One hundred and fifty thousand people took a long deep breath.

Five days later, oil was leaking from under Platform A—not just a little oil, but hundreds if not thousands of gallons.

II

THE FIRST YEAR

11

BACKGROUNDS

PEOPLE AND OIL had been interacting in the Santa Barbara Channel region for centuries before the blowout of Well A-21. The Indians who went to sea to greet the first white explorers in 1542 paddled plank canoes caulked with tar from natural seeps. George Vancouver, the English navigator, sailing through the channel in 1792, noticed a huge oil slick that must have come from natural submarine seepage. Early American settlers used tar to seal roofs and pave roads.

The first successful oil well in California was drilled in 1866 near Ojai, almost within sight of the channel, in what was then part of Santa Barbara County. An oil boom followed that extended from the channel shore at Rincon across the rolling hills of what later was named Ventura County, to Pico Canyon near Newhall in northwest Los Angeles County. There Andreas Pico, a Mexican Californian, had begun California's oil industry in 1855 by ladling petroleum from natural seeps, refining it in a crude still located near Mission San Fernando, and selling it as an illuminant, lubricant, and medicinal elixir.

Early production came by ladling or by draining natural seeps through tunnels. Successful tunnel operators included Leland Stanford's three brothers, Asa, Charles, and Josiah. They consigned some of their refined product to their brother's store at Sacramento. There it helped lay the fortune that financed the first transcontinental railway to California and founded Leland Stanford Junior University.

"Cable tools" were used to drill the first wells. The process resembled that of hammering a nail through a board. A heavy metal bit attached to the end of a cable was lifted and dropped repeatedly, crushing the earth and rock. Periodically, water was forced into the hole to flush it out.

Based on holdings in the Pico Canyon area, in the newly formed Ventura County, and in Santa Barbara County, the Standard Oil Company of California was incorporated in 1877. At first it had no connection with the Standard Oil Company of Ohio, organized in 1870 by John D. Rockefeller. However its parent company, Pacific Coast Oil, was later purchased by the Rockefeller interests, merged with Standard of Iowa, and became the modern Standard Oil Company of California.

The Union Oil Company was incorporated in 1890. Its headquarters were at Santa Paula, some twenty miles inland from the channel, in the heart of the new oil-producing district. One of Union's original fields was at Torrey Canyon. From there on a clear day you could see the channel's blue water. In 1892 a Union oil gusher in neighboring Adams field overflowed tanks and sumps, and oil poured down the Santa Clara River and entered the sea near Ventura. Not only did Adams Number 28 cause California's first big oil spill—at 1,500 barrels per day, it was the biggest gusher in California history; and it set off an oil rush comparable in feverishness to the Gold Rush of 1849.

But the rush to Santa Paula was overshadowed the next year when Edward L. Doheny dug a hole with a pick and shovel and found oil under his Los Angeles city lot at a depth of 46 feet.

The Los Angeles area quickly became the center of the California oil boom. When the boom played out after a few years, attention shifted to the Santa Maria area of northern Santa Barbara County, and then to the southern San Joaquin Valley, before finally swinging back to the region south and west of Los Angeles.

Discoveries made there in the 1920s, particularly in the Long Beach area, overshadowed anything so far.

Statewide production which had been a few hundred barrels annually in the 1860s, had reached 300 million barrels a year in the 1960s. Nearly a quarter of it came from offshore wells.

The first offshore drilling anywhere in the world took place near Santa Barbara, in 1896, when wells were drilled from piers at Summerland near the city's eastern limits.

With the Summerland strike, the interrelationship between the channel's oil and its human inhabitants took a decisive turn. The vicinity of Santa Barbara had its first oil boom. The *Summerland Advance Courier* reported glowingly that an average well cost about $300. A derrick cost $15. Drilling cost 80 cents per foot. Casing (5- and 5/8-inch diameter) cost $1.20 per foot, while 50 feet of cable was priced at $1.50. Operating expenses were $15 a month. An ordinary well yielded 4 barrels per day or 120 barrels per month. One hundred twenty barrels were worth $125, leaving a balance each month of $110 on a $300 investment.

Bonanza prospects loomed. But the oil gave out. Summerland, which had been a popular seaside resort, declined into a semi-deserted oil slum.

The Santa Barbarans next door asked themselves: "What if it had happened here?" Their community was already famous as a resort and residential area. But the times were expansive. Few people worried much about the negative aspects of oil development.

As if giving them another chance to do so, in 1927 oil was found from piers at Ellwood, fifteen miles west of Santa Barbara. The Ellwood strike proved rich. Santa Barbara was hemmed between the bonanza prospects at Ellwood and the sad example of Summerland.

In 1929, the community's predicament grew sharper still when oil was discovered inside the city limits. The scene was the newly opened Mesa Residential Tract. It was located on bluffs adjacent to harbor and beaches which had a magnificent view of shoreline and channel. As drills went down and wooden derricks went up, residential development ceased.

For the first time there was a concerted anti-oil protest, stemming not only from concerned landowners and realtors but from the community as a whole; but a city ordinance allowed oil development in the Mesa district and protests were ineffective.

Then fate intervened. The Mesa strike failed. The derricks gradually came down. Residential development haltingly resumed, but it was of decreased quality. A lesson had been learned.

The next challenge came from the sea. In the years immediately following World War II, Santa Barbarans were rudely shaken by a series of offshore explosions. They came from underwater charges being set off during seismic exploration for oil. Sound waves from the explosions penetrated the earth. When they met formations of varying densities, they were reflected in different ways. These reflections were recorded on instruments called geophones. They enabled geologists to determine the hidden geologic structure. The geologists were particularly interested to know if the structure included anticlines, or "domes," where layers of sedimentary rocks and sands of the Pliocene age had been folded upward and where oil might be entrapped.

The explosions continued for months, approaching steadily nearer shore. They became so powerful that they rattled windows, cracked plaster in buildings, and killed large quantities of fish.

"Santa Barbara's birthright as a paradise for sport and commercial fishermen is being blasted to extinction," the *News-Press* charged on May 2, 1948; and the paper alleged that this destruction was being accomplished with the full knowledge and cooperation of the State Division of Fish and Game, the agency responsible for protecting the channel's marine life as well as for issuing exploratory blasting permits.

When the City Council reacted slowly to the threat, aroused citizens, led by a commercial fisherman named George V. Castagnola, mounted a protest movement, secured sixteen hundred names on petitions, and presented the petitions to the council. The council voted to send a letter of protest and the petitions to Governor Earl Warren. One of the offending companies was the Union Oil Company.

The blasting was suspended, only to be resumed later under tighter controls.

The oil companies were looking for something rich under the channel's floor. Their findings were a guarded secret, but enough information leaked out to indicate that they had found what they wanted. One of the most promising reservoirs lay immediately off Santa Barbara, where Union was blasting.

An offshore oil field thus became an immediate possibility. What delayed its materialization was an argument over ownership of the channel's submerged lands. They had been claimed long ago by the state to a distance of three miles from shore. But in 1945 at the instigation of Harold Ickes, Secretary of the Interior in the Franklin D. Roosevelt and Harry S. Truman administrations, the federal government had made a counterclaim. Washington claimed it held "paramount interest" in all submerged land lying between "low tide level and the edge of the Outer Continental Shelf."

Urged on by hungry budgeteers and tax collectors as much as by oil companies, the opposing claimants went to court. In June, 1947, the U.S. Supreme Court decided in favor of the federal government. This threw the question of ownership of existing offshore leases into confusion. Were new applicants for leases under the recent Supreme Court decision entitled to priority over holders of previously valid state leases? Or were the older leases valid? In some cases, new applications covered lands previously leased. In other cases, the federal government was suing oil companies for trespass because they held what they claimed were valid leases on offshore lands near Santa Barbara.

Speculators added to this confusion by peddling interests in new lease applications, hoping that holders of existing leases would pay for quitclaims.

Itself confused, the federal government delayed issuing leases on its newly acquired submerged lands; while Congress threw the situation into complete chaos by indicating it would return the lands in question to state ownership.

Santa Barbara was temporarily saved, by these confusions, from immediate offshore oil development, as it had been temporarily saved from intracity development by the failing of the Mesa field. But oil companies continued seismic exploration and test-core drilling in the channel, and some of them went to great lengths to persuade Santa Barbara of their good intentions.

On July 7, 1952, Herbert Hoover, Jr., son of the former President of the United States and a director of the Union Oil Company, spoke to two hundred local leaders. He assured them that new methods of underwater exploration would kill few fish and that new techniques would make oil development compatible with Santa Barbara's environment. He added that the needs of the Korean War made such development immediately necessary.

The *News-Press* wasn't convinced. Warning against "plausible arguments in the name of patriotism," it said that offshore oil posed "the greatest community-survival problem in the city's long history."

Despite Hoover's assurances, growing anti-oil sentiment soon induced the County Board of Supervisors to join the City Council in opposing offshore blasting; and the council plugged a loophole in a 1946 ordinance, thus totally banning oil exploration or drilling within the city's limits.

Unperturbed, Hoover went on to join the Eisenhower Administration as its advisor on worldwide oil affairs; and unfriendly critics said that "Union had its man in the White House."

Hoover and others brought mounting pressure to remove the legal and political roadblocks delaying channel oil development. In 1953, Congress passed the Submerged Lands Act which gave California back its offshore lands to a distance of three miles from shore. This cleared the way for oil development of the Santa Barbara Channel out to the three-mile limit.

Santa Barbarans were ready. In an opening skirmish in Sacramento, they proposed an amendment to the state's public resources code. The amendment read: "Impairment of or interference with developed shoreline or recreational areas is prohibited."

Strictly interpreted, this amendment would have protected Santa Barbara's shoreline and that of the entire state from adverse effect by offshore oil development. Stanley Tomlinson, Santa Barbara's representative in the State Assembly, steered the amendment through the lower house despite known opposition from the powerful oil lobby.

"They were arrogantly snobbish, then," Tomlinson recalled. "They didn't pay much attention to the Assembly, knowing they controlled the Senate."

Tomlinson waited until Charles Stevens, the oil companies' veteran lobbyist, was ill. Then he slipped the restrictive amendment through the Senate in what was considered a legislative fluke.

Naturally, the oil companies struck back. They immediately proposed twenty-six liberalizing changes to the Resources Code.

Santa Barbara mounted a counteroffensive. Mayor John T. Rickard and former Mayor Norris Montgomery led a unified effort to establish a drilling-free sanctuary off the city's beaches. Montgomery got the idea from an existing bird sanctuary. "If Santa Barbara can be a sanctuary for birds, why can't it be one for people wishing to escape oil development?" he argued. Rickard and Montgomery hired Tomlinson, by now retired from the Legislature, to go back to Sacramento at public expense as a lobbyist, perhaps the first environmental lobbyist on record.

The bitter battle ended in compromise in 1955. While accepting most of the oil industry's liberalizing amendments to the Resources Code, the Legislature established an oil-drilling-free sanctuary, three miles wide and sixteen miles long, immediately seaward of Santa Barbara and its suburbs. Anti-oil forces had won a limited victory. It was soon limited further.

Oil development proceeded at an alarming pace along the coast on either side of the new sanctuary. In July, 1958, five tracts were leased in state waters westward of Santa Barbara and in the years between 1958 and 1966 eight major discoveries followed. This meant that state waters for forty miles west of Santa Barbara had become potentially one long oil and gas field.

Easterly, development was similarly extensive. In 1958, the Summerland offshore field was discovered by Humble Oil and Refining Company and by Standard of California. Also in 1958 there was accelerated development of the Rincon field where offshore wells had been drilled from piers since the 1930s. The new Rincon activity took the form of a man-made island, the first of its kind built in open ocean. Half a mile from shore, it was made of earth and rock deposited from barges in 45 feet of water and was known as "Richfield Island," after its corporate owner. Its two-acre surface accommodated 75 wells. The island was landscaped with palm trees in the manner of a coral atoll and became a familiar sight to motorists on Highway 101.

In 1966, Richfield and Standard of California developed another offshore field near Carpinteria.

Santa Barbara was hemmed by oil fields on both sides and it

watched with apprehension as the entire South Coast appeared destined to become an oil city. Incentives were keen. The cumulative value of offshore production had passed $150 million, with the state getting a one-sixth royalty. All this happened before the leasing of federal lands beyond the three-mile limit began. Meanwhile the State of California claimed that its shoreline ran seaward of the Channel Islands. If so, the entire channel was state property, a rich prize. The federal government, however, claimed that California owned only the three miles offshore from its mainland and from each of the islands. Until these counterclaims were settled, there could be no valid leasing beyond three miles from the mainland coast. The controversy happily gave Santa Barbara a final respite from the oil industry and its federal and state partners.

Many new developments indicated an onslaught was coming. Richfield's Island had been followed by another "first"—the completion of an oil well on the ocean's bottom, with all mechanical facilities submerged. In 1964 the first successful use of a mechanical-electrical underwater robot occurred in 240 feet of water at the Molino field near Gaviota. Between 1961 and 1965, the art of drilling from floating vessels ("drilling ships") was perfected in the channel. Clearly there would be few technical barriers to massive oil development once legal barriers were removed.

On May 17, 1965, the U.S. Supreme Court ruled that the channel's seabed beyond three miles from mainland or islands was federal property. This opened the way for the Department of the Interior to begin the leasing of half a million acres of the channel's richest oil land.

Even then some farsighted local anti-oil leaders wanted to prevent federal leasing completely. Fearful of the results of massive oil exploitation, they wanted to establish a dominant pattern of recreational use. Fred Eissler, a Sierra Club national director living in Santa Barbara, had helped introduce legislation in Congress to create a Channel Islands National Park. Eissler and the Club now proposed a Santa Barbara Channel Marine Sanctuary and Undersea Wilderness Area. It would be the first of its kind and might serve as forerunner of a marine system that would complement the national wilderness system existing on land. At the same time, State Senator Alvin Weingand put out feelers to see if federal leasing could be stopped by political action. He asked a veteran legislator, Virgil O'Sullivan, a former state senator, to talk to Santa Barbara civic leaders. O'Sullivan, who had dealt intimately with oil companies, had a simple message: "Fight. Once the oil industry gets a foothold, it will systematically ruin your beautiful surroundings."

But islands national park and undersea wilderness proposals failed to attract wide public support and there seemed to be no political ground on which to base the all-out fight O'Sullivan advised. Santa Barbara city and county officials decided that the leasing of the channel's federal lands was inevitable, but perhaps it could be controlled as state leasing had been. After receiving assurances from Secretary of the Interior Udall that their views would be considered before bids were called for on federal leases, they determined to cooperate fully with Washington. Bid calls were scheduled for sometime in 1967.

Thus the community was rudely shocked on December 1, 1966, when it learned, accidentally, that the federal government would be awarding its first channel lease within two weeks.

Supervisor Dan Grant learned of this critical event during a routine telephone conversation with Eugene W. Standley, the Department of the Interior's staff engineer, in Washington. Standley explained that the leasing involved merely a single tract, off Carpinteria, adjacent to an existing state lease that was allegedly draining its oil. When Grant expressed surprise that there had been no notification, Standley said that notice had been duly published in the *Federal Register,* the daily publication of the government's business affairs, about a month before.

The supervisors were not in the habit of reading the *Federal Register,* or relying on it to inform them of federal policy in the channel. They felt they had been taken advantage of. There had been no time to make in-depth studies of drilling problems, or to complete preliminary proposals on procedures and safeguards.

Their objections were ignored and, on December 15, 1966, the first of the channel's federal leases was awarded to a syndicate composed of Phillips Petroleum Company, Continental Petroleum Company, and Cities Service Oil Company. Their successful bid of $21,189,000 for the 1,995-acre lease averaged $10,619 per acre, a record high. It was a measure of what the oil industry thought the channel's federal leases were worth.

Unsuccessful bidders included an imposing array of big oil names: Signal, Sunray, Superior, Marathon, Pauley, Colorado Oil and Gas, Humble, Texaco, Mobil, Shell, and Union. Thoroughly alarmed, county and city leaders determined to go to Washington for a face-to-face meeting with Department of Interior officials responsible for the government's channel drilling program.

Rumors spread that the government—while agreeing to meet with them—was proceeding with its leasing arrangements. After what had just happened off Carpinteria, it was easy for the supervisors to believe such rumors, and they asked the State Senate for help. On February 17, 1967, the Senate adopted a resolution asking Congress to consult Santa Barbara city and county authorities before additional channel leases were granted.

On February 28, Grant, Clyde, and County Planning Director Whitehead, in company with Santa Barbara's mayor, W. Don MacGillivray, and the mayor of Carpinteria, Alan Coates, met in Washington with Assistant Secretary of the Interior J. Cordell Moore and members of his staff. The meeting had been arranged by California's senior senator, Thomas H. Kuchel.

Still aiming at cooperative control of expanding oil development, the local leaders urged that oil produced from federal leases be processed through existing onshore facilities and that any expansion of these facilities be done in cooperation with local authorities and made compatible with existing environmental and cultural values. The Santa Barbarans urged further that no submerged lands adjacent to the state sanctuary be leased, lest the state find it necessary to permit offsetting wells inside its sanctuary. Finally they asked that proliferation of drilling platforms be controlled and that underwater facilities be installed wherever possible.

Assistant Secretary Moore, and later his superior, Undersecretary of the Interior Charles F. Luce, assured the delegation that careful consideration would be given their requests and that Interior Department representatives would travel to Santa Barbara for conferences before further leases were awarded. This apparently sincere and cordial response somewhat allayed the fears of the Santa Barbarans.

Technically advising Luce, however, was Eugene W. Standley, the department's expert on petroleum problems. According to notes taken at the time, Luce asked Standley why channel leases could not provide for controls over drilling platforms and over the number and location of onshore processing sites. Standley said that department lawyers questioned the legal basis for including such controls in the terms of the leasing contracts. Luce replied that in Arizona, where he had been working on electrical power projects, the government had exercised strict control over facilities in order to reduce their impact on the surrounding area. Standley pointed out that the Arizona lands in question had been wholly federally owned and controlled, but Luce overruled the objection and directed Standley to investigate the matter further.

When Luce left government service a few weeks later, to head Consolidated Edison Company of New York, Santa Barbarans felt they had lost a friend. They also felt that Standley was a key figure in the leasing program and was more interested in developing the channel's oil resources than in protecting its environment.

Before returning, the delegation met with Vice President Humphrey's chief administrative aide, Neil D. Peterson. Humphrey had been designated by President Johnson as the President's liaison with local government. Peterson assured the visitors that Humphrey was personally concerned about Santa Barbara's oil problems.

In the end, the delegation returned to Santa Barbara believing they had impressed some key people in Washington with their views. To their dismay, they found growing apathy at home. "What's the use of locking the barn after the horse has been stolen?" one weary oil fighter put it. And a city official warned that the state's offshore oil sanctuary was as much in danger from Santa Barbarans as from outsiders. Two years earlier, attempts by oil companies to lease city residential property for oil drilling, despite anti-drilling ordinances, had forced oil's opponents into a crash campaign to amend the city charter. Passed by a two-to-one majority, the charter anti-oil amendment increased safeguards against drilling by placing the issue in the hands of the voters rather than in the hands of the City Council, where a four-to-three vote could be decisive. But now pro-oil sentiment was growing. The charter amendment could be repealed.

Encouraging this attitude, word came that the state was going to make money from oil companies operating on federal leases by charging rental for pipelines across state-owned submerged lands. Other reports said that the state would certainly open the sanctuary to drilling, should drilling occur on nearby federal tracts. There was rising pressure to cash in on the boom, while it lasted.

But on March 18, 1967, pro-oil sentiment received a setback. The Union Oil tanker *Torrey Canyon* ran aground on Seven Stones Reef off England's southern coast. The appalling damage to beaches and marine life, coupled with the inability of defense forces to cope with the inundating oil, reawakened Santa Barbarans to their own danger. George Clyde wondered publicly if a year's moratorium on channel leasing might not be a good idea. A moratorium would allow time to study problems raised by the *Torrey Canyon* disaster, as well as other problems not yet identified, let alone answered, as result of the federal government's hasty leasing program.

The Board of Supervisors incorporated Clyde's idea into a resolution asking Congress to declare a one-year moratorium on channel leasing. The resolution also asked that the state oil sanctuary be complemented by a federal sanctuary extending across the channel to the state waters adjoining Santa Cruz Island.

The only opposition to the resolution expressed locally came from the Western Oil and Gas Association's representative, Henry Wright. Wright, a former English professor and professional football player, warned the supervisors they were becoming an adversary of the oil industry, which had been a major factor in Santa Barbara County's economy for seventy-five years and intended to remain so. Though the county derived no revenue from federal offshore leases, its tax revenue from state leases and from onshore oil production amounted to about $4 million annually. Wright questioned the extent of local anti-oil sentiment. He said his association had sampled public opinion throughout the county and found that 63 percent of adult males were indifferent to the oil issue, 20 percent were against offshore leasing, while 17 percent were in favor.

WOGA, a Los Angeles-based association representing 90 percent of the oil industry west of the Rockies, had also made a survey of onshore facilities needed to process oil from federal leases. It was objecting to restrictions proposed by the supervisors. The association had become a presence in the community, a giant but amorphous one, representing forces of untold wealth and power that were not going to be pushed aside easily.

The federal government's response to the supervisors' request for a moratorium and for a cross-channel sanctuary came during a visit to Santa Barbara, in mid-May, 1967, by Assistant Secretary of the Interior Moore, accompanied by Eugene W. Standley. Moore said the government could not grant a year's moratorium "without incurring a lot of pressure from the oil companies." He was dubious about the cross-channel sanctuary, too. But in response to a question from a county supervisor about pollution, he assured the Santa Barbarans that they had nothing to fear. New technology rendered accidents an insignificant possibility.

After touring the channel area, Moore's party returned to Washington to prepare the government's decision.

Searching for support, the supervisors turned to unusual measures. Learning that President and Mrs. Johnson were planning to visit Los Angeles, they invited the Johnsons to overfly the channel and view the problem area. The President could see for himself a situation where the federal government was deeply involved. As chairman of the America Beautiful Committee, Mrs. Johnson might influence her husband toward keeping Santa Barbara's part of America beautiful. But the supervisors' invitation was not accepted by the Johnsons.

In mid-July came further discouraging news. During the ten years since 1958, when the state's first offshore channel lease went into production, oil companies had recovered oil and gas worth approximately $190 million from their Santa Barbara Channel leases. Despite this staggering sum, the companies had shown no profit from their channel operations. Still they continued to operate. The reason was simple enough, according to one expert. The "unprofitable" operation permitted the companies to develop new fields while enjoying tax writeoffs. While growing richer, they had been "losing money." The labyrinthine reasoning that lay behind development of the channel's oil never ceased to amaze Santa Barbarans.

Labyrinthine reasoning was also taking place in the Interior Department. On August 7, Stanley A. Cain, Udall's assistant secretary for fish, wildlife, and parks, recommended that the Santa Barbara Channel be made a marine sanctuary. But a few days later, after discussions with the Budget Bureau and with Cordell Moore, the assistant secretary in charge of mineral resources, Cain withdrew his recommendations.

The long and bitter contest between citizens on the one hand and government and oil industry on the other was nearing a climax. On September 22, 1967, Assistant Secretary of the Interior Harry R. Anderson arrived in Santa Barbara to present Washington's final terms. Anderson was accompanied by Eugene W. Standley and D. W. Solanas, regional oil and gas supervisor for the Department of Interior. They met with city and county officials and proposed a two-mile-wide buffer zone immediately seaward of the state sanctuary. There would be no oil development in this zone. It would thus, Anderson argued, eliminate the possibility of wells in federal tracts draining oil from the state sanctuary. The buffer zone represented a considerable sacrifice on the part of government and industry. It would cost the government an estimated $40 to $60 million in bonuses, not to mention royalties; and it would deprive the industry of needed production and income.

Nevertheless the government's decision in favor of the buffer was firm, and bids would be called for on some half a million acres of the channel's lands on October 15, three weeks hence. The bids would be opened in December.

The supervisors felt as if a gun had been pointed at their heads. Though the buffer proposal was encouraging, it was not the cross-channel sanctuary they had asked for. They were not sure it would protect the state sanctuary adequately. There were additional undetermined issues such as the number of platforms to be allowed on each tract and the responsibility for control and cleanup of spills. The entire matter seemed too complex and too far reaching to be settled so quickly.

The supervisors decided to appeal directly to Secretary Udall. On September 24, in a transcontinental telephone conference, they asked Udall to postpone the bid-call for six months. Udall agreed to consider their request and two days later granted a sixty-day postponement.

The delay was protested by the oil industry. Rigs and crews

were ready to move. Changes in schedules cost thousands of dollars. There were similar protests from government sources. The Santa Barbara Channel had had enough consideration, some government people thought, and the U.S. Treasury sorely needed income to support the war in Vietnam.

Conservationists were raising their voices too. The Sierra Club had asked for public hearings on the leasing program. Prominent citizens joined in. But to no avail since hearings had been denied "for fear," as Eugene Standley bluntly said later, "of stirring up the natives."

Faced with a deadline sixty days away, the supervisors debated what to do. They badly needed to know: (1) if the government's proposed buffer zone would, in fact, protect the state's sanctuary; (2) if lease holders could reasonably be required to install underwater facilities, rather than platforms; and (3) if it were feasible for leaseholders to unitize, or share facilities, off shore and on shore, thus eliminating duplication and reducing technological sprawl.

They had no way of answering these questions from information available to them. Vital technical data regarding the channel's geologic and petroleum engineering problems was the private property of the oil companies. It had cost them dearly over many years and they were not willing to share it with opponents or competitors. As for the federal government, it was nearly as poorly informed as the supervisors. The government supervisorial agency for offshore oil purposes, the Geological Survey, put it bluntly: "We're not in the oil business." The Survey conducted no seismic exploration or core drilling programs. It erected no platforms. It operated no floating rigs. In the forthcoming leasing, the government would be relying on oil company information as to what its leases were worth; as it was now relying on oil company information in the controversy with the supervisors as to conditions under which leasing should begin. Thus the oil industry controlled crucial information needed by its partner, the federal government, and by its adversary, the people of the South Coast.

This monopoly of information became an issue aired later in congressional hearings, but this was of no use to the supervisors now. They instructed the County Petroleum Engineer to hire experts and make a $20,000 crash technical study of the channel's geology and petroleum engineering problems. The study must be completed within forty-five days so that there would be time to act on it before Udall's sixty-day grace period expired.

On November 17, the Engineer's report was ready. It was the most comprehensive and authoritative document of its kind yet made public. It recommended, among other measures, that not more than 25 percent of the channel's federal lands be leased initially (10 percent would be preferable) and that this area be considered an "experimental area" where techniques and regulations could be developed slowly and carefully. Erection of additional platforms, including the controversial new Phillips Platform Hogan, should be opposed. The county should encourage unitization of facilities, off shore and on shore. Finally the report called attention to "a large oil pool" directly off Santa Barbara. It foresaw drainage of oil from federal buffer zone and state sanctuary if this pool were leased and recommended inclusion of its tracts (among them Tract 402) in an enlarged buffer zone.

Armed with the findings of their special report, the supervisors made a last effort to defer or regulate channel leasing. Through the ubiquitous Eugene Standley, they arranged a meeting with Udall and Undersecretary Moore, to be held in Washington on November 27, 1967. But before they could leave, an event occurred which gave them increased local support and greater moral justification for their final appeal.

On Monday evening, November 24, the Army Corps of Engineers conducted a hearing in the City Council chambers on Phillips Petroleum's request for a permit to erect Platform Hogan in its federal lease off Carpinteria. The Army Engineers were involved because a federal statute gave them authority to approve or disapprove structures in U.S. navigable waters.

Pro-oil forces, largely from out of town, arrived at the meeting early and occupied most of the seats. Most Santa Barbarans present were standing when Colonel Norman E. Pehrson opened the proceedings. Pehrson tried to confine discussion to what he said was the issue: Phillips' request for a permit to construct a platform; but the hearing soon became a free-for-all on the subject of channel oil development. When it was revealed that the platform in question was already en route to Santa Barbara from New Orleans via the Panama Canal, Santa Barbarans indignantly labeled the hearing a mockery and a travesty on the democratic process.

The official delegation departed for Washington, leaving behind a community seething with anger at what seemed renewed government perfidy: a hearing with a foregone conclusion.

In Washington, the supervisors got much the same treatment as citizens had received at the recent hearing. All of their suggestions, based on their $20,000 crash report, were refused. Udall did not attend the meeting. Undersecretary Moore and Eugene W. Standley made the government's position clear. Bid calls were announced for February 6, 1968.

Oilmen were jubilant. The general manager for the Western Oil and Gas Association pledged that the industry would conduct operations in the channel "in such a manner that few, if any, local residents will be aware of the activity."

But on December 2, Santa Barbara's representative in the State Assembly inspected a platform operated by Texaco in state waters near Gaviota and saw oil gushing into the sea from a hole in a rusted pipe. The news inflamed the South Coast. The *News-Press* angrily asked who would pay damages caused by an oil spill. It warned of major leakage that might seriously injure onshore property and the area's tourist economy, and it proposed that 1 percent of the government's income from channel leases go to an insurance fund to finance cleanup of oil spills. Responsibility for cleaning up pollution was one thing the Department of Interior had not gotten around to settling, before permitting leasing to start.

Lieutenant George H. Brown, III, newly appointed Santa Barbara Coast Guard Group Commander, made the situation abundantly clear when he told a group of disgusted and discouraged civic leaders: "If an oil spill occurs, we'll advise and monitor but you'll have to contend with it when it comes ashore."

D-Day, lease day, was Tuesday, February 6, 1968. The scene was the Renaissance Room of the Biltmore Hotel in downtown Los Angeles. Cigar smoke, speculation, and huge sums of money burdened the atmosphere, and it was thick with Texas and Louisiana drawls. Until 9:30 A.M. bids were accepted on 110 channel tracts containing 540,000 acres. Bidders were required to submit a cashier's check or bank draft for 20 percent of the amount bid. Before leases were awarded, the additional 80 percent of the so-called bonus, or nonreturnable advance payment, was required, as was the first year's rental of $3 per acre.

At 10 A.M. the sealed bids were opened and read aloud by William E. Grant, of the West Coast office of the Bureau of Land Management, the Interior Department agency responsible for the leasing. Laughter mingled with gasps of amazement during the hour and a half it took Grant to read 165 sealed bids. Most of the sums were staggering. At the end, high bids had totaled $603,204,284, a new world record. But all bids, high and others, had totaled $1,293,601,113.26, an amount larger than the annual budget of many nations. Humble—a wholly owned subsidiary of the Standard Oil Company of New Jersey—was the largest successful bidder, with approximately $217,880,727. But a combine headed by Union made the highest bid ever recorded for a single tract: $61,418,000.25 for Tract 402, five and one-half miles off Santa Barbara—or $11,373.70 for each of its 5,400 acres.

Oilmen were smiling. So were Department of Interior officials sitting at the head table with Grant. Among them was Eugene W. Standley, who had attended all top-level meetings on channel oil matters and who had probably done more than anyone else to see the leasing through to this remarkable conclusion.

Seventy-five parcels were bid for, but the government rejected four bids as too low. This reduced the net total payable to the U.S. Treasury as the result of the morning's work to just under $603 million.

Many Santa Barbarans despaired. With such wealth arrayed against them, the task of resisting oil development seemed hopeless. Gloom grew deeper on March 20, when the Union Oil Company announced discovery of a major oil field in Tract 402 within sight of the city's waterfront. The discovery well (drilled from a floating rig) was rated at 1,800 barrels a day of medium-grade (27.8 gravity) oil. Union announced plans to install two platforms and exploit its find. It named its new field "Dos Cuadras," in keeping with the Spanish tradition of the Santa Barbara area. The name, literally "two squares," was derived from the adjacent square-shaped tracts, 402 and 401, under which the oil lay. Tract

401 was leased by a group consisting of Sun Oil, Marathon Oil, Sunray DX Oil Company, and Superior Oil Company.

Resistance seemed more than ever futile, but things began to look up when oil companies began making leases inside the city limits. Apparently they were betting that defeatism and desire for gain would lead to a change in community opinion and repeal of the charter amendment banning oil development. Signal Oil and Gas was the firm chiefly involved. It was owned by a Santa Barbara millionaire named Samuel B. Mosher, who raised orchids on a 5,000-acre ranch west of the city. Mosher's people were revealed to have executed more than 1,200 leases with landowners on the city's east side, including property near the waterfront and the city's finest beaches.

"Your Oil, Home and Community in the City of Santa Barbara—Presented by Signal Oil and Gas Company" read the title of the handsome fourteen-page booklet presented to prospective customers. Property owners were reportedly offered $10 and royalties of 12½ percent for a 10-year lease.

Fighting anger rose in the city at the news of the leasing, even though the community had few weapons to fight back with except its hands and its will. Then, on June 7, 1968, two thousand gallons of crude oil gushed into the sea from a tank on Phillips' newly erected Platform Hogan, and the people of Santa Barbara saw an opening.

They focused their counterattack on platform emplacement. It was easy to imagine what could happen when every one of the channel's seventy-one federal leases had a platform (and some were expected to have more than one) with tanks that could overflow and pipes that could rust out. On June 21, a phalanx of local organizations joined together in petitioning the Army Engineers for a hearing on Union's request to erect two platforms in Tract 402.

The petition was refused. The chief district counsel for the Army Engineers said that no significant information had been advanced showing that the proposed platforms would be a hazard to navigation. He reiterated Colonel Pehrson's earlier statement that the Corps concerned itself only with navigational hazards.

Fred Eissler of the Sierra Club produced a letter from the Army

Department stating that Engineer Corps hearings involved "the evaluation of a structure's effects on water quality, recreation, fish and wildlife, and other natural resources."

The Army Engineer counsel replied that this was true only if some other agency had not evaluated these effects, and in this case it had been done by the Interior Department. Later evidence showed that the Interior Department had made no such survey. Petition denied, Union was free to emplace its platforms and did so. Santa Barbarans were convinced they had been the victims of high-level buck passing.

Local resistance was weakening. Even before the Army Engineers denied the citizens' request for a hearing, the City Council had dropped its request for one, saying that the city's prime concerns—platform design, submerged facilities, and spillage control—were not within the jurisdiction of the Engineers.

Next the county supervisors lost some of their resolve. On July 27 they granted Humble Oil permission to construct onshore facilities adjacent to existing Standard Oil Company of California facilities in the Carpinteria area. Although this was in keeping with the official policy of consolidating onshore facilities, many citizens disagreed with it. An energetic group led by Weingand, Eissler, and Mrs. Sidenberg collected more than twelve thousand signatures, more than enough to place the issue on the November 5 general election ballot as a referendum measure.

Infighting began. Later it was referred to as the "oil civil war." George V. Castagnola, who had led the citizen protest against seismic blasting back in 1948, headed a citizens group supporting the supervisors, the oil companies, and the expanded Carpinteria facility. Castagnola now held the franchise for commercial operation of Stearns Wharf, an important staging point for offshore oil operations, and he was publicly inviting such business.

On November 5 after bitter infighting among the pro and con oil factions, the referendum insurgents won a surprising victory. The vote, county-wide, was 44,324 to 41,434. Along the South Coast, the "no"—no more oil—vote was overwhelming.

Opponents of oil were not surprised but were further enraged that oil and drilling companies had furnished substantial financial support to the pro-oil group. Leading contributors were Humble, Phillips, and Sunray. Petroleum, which had been a benevolent natural phenomenon to the area's Indians and early white settlers, had become a divisive force which set the community against itself. Oil now had a powerful life of its own, was worth billions, influenced the welfare of thousands of people, and threatened to disrupt the ecology, as well as the civic peace, of one of the most beautiful places on earth.

On January 17, 1969, the Sun Oil Company announced plans to emplace its first platform in the Dos Cuadras field less than a mile east of Union's newly emplaced Platform A. Sun said it was taking "elaborate precautions against oil pollution in the Santa Barbara Channel."

All drilling and production equipment on the new platform was to be operated by electric power, thus eliminating hazardous diesel engines. All oil and salt water produced from Sun's wells were to be piped ashore and separated there, instead of at the wellhead. Sophisticated instrument systems would prevent spillage of oil or danger to the crew in case of accident. Finally, the entire structure was to be painted blue to match the ocean.

Despite such assurances, Santa Barbara's animosity toward the oil industry continued to grow and the bitter divisions created by the oil referendum fight widened. Castagnola's stand with the oil companies against the majority of city residents now raised the issue of the proper use of the city-owned wharf, which he controlled by contract with the city.

At the same time, Santa Barbara's small-boat harbor was taking on the appearance of an oil port. It was becoming overrun by service boats, derrick barges, mobile cranes, and commercial craft of various types.

Tourists began to complain when their view was blocked by cargo barges anchored close to shore. Prospective home buyers complained, too, as they looked at twenty-story-high platforms rising from the channel. There were twelve platforms now, counting Union's two new ones, and Union was talking about a third, also to be placed in Tract 402.

As time drew near for the inauguration of Richard M. Nixon as President and for the confirmation of his Cabinet appointees by the Senate, Santa Barbara's attention focused on the Washington scene. New national leaders might agree to new policies in the channel. On the other hand, there was the President's controversial nominee for Secretary of the Interior, Walter J. Hickel, who was reported to have close ties to oil and gas interests. One report said that Robert O. Anderson, president of Atlantic Richfield, had recommended Hickel for the Interior post. Anderson, who had known Hickel in Alaska, was a Republican National Committeeman from New Mexico and reportedly had contributed $60,000 to Nixon's election campaign.

Members of both parties opposed Hickel's nomination. During questioning by Democratic senators, Hickel at first said he owned no oil investments; but on cross-examination he admitted he had about a million dollars invested in the Anchorage Natural Gas Company, of which he had been chairman. Hickel was also described as having close ties with Texas oilmen. Conservationists joined in the attack with letters, telephone calls, and petitions to senators. But former President Johnson, himself close to Texas oilmen, used his Senate influence on Hickel's behalf, Hickel said later; and finally the controversial nominee was confirmed as Secretary of the Interior. To many Santa Barbarans, it seemed open encouragement of the forces that threatened to overwhelm them.

Allaying the possible menace of Hickel's appointment, Senator Alan Cranston brought some encouraging news. Cranston would support two congressional measures helpful to Santa Barbara's side of the oil battle, now referred to as the "Thirty Years War." The first measure gave permanent status to the two-mile-wide buffer zone established by order of the Secretary of the Interior. The second would establish a revolving fund to finance cleanup of oil discharged from a vessel or from offshore or onshore oil installations. The legislation had been introduced earlier in the month by Republican Congressman Teague.

Cranston's support for Teague's measures indicated that bipartisan backing was available for legislation dealing with Santa Barbara's environmental problems. But time had run out. The moment had arrived in which the past and future of a community, an industry, and a government were to meet. It was a moment that would decisively influence national attitudes and the course of U.S. policy.

On January 28, Well A-21 blew out. A Western Oil and Gas Association executive, flying overhead in a commercial airliner, happened to look out the window and see the column of oily mud gushing over the top of the derrick. Touching the oilman sitting next to him, he said: "Look!"

The oilman leaned over and looked out the window. "My God!" he said, and turned visibly pale.

12

CRISIS RESUMED

WHEN WELL A-21 was finally choked with cement on the night of February 7, it had flowed wildly for ten and a half days. Two hundred and thirty thousand gallons—or perhaps 2,300,000 gallons—of oil had gushed into the Santa Barbara Channel. The amount varied with the estimator. Union's figure was the lower. Scientist Alan A. Allen's was the higher and later findings supported Allen's estimate.

Though now cut off at its source, the huge, still-dangerous slick wandered up and down the coast. Beaches and harbors were contaminated when wind and current brought the oil ashore. Off shore, the leases remained. Drilling on them had been suspended, but their potential for future blowouts and spills remained great.

For most Santa Barbarans, there was no going back to the days of cooperation in channel oil development. Their disillusion was nearly complete. They were determined to push ahead with their opposition. The only question was how.

Sounding a keynote, GOO staged a rally Saturday morning, February 8, in De la Guerra Plaza in front of the City Hall. Alvin Weingand told of plans to take 40,000 Get Oil Out! signatures to

Washington and present them to the President. Bud Bottoms suggested that citizens go to the beach, scoop up a sample of crude oil, seal it securely, and mail it to senators and congressmen.

George Clyde articulated Santa Barbara's new view later in the day. He said that on Monday he would ask the Board of Supervisors to follow Congressman Teague's example and request a "permanent stop to all drilling in the federal waters of the Santa Barbara Channel." To some, it sounded presumptuous. It amounted to a formal declaration of war on national government and oil industry. It implied a level of leadership and citizen commitment beyond anything yet seen and it demanded an unconditional surrender by forces of monumental power.

But Clyde and like-minded citizens were already receiving help from unexpected sources. In a front-page story, the *New York Times* revealed that former Secretary of the Interior Udall had accepted full responsibility for the decisions that led to the spill. Udall said he was "sickened" by the consequences of his action and wondered whether "we should not hold back" on further channel drilling. Udall said that when Interior Department experts were asked their opinion on the drilling, there had been no dissent. The question of stricter regulations had never come up "though geological conditions in the Santa Barbara Channel were known to be unstable."

When Santa Barbarans learned of Udall's comments, they took fresh hope. With Udall admitting government culpability, the government might correct its mistake. Certainly his statements opened the door for the Nixon Administration to blame its predecessor, while taking corrective action.

On February 10, the board met in an overflowing supervisors' hearing room to consider George Clyde's motion for a permanent cessation of drilling in the channel. The crowd groaned in dismay when Supervisor Tunnell of the Santa Maria oil-producing district objected to the motion. In a rising tide of determination, the citizens returned in greater force after the noon recess, and heard Clyde's motion, broadened to include "permanent cessation of drilling on state leases and removal of all platforms which do not have producing wells," pass unanimously.

Thus the state was included among Santa Barbara's adversaries, heightening the David-Goliath aspects of the situation. But next day the City Council followed the example of the Board of Supervisors, and Mayor Firestone asked Congressman Teague to arrange a meeting with President Nixon, so that he could personally convey to the President "the community's official convictions."

Citizens and their elected representatives were thinking with one mind. An electrifying feeling ran through the community as people felt themselves influencing the decision-making process. The significance of their cause—and its justice in their minds— gave them a sense of living in history. If called upon to attend a meeting, make a talk, write a letter, telephone a councilman or supervisor, staff a sidewalk table where petitions were being signed, or send a telegram, or donate money, people were ready to act. Marvin Stuart, co-founder of GOO, had read about the environmentalist lawyer, Victor J. Yannacone, Jr., and about EDF, the Environmental Defense Fund of scientists, and had picked up his telephone and invited Yannacone to come to Santa Barbara. Now the Santa Barbara Audubon Society was raising money to pay Yannacone's round-trip plane fare. It was characteristic of what was happening throughout the community.

On the beaches themselves, 1,200 men, many of them local residents, were involved in the cleanup. About 800 of them had been hired by Union or its contractors. Some 400 were convicts from state prison camps, paid wages of a few cents a day by the state. Their living expenses of $9.50 a day were paid by Union. Labor leaders protested the use of prisoners, which had been personally authorized by Governor Reagan. After ten days, during which intensive political pressure built up in Sacramento, the convicts were withdrawn and their jobs taken over by union laborers, at $3.97 per hour.

Straw continued to be the workers' chief weapon of defense. Truckloads of it were arriving from as far away as Arizona, bringing as many as 2,500 bales a day. Dissidents protested the paradox that in a day of moon walks, straw was the best material to be found to combat an oil slick, and estimated that the baling wire involved would stretch twice the length of California. Men and

Clean-up crew at work on Santa Barbara beaches, February, 1969. DICK SMITH PHOTO.

machinery continued to spread the straw on beaches and water, and then to pick it up again and haul it away. The first truckloads of contaminated straw were taken to the city's Las Positas dump; but when the dump began oozing oil, city officials closed it. The trucks were now going to a dump near Oxnard in Ventura County, more than thirty-five miles away. They made a long smelly procession on U.S. Highway 101. Later loads were dumped west of Santa Barbara at Tajiquas, where their oil eventually seeped back into the sea.

A new feature of the cleanup effort was the use of pressurized hot water on oil-stained rocks and seawalls. Though it tended to kill such marine life as remained, it seemed the best way to erase the black scars. High tides had flung oil fifteen feet high on cliff faces. And every rock in the breakwater had to be cleaned by hand by the hot-water crews. Union's cleanup costs eventually totaled $5 million.

Local, state, and federal agencies now involved in Lieutenant Brown's National Contingency Plan numbered more than twenty. A United States Weather Bureau mobile meteorology station provided round-the-clock information and weather forecasts, from which Brown could predict movements of the oil slick. Personnel from the Department of Interior's Bureau of Sport Fisheries and Wildlife had arrived, bringing an airplane, from which the effects of the spill on marine life could be observed. Representatives of the White House's Office of Emergency Preparedness were on hand transmitting reports to be used in presidential briefings. They helped keep Nixon as well informed as Senator Muskie. But they represented problems. If the spill were to be declared a disaster by the President, under provisions of Public Law 875, the federal government would take over the recovery effort, as it did in the case of hurricanes and floods, and the Office of Emergency Preparedness would take charge—freeing Union of an important responsibility.

The National Park Service had become involved because it managed oil-threatened Anacapa and Santa Barbara islands comprising the Channel Islands National Monument. Its rangers were making sea and shore surveys. And the Bureau of Commercial Fisheries was preparing its research vessel, *David Starr Jordan*, for a cruise to the vicinity of Platform A. The submerged observatory of the *Jordan* would provide some surprising first looks—just how surprising no one yet guessed.

Meanwhile the cost of the spill to local, state, and federal agencies involved was approaching an estimated $1 million, according to an informed Coast Guard official.

By Tuesday, February 11, a variety of new forces had emerged. State Senator Lagomarsino and Assemblyman MacGillivray, for example, were now backing Santa Barbara's official determination to get oil out of the channel. Conservative U.S. Senator George Murphy had not been heard from. The president of Union Oil telephoned the president of the Santa Barbara Audubon Society to apologize for the deaths of more than six hundred birds as result of the spill. But the bird toll was steadily rising. Alvin Weingand had talked by telephone to the mayor of St. Ives, Cornwall, one of the English communities hit hard by oil from the *Torrey Canyon*. The English mayor had offered moral support and warned of the adverse effects of oil spills on a tourist economy. The curator of the Museum of Vertebrate Zoology at the University of California at Santa Barbara had found a dead dolphin on the beach. The breathing hole of the once-beautiful animal was clogged with oil. Apparently it had suffocated. But a State Fish and Game Department spokesman said: "We must have firm proof that these mammals are affected by oil, and that is difficult to determine."

His statement further exacerbated public opinion. Citizens seemed to be finding things public officials did not. They wondered if they could trust a federal government whose former Secretary of the Interior accepted responsibility for the conditions that led to the oil spill and a state government whose director of Fish and Game matters was an oilman.

As if in response, the *Los Angeles Times,* next morning, raised the issue of conflict of interest on the part of regulatory agencies. What particularly struck the *Times* was the fact that during the height of the Santa Barbara Oil Spill the state's "pure water" agency—its water resources control board—had been holding hearings on toothless proposals to improve water quality. Witnesses, including a Western Oil and Gas Association spokesman, had defended the practice of polluting Los Angeles Harbor at the rate of 60,000 barrels of petroleum refinery waste per day. The reluctance of state and regional water-quality control boards to act on pollution problems had become notorious. Was this because of their composition? the *Times* asked. By law five of the seven seats on such boards were occupied by actual or potential polluters: industry, government, agriculture, public utilities. One was occupied by fish and game interests. Only one was allotted to the general public.

The industry member on the Los Angeles Regional Board happened to be Thomas Gaines of Union Oil, who had been placed in charge of the company's pollution-control effort at Santa Barbara. Yet for years Union had been dumping oily refinery waste into Los Angeles Harbor. For more than fifteen months it had been contesting a pollution citation issued by the Department of Fish and Game, not denying guilt but claiming the department had no jurisdiction. Meanwhile Union's pollution of the harbor had continued.

The *Times* commented: "The ridiculous, built-in conflict of interest in the state's regional water quality control boards should end."

A web of circumstances and attitudes was coming to light. Union Oil and the Santa Barbara spill occupied a position at or near its center.

The Bureau of Commercial Fisheries research vessel, *David Starr Jordan,* was making observations in the vicinity of Platform A. It found phytoplankton and microzooplankton drastically reduced in comparison with counts made a month before in the same area. Fish eggs and larvae were present in usual quantity, including eggs and larvae of anchovies and larvae of rockfish and hake. Near-surface nutrients such as nitrates, silicates, and phosphates from under the slick showed no chemical differences when compared to samples from nearby clear water. However, dissolved-oxygen content below the slick was significantly less than in non-oily water. But that was not all. Scientists in the *Jordan*'s submerged observatory, who thought that Santa Barbara's spill had ended, were surprised to see oil rising from the ocean floor. It rose in company with three gas boils each about ten yards in diameter. Thick oil covered an area approximately twenty times as large as that of the gas, or about 1,600 square yards. The scientists estimated the flow rate of the oil at 1,500 to 3,000 gallons per day. On the surface, a slick extended downwind as far as they could see.

When the *Jordan* returned to its berth at San Pedro on Wednesday morning, February 12, Dr. Paul Smith, its research director, notified Eleventh Coast Guard District Headquarters of the escaping oil and the growing slick. District Headquarters in turn notified Lieutenant Brown.

Late Wednesday afternoon, the *News-Press* received an anonymous telephone call. A man's voice said that oil was escaping in large quantities from under Platform A and a new slick was developing. It was too late to send a plane up, but an overflight by reporters next morning confirmed the truth of the call.

The fact that, once again, private individuals—not government or oil company spokesmen—had revealed the existence of the leak, added fuel to the popular fury. It strengthened the community's new determination to rid the channel of all oil operations, no matter how long and hard the struggle.

13

"THE PRESIDENT MAY SAVE US"

WHAT HAD CAUSED the new leakage? A Union spokesman said it came from shallow sands pressurized by gas from below. A few days later the oil was described as rising up the bore of Well A-21 and reaching the surface through ocean-bottom fissures with openings as wide as twenty feet. A two-man submarine had descended into one of them. By then the flow was estimated by Union itself at 2,000 to 4,000 gallons per day.

Why hadn't the government or the oil company detected the leakage and made it publicly known? Bad weather had curtailed the Coast Guard's surveillance flights; but Lieutenant Brown learned later that the leakage had never really stopped, it had been going on all the time. Union Oil officials declined to be interviewed on this controversial question.

Santa Barbarans turned to the White House for help in a situation that seemed to them intolerable. The President's interest was already evident. He would, it seemed, gain political mileage from the new public concern for the environment if he intervened on Santa Barbara's side. On the day after the new leakage at Platform A was detected, he had announced the appointment of a special investigative panel. Known as the President's Panel on Oil Spills, it was headed by Dr. John C. Calhoun, Jr., vice president of Texas A&M University, a former Department of Interior science advisor and a recognized expert in petroleum engineering. Its thirteen members were authorities in geology, engineering, and marine science from California and other states; and its announced purpose was to "consider problems relating to oil spills, beginning with the one at Santa Barbara."

The panel appeared on-scene on February 18. It inspected the shoreline, overflew the channel, and held an executive session at the University of California's campus from which press and public were barred. This created further resentment among Santa Barbarans, who had been excluded from more conferences on their environment than they cared to remember. Emerging from the executive session Chairman Calhoun promised recommendations soon. He said that, in a sense, Santa Barbarans were "guinea pigs" undergoing an experience for the benefit of the rest of the nation.

The guinea pigs were not flattered. The cost of the experiment seemed to them too high. Still, the President had acted. He might do more despite the fact that Hickel had already indicated what the Administration's course of action would probably be. On February 19, he issued stricter regulations for federal offshore leases. One of them held oil companies absolutely liable for the cost of cleaning up pollution. Hickel's new regulations told the companies: "You can have your oil but you've got to be more careful how you get it." The regulations told Santa Barbara it was not going to get oil out of the channel, not yet, anyway.

Hickel's guidelines seemed confirmed when Nixon announced he could not see Mayor Firestone. The President was leaving soon for his first official visit to Europe. But on February 20, Nixon took note of pollution problems, including oil spills, while commending Hickel for his handling of them. Hickel had announced suspension of all U.S. offshore oil lease sales. Next day, February 21, the White House announced it was resuming control of the nation's oil import program. Control of the program had been entrusted to the Interior Department during the Johnson Administration, ostensibly to avoid conflict of interest on the part of a Texas President closely tied to the oil industry. By resuming control at this moment, the President seemed to express personal concern with the issues aroused by the Santa Barbara spill.

While Santa Barbara and the oil companies waited for the report of the President's Panel on Oil Spills, Hickel gave Union permission to pump oil from one of Platform A's completed wells, A-38, with the idea of relieving pressure on the shallow sands it penetrated. A-38 was a slanted hole completely cased and sealed off in its lower reaches by a cement plug. The company planned to perforate the casing for a distance of 60 feet opposite shallow oil sands, beginning about 300 feet below the ocean floor. This might permit oil and gas to flow into the well and thus relieve pressure on the leakage area. But after a day's trial there was no change in the amount of the leakage.

Hickel then approved reopening of Well A-21 to a depth of 175 feet and the perforation of its casing in the hope that two pumping wells might reduce the flow of oil. They did not.

Next, on February 22, the President's panel recommended that all five wells on Platform A be reopened and pumped "at maximum rate" to relieve subterranean pressure that might be forcing oil to the surface.

Santa Barbarans protested loudly. Pumping oil from under Platform A seemed to them like playing Russian roulette with the channel's ecology and the city's future. As if confirming their fears, the leakage increased. A southeast wind blew the oil ashore, re-blackening the beaches in time for the impending visit of Senator Muskie's Senate Subcommittee on Air and Water Pollution.

While Union talked of placing funnel-shaped metal chimneys over the leaks, oil floated away by the hundreds of gallons and joined older oil that was drifting up and down the coast. Northward, the slick had rounded Point Conception, fouling beaches as it went, and creating a public uproar, and touched at Pismo, about 80 miles from Santa Barbara. Southward, oil had appeared off the western end of Santa Catalina Island, 100 miles away.

Even the beach cleanup had hit a snag. There was no place to put the debris. Dumps were full. Union began burning piles of oily straw and driftwood on the beaches. This in turn polluted the atmosphere with oily black smoke. Confusion and ineptness prevailed, while the earth continued to bleed from its man-inflicted wound, and the environment continued to suffer.

Union's efforts to contain the oil escaping to the ocean's surface were no more successful than its efforts to clean it up. "Operation Sea Sweep," with its huge V-shaped booms, had not worked. Each arm of the "V" was a 20-inch-diameter steel pipe 800 feet long. The huge apparatus was towed by two tugs; and a vacuum barge was waiting to be stationed inside the neck of the "V" to pump out the trapped oil. But the booms were damaged by heavy seas and the whole device was taken ashore and dismantled.

Against this background, Senator Muskie's Subcommittee on Air and Water Pollution met in Santa Barbara on February 24 and 25. Santa Barbarans pinned their hopes to the hearing. Congressional attention might spur presidential action. There was a clearly developing rivalry between Muskie and Nixon for leadership in the oil-spill issue and in the national environmental questions it represented.

At their own level, local citizens took the well-trodden path to the supervisors' hearing room hoping that hidden truths about what had happened and was happening at Platform A—and what the oil spill was doing to the channel's ecology—would be revealed. They already knew that, except for birds, damage to animal and plant life had been less than expected. In intertidal areas where contamination had been particularly heavy, many sand fleas, sand crabs, red worms, anemones, alga, mussels, barnacles, rock oysters, and cockles were dead or injured. They had literally been smothered in the oil. But sea lettuce and other bottom-growing plants had apparently escaped massive injury. It was too early to tell about the giant kelp beds, and long-term effects on all forms of intertidal and near-shore life remained to be seen.

There was sharp disagreement about the effect of the spill on fish. Some reports said that no fish had been caught in commercial quantities since the spill began; but whether this meant that fish were being killed by oil, or were merely avoiding it, was debatable. Some observers claimed that absence of visible dead fish indicated that few were being killed; others insisted that dead fish sank or were quickly eaten, and thus absence of corpses proved nothing. Still others attributed a lack of commercial-size schools to an unusual drop in water temperature and heavy siltation following the recent floods.

Similarly with marine mammals, some authorities found evidence of serious damage; others did not. Dead or dying seals (six in one week) or sea lions were found coated with oil, but Fish and Game Department spokesmen insisted their number was normal and that the fact that they were stained by oil might be incidental.

Attention had focused on the gray whales, migrating northward in large numbers. Fred Hartley had photographed them and informed his stockholders they were apparently in good health and untroubled by Union oil. But Dr. Robert Orr found oil in the mouth and baleen of a 30-ton gray whale that was washed up dead on a San Francisco beach. Dr. Orr, curator of mammals at the California Academy of Sciences, said oil could have caused the animal's death; and he found it significant that three dead whales should have come ashore in Northern California, after passing through the Santa Barbara Channel. When two more were found dead in the same area within a few days, there was a loud public protest and the Interior Department ordered an inquiry. Clark T. Cameron of Los Angeles, president of the American Cetacean Society, wired President Nixon asking him to convene a meeting of experts to devise a means of diverting the whales from their usual route through the channel. Cameron told newsmen that the number dead was "too large to be mere coincidence" and that for every known dead whale "many more might rest on the bottom."

In the cold water of a winter sea, bacterial action would be inhibited, scientists pointed out, and bloating would not occur, thus permitting carcasses to sink to the bottom.

At the last moment Senator Muskie could not be present for the Santa Barbara hearing of his Senate subcommittee. His colleague, Senator Joseph Montoya, a New Mexico Democrat, presided. Under Montoya's questioning, D. W. Solanas, speaking as Regional Oil and Gas Supervisor for the Department of Interior's Geological Survey, disclosed that there had been only one inspector on duty for all of the channel's federal drilling operations at the time of the Well A-21 blowout. The inspector had not visited Platform A once during the time Well A-21 was being drilled. Solanas denied, however, that the presence of an inspector would have prevented the blowout. The drilling of Well A-21 had followed procedures approved in advance by his office. It was "Mother

Earth" who broke down, Solanas said, echoing Hartley's statement at the earlier hearing. Solanas defended the waiver of rules which had permitted Union to place casing to a depth of only 239 feet below the ocean floor, rather than 880 feet, before drilling further. An oil-bearing sand began immediately below the 239-foot level. To drill into it without first placing casing and installing blowout-prevention equipment would not have been safe. In response to questioning from Montoya and Cranston as to why Union did not add casing periodically as the well went deeper instead of waiting until it was finished, Solanas said this would not have been feasible because there was no geologic structure strong enough to cement the casing to.

Solanas' testimony was contradicted by John Fraser, the Union vice president, who said it would have been feasible to cement the casing at 1,200 feet or at 1,800 feet. Had this been done, said Fraser, there might have been no blowout.

Francis J. Hortig, executive officer of the California State Lands Division which supervised drilling in state waters, said it was standard practice in state wells to require casing to 1,000 or 1,200 feet, or to a geologic formation firm enough to cement to. Hortig said he would have required such casing had Well A-21 been in state waters.

Senator Cranston asked Hortig what he would have done had there been a continuous sand from 260 to 3,000 feet, as Solanas suggested there was. Hortig said he had never heard of such a geologic structure but if confronted with the problem of drilling through it, "very definite additional protective measures would have to be considered." They would depend upon pressures known or believed to exist, upon the terms of existing safety programs, and upon the weight of mud employed; and they might include the use of double blowout-prevention equipment and of heavier surface equipment "so there could be assurance that the entire sand body could be penetrated without any hazard of having a blowout."

The hearing was going favorably for Santa Barbara. It was about to go more favorably.

Lieutenant Brown had been called out of the room. When he returned somewhat breathlessly, there was a stir at the witnesses' table. Brown brought interesting news. A large new outbreak of oil had occurred at Platform A. Down-hole work by Union in Well A-41, intended to relieve the leakage from Well A-21, had caused the new outbreak.

The Senate subcommittee hearing revealed that both government and oil company might have been negligent, even grossly negligent, in their supervision and drilling of Well A-21; while the renewed outbreak of oil seemed to say that God was not dead but active on Santa Barbara's side.

As if to prove His presence, on the night after the hearing a bolt of lightning struck Platform Hilda, owned by Standard of California, situated in state waters about four miles from Platform A. The bolt ignited a gas vent which burned spectacularly for three hours. Oil people dismissed the incident as minor. Anti-oil people thought they knew better: someone up there cared. From far corners of the earth came telephone calls and letters assuring them that they were right. If further evidence was needed, the Santa Clara River near Ventura rose next day, snatched three Union Oil storage tanks off their foundations, and carried them out into a channel already awash with Union Oil.

The new outbreak of oil played into Santa Barbara's blackened hands. It revealed Goliath's ineptness, and it invited an end to public patience. The associated students organization at the University of California at Santa Barbara had already endorsed the community's get-oil-out position. Many of them had attended the subcommittee hearing. A student environmental study group called Campus Organization for a Pure Environment had adopted the oil spill as one of its projects. A militant disillusion was growing among young and old; but it was particularly prevalent among the young who saw their beaches and their future being polluted, in a grandly inept display, and they tended to blame it on their elders and on the prevailing social system.

The new leakage also radicalized legislators. A few days before it occurred, Congressman Teague had introduced a bill to ban all channel drilling permanently. Teague's bill called for the federal government to buy back its leases. Told this might cost a billion dollars, Teague replied: "If you had another of these disasters, there could be a dead sea off Southern California. And that's worth more than a billion dollars!"

Three days after the February 25 outbreak, Senator Alan Cranston, the California Democrat, took the hard line, too. He also introduced a bill to ban totally all drilling in the channel's federal water. Cranston said he had been convinced by experts that offshore oil platforms, wells, pipelines to shore, and storage tanks on shore were not built strongly enough to withstand Santa Barbara earthquakes. Major quakes rocked the fault-flawed channel region on an average of every fifty years and lesser ones every ten years. No less than sixty-six small quakes had centered in the channel during the summer and fall of 1968, while Platform A was being erected. Quoting a well-known geologist Cranston went on to say that drilling for oil on a sea floor in such a state of geological ferment could be compared with gambling. He strongly advised revoking all leases and declaring all oil fields off Southern California to be federal petroleum reserves.

Following the Senate subcommittee hearing, the Nixon Administration's representative, Senator Robert Dole of Kansas, remained an extra day in Santa Barbara to investigate the situation personally. After visiting Platform A and conferring with federal officials, Dole telephoned Secretary Hickel and proposed a solution to the interdepartmental conflict between the Brown-De Falco-Biglane command trio and the offshore command authority represented by Standley, Acuff, and Solanas. Hickel agreed with Dole's proposal and ruled that the U.S. Geological Survey had jurisdiction over pollution problems seaward of the three-mile limit, while the Federal Water Pollution Control Administration retained control within three miles from shore.

As on-scene Contingency Plan commander, Lieutenant Brown retained coordinative control of the entire defense effort. However, ironically enough, Eugene W. Standley, who had done so much to bring about channel leasing, was placed in charge of controlling pollution at Platform A.

Meanwhile the Washington scene was not without ironies of its own. On February 28, Secretary Hickel told another session of the Muskie subcommittee that "we, the public, are the real owners [of offshore oil lands]," and that the federal government should acquire its own offshore geological information rather than rely on oil companies. Hickel, echoing sentiments expressed by the Santa Barbara supervisors two years earlier, followed up his statement with telegrams to all channel oil operators asking for geological data on their wells.

For Santa Barbara as well as the rest of the nation, a new Hickel was emerging. Three days later he told a wildlife resources conference: "We must take into consideration whether revenue from offshore leases . . . offsets the harm that might come to the surrounding area." And on March 13, Hickel urged the House Merchant Marine Committee to confirm by legislation his right to impose absolute unlimited liability on oil companies—without proof of fault—for pollution resulting from offshore drilling. Even Senator Muskie was pleased. Originally one of Hickel's severest critics, he was finding the Secretary's attitude "positive and constructive."

The spill was making itself felt in Washington in further ways. Dr. Walter Mead, one of the nation's leading petroleum economists, had come from Santa Barbara to testify before the Senate's Antitrust and Monopoly Subcommittee. Mead told Senator Edward M. Kennedy, the committee's chairman, that federal subsidies to oil companies cost consumers at least $4 billion a year and that such subsidies should be phased out. Kennedy replied that proponents of subsidies claimed they were necessary for national security because they made certain that the United States would have adequate domestic petroleum supplies in time of war.

Mead, a professor at the University of California at Santa Barbara and president of the Western Economic Association, answered that oil companies maintained several years' supply of domestic reserves; in addition there were about 600 billion barrels of oil contained in the oil shale of Rocky Mountain states, which technology could make available during an emergency.

At the conclusion of the hearing, Kennedy said that subsidies and import quotas "appeared to have cost the American consumer $40 to $50 billion over the past ten years." Earlier Mead had explained how these subsidies worked. The price of oil was artificially high, he had said, because of restricted supply. Oil industry costs were artificially low because of special benefits. High price and low cost were the result of four federal subsidies. The first of these was the depletion allowance which exempted $27\frac{1}{2}$ percent of an oil producer's gross income from federal tax (up to a limit of 50 percent of his net income from an oil property). The depletion allowance reduced a producer's tax by about half, while greatly encouraging production.

The second subsidy was production control. By restricting production, it kept prices high.

The third subsidy was taxpayer support of U.S. oil companies' foreign operations. When an oil company produced oil from lands owned by others, it normally paid a royalty to the resource owner. In the United States, such royalty payments were tax deductible expenses like other necessary expense of doing business; but when paid to foreign governments, they were deductible from U.S. federal income tax.

This meant that highly profitable operations might pay small or no income tax if their expenses included substantial royalty payments to foreign governments. For example, most large U.S. corporations not in the oil business had an effective federal income tax rate of about 50 percent. By contrast, the Standard Oil Company of New Jersey, with large foreign operations, had an effective rate averaging less than 4 percent during the 1962–1966 period, although the firm had net income greater than $1 billion annually.

Finally there was a fourth subsidy. It arose because oil companies without access to extensive foreign supplies found that imports were depressing the price of domestic oil. They exerted pressure on the federal government to impose import quotas. (The import quota program was established in 1959, during a period when Herbert Hoover, Jr., the Union Oil Company director, was advising the Eisenhower Administration on worldwide oil matters and serving as Undersecretary of State.) The effect of import quotas, together with production control, was to maintain an artificially high domestic price. For example, in February, 1969, the world price of a barrel of oil was less than $2; the domestic price was more than $3.

"If subsidies were removed," Mead argued, "the price of oil in the United States would decline to about $2 per barrel, and the cost of oil production would rise. Under these conditions, there would be no drilling in the Santa Barbara Channel, because it would be unprofitable."

Mead had suggested that Santa Barbarans work for a phasing out of the four-point subsidy system as a means of bringing channel oil operations to an end.

Airing such statements in a forum as conspicuous as Capitol Hill put the oil industry on the defensive as it never had been before. Santa Barbara's counteroffensive against oil was becoming a national counteroffensive.

"If you have a feeling the petroleum industry is taking a public beating these days in Washington you are right," the *Oil and Gas Journal*, the industry's leading mouthpiece, commented.

Over on the House side of Capitol Hill, Congressman Henry S. Reuss, a Wisconsin Democrat, was charging that a secret White House-authorized study showed that oil and gas companies had escaped some $2.25 billion in federal income taxes in 1968 alone. According to United Press International, the study, made by the Consad Research Corporation of Pittsburgh, had investigated the 27½ percent tax depletion allowance and other benefits allegedly enjoyed by oil and gas interests. "Now the study is completed and its results printed and the public can't see it," Reuss charged. He added that the study might be just what was needed to speed congressional action to plug the depletion allowance loophole.

In fact, the Consad Report, instigated by the Johnson Administration, supported Walter Mead's contention that tax-law loopholes encouraged excessive drilling and inefficient oil production.

Three days later, the White House released the controversial report without comment. White House watchers interpreted this noncommittal release as favorable to oil-tax reform and to new controls over the oil industry. Further, Republican Senator Clifford P. Case of New Jersey had raised the question of the possible threat to Atlantic Coast beaches caused by offshore drilling there; and Representative Keith Hastings, a Massachusetts Republican, had urged the House Merchant Marine and Fisheries Committee to propose a two-year moratorium on offshore drilling in federal waters, so that studies could be made of ways to prevent Santa Barbara-type disasters.

By March 15, there were forty-four bills in Congress dealing with pollution, chiefly oil pollution. Most of them had been introduced since the Santa Barbara spill.

Former Secretary Udall's testimony before the Muskie subcommittee had been a chief feature of the new congressional interest in environment. "A presidential decision had been made about getting more money to balance the budget," Udall said, describing the origins of federal leasing in the Santa Barbara Channel. He labeled the oil spill "a conservation Bay of Pigs." But Udall pleased the Nixon Administration by saying he favored tighter drilling regulations, tougher enforcement, and improved geologic information; and he pleased the oil companies by declining to recommend a permanent ban on channel drilling.

Udall's testimony seemed to make presidential intervention more than ever unlikely.

While these developments were taking place in Washington, there had been new legal action at Santa Barbara. On February 18, the State of California joined with the County of Santa Barbara, and the cities of Santa Barbara and Carpinteria, in filing a $500,000 claim against the Interior Department. On February 24 the same public entities had filed a $560,006,000 damage suit in Superior Court in Santa Barbara against the four owners of Platform A and their contractor, Peter Bawden Drilling Incorporated. Like the claim against the Interior Department, the suit asked payment for damage to wildlife and beaches, plus payment for general damages including injury to offshore lands that supported marine life and to resort areas that attracted tourist trade.

When added to the earlier class-action claims, these new moves brought the total sought from oil companies and drilling contractor to $1,860,006,000 and total claims of all kinds resulting from the spill to $2,360,006,000.

A few days later, a Santa Barbara attorney, James Oppen, filed a $1.51 billion antitrust, class suit against the oil companies and their insurance companies on behalf of local boat owners. Oppen's complaint alleged that Aetna, All State, Travelers, State Farm Mutual, and other insurance firms involved on behalf of the Platform A group, had entered into a "conspiracy" not to pay oil-spill damages to boat owners unless the owners agreed not to sue for "loss of use." Oppen's suit brought total claims against oil companies and government to nearly $4 billion.

On March 1 the environmentalist lawyer, Victor J. Yannacone, Jr., arrived in Santa Barbara. He came as a potential savior. Backing him was the prestigious Environmental Defense Fund numbering more than one hundred distinguished scientists headed by Charles F. Wurster, Jr., of the State University of New York, who had done probably more than anyone else to demonstrate the harmful effects of DDT on living organisms. Yannacone had a powerful sector of the U.S. scientific community behind him. At a time when scientists were reluctant to involve themselves in public issues, this was an important factor. Yannacone had just gained a milestone victory in the New York State DDT case (*Yannacone v. Suffolk County Mosquito Control Commission*) and was pressing actions against DDT in Michigan and Wisconsin and air pollution in Montana.

Nobody had higher visibility in the field of environmental law. If Yannacone took Santa Barbara's case to the U.S. Supreme Court, the least it could do would be to put pressure on White House and Congress to take action in the channel. The most it could do would be to halt channel drilling through legal injunction.

The thirty-two-year-old Yannacone proved to be fiery, intelligent, and abrasive. "The next revolution will be the Environmental Revolution!" he announced, adding that what can't be settled in the courts will be settled in the streets. He hoped to establish a body of environmental law analogous to the civil rights law established by the American Civil Liberties Union, the NAACP, and similar litigants.

So far the courts had not accepted Yannacone's novel doctrines about the individual's constitutional right to a livable environment, but he was not discouraged. "We'll keep on suing the bastards," he said. However, his estimate of the cost of a full-scale suit based on the Santa Barbara disaster—$214,000 plus or minus 10 percent—was discouraging to Santa Barbarans. Many anti-oil leaders were put off. But a new citizens organization had taken shape under the impetus of Yannacone's visit. Composed of scientists, lawyers, teachers, writers, housewives, and newsmen, Santa Barbara Citizens for Environmental Defense was making legal action its primary objective. It decided to investigate Yannacone's offer further. Its chairman, Dr. Norman K. Sanders, an environmental scientist at the University of California at Santa Barbara, went to New York with Dick Smith of the *News-Press* staff and met with Yannacone and leaders of the National Audubon Society who were helping Yannacone financially through their Rachel Carson Fund. Sanders and Smith learned that law school professors had been working with Yannacone to gain experience in environmental law, their salaries paid by National Audubon. Unpaid volunteers were coming forward too. Scientists were donating their time. Perhaps something similar could be arranged in Santa Barbara on a do-it-yourself basis that would bring the oil spill to the Supreme Court as an environmental and civil rights issue, at a cost of less than $214,000.

"The President may save us," a Santa Barbaran said wryly, "but he may need a little help from us."

Helpful pressures were arising, too, in the channel itself. One year after oil operators had spent $602,719,261.60 on its leases, it was proving a surprising disappointment. Oil had been found in only three places: Union's Tract 402, Sun's adjacent Tract 401, and Humble's Tract 342 about five miles off Point Conception. Of 44 wells reported drilled, 31 had been dry holes or been abandoned for other reasons. At a cost of $250,000 to $1,300,000 per hole, this was hurting. In addition, the enforced shutdown of drilling and production was costing operators an estimated $300,000 a day.

"It's ironical," said the *Oil and Gas Journal*, "that after the millions spent on leases and explorations, the first oil produced came in on the tide."

There was even a feeling that channel oil operations were jinxed. Before the blowout, two work boats had sunk and a ferrying helicopter had crashed. After the blowout, a kelp-cutting vessel had sunk without a trace during the height of the leakage. Then the leakage had resumed. Then it had increased. Then lightning had struck Platform Hilda, and flood waters had carried away Union's storage tanks. More than a dozen men had died in events connected in some way with channel oil operations.

Now, on March 14, a rumor spread that Pauley Petroleum Incorporated was asking the Interior Department for the return of the $73,854,594 bonus it and its associates had paid for channel lease tracts 375 and 384, off Rincon. When the report was confirmed, it became the first break in the industry's solid front—the first tangible evidence of victory Santa Barbara oil fighters had yet been given.

At the same time Congressman Teague and Senator Cranston were proposing an exchange of channel leases for similar leases in the U.S. Navy Elk Hills Reserve in nearby Kern County, itself once the subject of a national controversy. The Elk Hills Reserve had achieved notoriety in the 1920s as part of the disgraceful Teapot Dome Scandal. President Warren G. Harding's Interior Secretary, Albert Fall, had persuaded Secretary of the Navy Edwin Denby to transfer the Elk Hills and Teapot Dome, Wyoming, oil reserves to the Interior Department. Fall then leased both of them, without competitive bidding, to two private oil producers, Harry F. Sinclair of New York, and E. L. Doheny, the Los Angeles oilman. In return for arranging the deal, Fall received $100,000 from Doheny for Elk Hills and $300,000 from Sinclair for Teapot Dome. A Senate investigation and court trials forced Fall and Denby to resign from Harding's cabinet. Fall was later convicted of accepting a bribe and was sent to prison.

Since 1928, Elk Hills' 46,000 arid treeless acres at the southern extremity of the San Joaquin Valley had been administered by the Navy, with the Standard Oil Company of California as standby operator. Production had been 65,000 barrels daily at the end of World War II. It was now reduced to 6,500 barrels, against a capability of 175,000 barrels. Total reserves were at least 1.3 billion barrels, perhaps twice that amount.

The Teague-Cranston plan called for channel oil operators to receive Elk Hills oil to the value of whatever their channel leases proved to be. Details would require working out, but the plan had the appeal of an arrangement in which relatively little cash would change hands.

At last the mechanics of how oil might be gotten out of the channel were appearing. But would the President heed them?

GOO was presenting guerrilla theater. If nothing else, it let off steam and helped raise money. Entitled *Barbara's Fatal Fault,* or *Oil's Well That Ends Well (Drilling),* The People's Melodrama and Variety Show had been written and produced by volunteers from the South Coast community. Its message was not hard to follow. The hacienda of Barbara, a virtuous maiden, was coveted by greedy men in search of buried treasure. They were led by Derrick, Earl of Union, and by Lawyer Clutch. Sludge and Ethyl did their bit, as did Scoop, the crusading editor who uncovered hanky-panky between the exploiters and their two agents in government, Uncle and Stu Weedall.

Barbara's Fatal Fault played to full houses at San Marcos High School auditorium and netted $3,500 for GOO's needy budget. At GOO's downtown office, provided rent-free by a cooperative attorney, seventy-five women were answering letters and mailing literature. Ten thousand copies of a special *News-Press* oil-spill supplement went to newspapers and radio-TV stations throughout the United States, to all members of Congress, and to hundreds of individual inquirers. The Illinois Division of Beaches and Parks requested ten thousand anti-oil petition forms, and twenty-five Americans living in Switzerland had already signed. Australians wrote offering help and asking assistance in protecting their shoreline from drilling. Canadians and Americans living near Lake Erie, often described as North America's "dead sea" as result of pollution, were particularly interested. GOO offshoots had appeared in Sacramento, Laguna Beach, Harvard University, and Washington, D.C., to name some of more than a dozen that had sprung up; and GOO's leaders were preparing to take sixty thousand signatures to the White House, now that the President had returned from his meetings with Charles de Gaulle and Prime Minister Wilson.

The White House itself was being flooded by mail from many quarters. Some 1,300 letters and telegrams had been received. Congressional offices reported about 7,750. The Federal Water Pollution Control Administration announced it was receiving so many inquiries and suggestions concerning the spill that it was establishing a special office to cope with them. More than 3,500 ideas were eventually processed.

But was the President heeding and if he was, would he act?

On the fiftieth day of the Santa Barbara spill, oil was still seeping from locations from which it seeped on the first day, along an east-west line about 1,500 feet long generally following the fault line under Platform A; and Union was still trying without much success to stop it. Cleanup crews were working as far away as Gaviota, 35 miles to the west. They might have spread out over 250 miles, because oil had come ashore at beaches from Pismo to the Mexican border—severely contaminating Southern California's prime recreational seashores at Santa Monica, Laguna, and San Diego.

Was the President heeding? His connections with the channel

area were long and personal. As a student at Whittier College he had visited Santa Barbara and enjoyed its beaches. As a young Communist-hunting Republican Congressman, he had made his decision to run for the Senate at Democrat Alvin Weingand's secluded San Ysidro Ranch Hotel. Nixon's two daughters had attended boarding school in Montecito. He would be no stranger to Santa Barbara if he came.

Suddenly he was coming. On Wednesday, March 19, he announced he would visit Santa Barbara the following Friday, stopping in Independence, Missouri, to see former President Harry Truman on the way.

14

"CONGRESS MAY SAVE US"

NIXON BOARDED a Navy helicopter at Point Mugu Naval Air Station and flew forty miles over oil-stained channel and beaches, arriving in Santa Barbara at 3:25 P.M. on a cloudy afternoon.

Three thousand people were waiting for him at a roped-off area on the waterfront. Many were school children. Some carried Get Oil Out! signs. Weingand was waiting with sixty thousand anti-oil signatures to be presented to the President. On the beach itself, workers in yellow rainsuits were making a show of raking a beach they had already cleaned several times.

It was an emotional moment. The President of the United States had heeded the citizens' call of distress. His plane would land in an ocean-front parking lot and he would walk on oil-soaked sand. If there was a bond between government and governed, here it was in the flesh, its meaning heightened by the events of the past fifty-four days. A young mother held her small child above her head so that he could see the President.

Bareheaded, wearing a dark suit, Nixon emerged from his helicopter smiling and relaxed. He was preceded by Mrs. Nixon, who wore a light green suit, and followed by Paul De Falco and

Dr. Gordon J. F. MacDonald, vice chancellor of the University of California at Santa Barbara, a member of the President's Oil Spill Panel.

Mayor Firestone and Supervisor Clyde greeted the presidential party. Waiting nearby were 150 newsmen, who surrounded Nixon and local officials, and all moved together toward the beach, while Firestone hammered away at a single theme: "Mr. President, the people of this community want the drilling stopped and the platforms removed!"

"Mr. Mayor," Nixon finally replied, "I think you've made your point!"

The President chatted with members of the cleanup crew, and then told newsmen: "The Santa Barbara incident has frankly touched the conscience of the American people." It was "sad," he said, that the oil spill was the example necessary to waken public and government to a new awareness of their responsibilities. He promised that his administration would do a better job on environmental problems than had been done in the past. While he was talking, an oily wave came up and soaked his shoes.

In the distance, the roped-off crowd was chanting: "Get Oil Out! Get Oil Out!"

Nixon brought word that the channel's 21,000-acre federal buffer zone was being converted to a "permanent ecological preserve" and that a new buffer zone of 34,000 acres was being added seaward of it. Furthermore, new and tougher drilling regulations were being put into effect for the entire California coast. Hickel had announced them in Washington earlier in the day.

The President promised to consider a permanent ban on drilling. Then he was airborne, whirling away toward Platform A, while a shaft of sunlight came through the clouds and spotlighted the source of the disaster for him.

He left mixed feelings. Most of the spectators were surprised and hurt that he had paid them no attention whatever. There had been no opportunity for Weingand to present the sixty thousand signatures.

Was the presidential visit merely a political show or would it lead to action? To have the Chief Executive bring proposals for protecting the channel environment was flattering. But there was probably little if any oil in the new buffer zone (no oil companies had bid on it after years of exploring it) and the new regulations (including additional casing requirements and increased blowout-prevention equipment) sounded like a poor substitute for banning channel drilling permanently.

The answer came soon but not in the form Santa Barbarans expected. Although on March 21 Hickel had announced that the drilling ban would "continue indefinitely" while "exhaustive studies" were made, on April 1 he announced that the ban had been lifted. Ten days earlier he had said that it might be necessary to abandon Platform A entirely. Now he authorized renewed drilling on five leases: the original one held by Phillips off Carpinteria, two held by Mobil at the eastern end of the channel, and two by Humble off Point Conception. Hickel gave as justification for his action: (1) geological and engineering analyses of the five leases showed that more than 2,000 feet of protective geologic formations lay above the oil-bearing beds, (2) the oil companies had agreed to operate under stricter regulations, (3) the leases were at a substantial distance from Santa Barbara and from the blowout site.

Hickel might have added that he was under severe pressure from the oil companies. They had been losing upward of $300,000 a day for fifty-two days while the ban prevailed.

To most Santa Barbarans, the renewal of drilling was a further example of government perfidy. It seemed incredible.

George Clyde telegraphed the President: "A tragic mistake is being made which only you can correct." The *News-Press* published an open letter to Nixon on its front page, reminding him that when he had walked on Santa Barbara's beaches he had promised "to consider a permanent ban on drilling" and had rekindled community hopes. "We feel betrayed!" the *News-Press* said, and asked its readers to sign the editorial and mail it to the White House. Hundreds of them did. Many sent telegrams. Some telephoned the White House and expressed their views to presidential aides.

Any bond of confidence between Santa Barbara and the President relative to oil matters had been broken, and the harassed community was forced to look elsewhere for immediate relief.

Dr. Norman Sanders, a former member of the U.S. Fish and

Wildlife Service and now chairman of Santa Barbara Citizens for Environmental Defense, was making contact with scientists in various parts of the country. He hoped to enlist their help as expert witnesses in a citizens' lawsuit to halt channel drilling by injunction. But Sanders was meeting with difficulties. One prominent academic geologist had just received a grant from an oil company. Another was afraid he would lose his chance for promotion if he became involved. Several were working on federal grants, or hoped to get them. Despite the urgency and wide social significance of the problem, experts were reluctant to commit themselves.

The State of California was having similar difficulties in preparing its cases against oil companies and federal government. "There is an atmosphere of fear," Charles A. O'Brien, California's chief deputy attorney general, charged. "Experts are afraid that if they assist us in our case they will lose their oil industry grants." O'Brien attacked what he called industry domination of university researchers. "Should a University of California professor being paid $20,000 a year by the taxpayers have outside employment for say $65,000 a year which may interfere with his giving his expert knowledge to the state on an important matter such as oil pollution?"

O'Brien noted that lawyers in the attorney general's office were forbidden to take outside cases or do private legal consulting and suggested that the rule be extended to cover state university and college professors.

The chairman of the department of petroleum engineering at the University of Southern California admitted that universities were beholden to oil companies for financial support. "There isn't any doubt about it," he was quoted as saying. "We train people mainly for the oil companies, but that doesn't mean we have sold out to them." Similarly, a professor of petroleum engineering at the University of California at Berkeley said he would not testify for the state "because my work depends on good relations with the petroleum industry. . . . I view my obligation to the community as supplying it with well-trained petroleum engineers."

The University of Southern California declined to reveal the sources of its oil industry funding; but the California Institute of Technology, where Fred Hartley was a trustee and whose president, Dr. Lee A. DuBridge, had recently become White House science advisor, revealed later that it had received $1,379,035 from oil or gas companies during the period 1966 through 1969. Among Caltech's major donors were Standard of California with $176,755, Atlantic Richfield with $133,500, and Union with $111,850. The American Petroleum Institute gave $139,230.

The University of California, where oilman Edwin W. Pauley was a member of the Board of Regents, said it had received $987,768 from oil or gas companies during the period 1966 through 1969. Leading donors were Shell with $283,567 and Standard of California with $157,253. The American Petroleum Institute contributed $143,556.

University spokesmen were quick to point out that oil industry gifts represented a small percentage of total private donations. At Caltech it was 5 percent; at the University of California about 1.6 percent. Nevertheless, petroleum was a presence in academia. At the University of California, for example, Regent Pauley was shown to have been a substantial contributor in an arrangement some people questioned. Senior officials of the university had formed a nonprofit corporation and reached an agreement with Pauley Petroleum Incorporated whereby the nonprofit corporation borrowed $5.8 million from the First National Bank of Chicago and loaned it to Pauley. The loan was to be repaid to the bank at $6\frac{1}{4}$ percent interest, while Pauley was to repay the university's nonprofit corporation at $6\frac{3}{8}$ percent. The difference of one-eighth of one percent, amounting to an estimated $30,000, was to be retained by the university.

Repayment money was to come from the sale of oil and gas produced in the Huntington Beach and Santa Barbara Channel areas. To oil's opponents in Santa Barbara and elsewhere, this was an edifying if not particularly encouraging disclosure.

Two Republican state assemblymen, one from Leucadia, the other from Huntington Beach, charged that Regent Pauley, and University of California President Charles J. Hitch, and the university, were involved in a possibly improper deal that might result in tax advantages of $823,000 to Pauley. They called for an investigation by the State Legislature.

The Pauley-U.C. arrangement had its origins in federal tax law that set a limit on the amount of deduction an oil producer could claim under the 27½ percent depletion allowance. Under an arrangement called a "carve out," a producer, through a middleman, could negotiate a loan secured by potential oil production. The middleman received a profit from merely conveying the loan.

Universities throughout the United States were described as eager to enter into this kind of an arrangement, because it brought them money with no risk. Pauley had already made similar arrangements with the universities of Chicago and Southern California.

The Santa Barbara Oil Spill thus reached further into the contemporary social structure.

By April 1, the Western Oil and Gas Association had contracted with the University of Southern California for a "no-strings-attached" scientific study of the oil spill's effect on the channel's ecology, to cost $240,000; and the federal government had let research contracts to: (1) Battelle Memorial Institute to develop a complete report of the oil-spill incident; (2) the San Diego Zoo to study the effects of oil on birds, and procedures for cleaning animals; (3) the University of California at Santa Barbara for a variety of studies related to the spill.

Meanwhile, a new and distressing aspect of the channel controversy appeared. As far back as March 19, oil had come ashore at Point Bennett on San Miguel Island in the vicinity of the seal herds. A ranger of the National Park Service had reported it to the State Fish and Game Department, but no public mention of it had been made by either state or federal officials. But on April 3, two scientists from the University of California at Santa Cruz, Richard Peterson and Burney Le Boeuf, reported that 200 of 1,250 young elephant seals they had tagged for study, during a four-day visit to the island, had been contaminated with oil. Oil covered nearly a mile of two rookery coves and was six to eight inches deep between the rocks there. Peterson and Le Boeuf had seen dead elephant seals and sea lions coated with oil. Several oil-smeared pups were having difficulty opening their eyes.

"This is really the first evidence of damage to vertebrate

Oil-soaked elephant seal, San Miguel Island.
B. J. LE BOEUF.

animals on a large scale from the oil slick," Dr. Peterson told newsmen.

Why hadn't public announcement been made? A spokesman for federal authorities said that calling public attention to the situation would invite intrusion by unauthorized visitors and that any attempt to clean up the oil or the polluted animals would disturb the seal herds and do them more harm than good. Though some experts agreed with him, public anger mounted. Once again government officials seemed to be concealing facts about the spill, while private citizens were revealing them.

Increasing these feelings, on Friday, April 4, a team of citizen divers, sponsored · by the Sierra Club, investigated ocean-floor conditions near Platform A. The group was led by a Jacques Cousteau aquanaut and included Dr. Glen Egstrom, a professor of physiology from the University of California at Los Angeles, and California Congressman John V. Tunney, son of the former heavyweight boxing champion. At a depth of 200 feet, Tunney found "a constant stream of gas bubbles and oil coming from holes in the sand." The holes were about a foot wide and eighteen inches deep. Oil was streaming from their centers. Dr. Egstrom said he saw four or five such holes in an area of thirty feet. He estimated the flow from one hole at one-quarter gallon per minute. Later findings indicated that holes of this type might have been blown open by the blowout, while others had been caused by centuries-long natural seepage.

The Sierra Club investigators concluded that approximately ten times more oil was escaping than the 1,000 gallons per day which Union and the U.S. Geological Survey estimated. Tunney called for a renewal of the drilling moratorium until the government's channel oil program could be investigated at public hearings.

In mounting anger and distrust over events such as these, a group of citizens headed by W. H. Ferry, vice president of Santa Barbara's Center for the Study of Democratic Institutions, announced that a public meeting would be held at the waterfront on Sunday, April 6. Hickel's peremptory lifting of the drilling ban was a further cause of grievance.

By the time people assembled for the meeting, the District Attorney had served notice on the channel operators who had resumed drilling that he would file charges against them under the California Criminal Code unless they stopped. The D.A. claimed that though drilling in federal waters was technically outside his or the state's jurisdiction, its effects—namely, a contaminating oil spill—were likely to be felt in the state's waters and on the state's shores, and thus drilling was actionable as a public nuisance. In Washington, Congressman Teague had written Secretary Hickel asking him to fire Dr. William T. Pecora, head of the U.S. Geological Survey, Teague saying he questioned the validity of Pecora's judgment in channel oil matters. State Fish and Game officials and *Los Angeles Times* reporters had visited San Miguel Island and found nine dead elephant seals coated with oil and thirty-five heavily coated and not likely to survive. Thirty more were seen with oil on their bodies. "The count was minimal," a department biologist said. "We don't know how many dead or dying seals were washed out to sea."

An irate Santa Barbara public next learned that the Signal Oil Company had been fined $500 in Municipal Court for permitting an onshore tank at Ellwood to overflow and spill some fifty barrels of oil into channel waters. It was a familiar human-error situation. A valve that should have been open was closed. A valve that should have been closed was open.

In addition to all this, Secretary Hickel, in an interview in Washington, described the Santa Barbara Oil Spill problem as "solved."

The citizens who gathered under the tall palms at the foot of Stearns Wharf, Sunday at 3 P.M., were in an angry and determined mood. Chairman Ferry stood on a natural podium of grass, an American flag on a staff at his right hand. At his left was an improvised resistance banner. It consisted of a black rattlesnake coiled on a yellow background, bearing the inscription, *Don't tread on me!* At his back was the troubled channel. He told his hearers they were up against the three "Ps"—Privilege, Politics, and Pollution. "Other Americans may not realize it but we are fighting their battles too."

As the meeting progressed, the violent feelings that had been seething rose nearer the surface. Finally, Vernon Johnson, an Air Force veteran, and the last speaker, suggested that something be done before the meeting broke up. "Let's walk out onto the wharf and write our names on some of those pieces of oil machinery!"

His suggestion found favor, particularly among younger listeners. One of them seized the American flag, another the yellow resistance banner. With the two flags at their head, about four hundred people, young and old, began marching out onto Stearns Wharf, to the surprise of scores of Sunday sightseers along the waterfront.

When they reached the end of the wharf, some of the marchers wrote their names on pieces of heavy equipment, others joked with workmen. One got into a scuffle with crewmen when he tried to smear grease on a work boat's side. Three policemen arrived. As they talked with some of the leaders, the atmosphere began to cool. All might have ended there; but as the crowd was returning along the wharf, it met two large trucks loaded with pipes that looked like oil-well casing. About a dozen persons sat down in front of the trucks.

As the police moved in, more protesters sat down, until about forty were seated on the splintery boards in front of the first truck. In resignation, the driver turned off his engine; the crowd began to sing "We Shall Get Oil Out!" to the tune of "We Shall Overcome!" followed by "America the Beautiful."

The driver restarted his engine and blew a blast on his horn. But the protesters refused to budge. Then the police moved in. The driver turned off his engine again and the crowd cheered. At 5:17 both trucks began backing off the wharf as the crowd roared its approval. It moved back to shore triumphantly, along with the trucks, and watched them drive off.

The march on the wharf raised serious questions. Was civil disobedience to become a weapon in the anti-oil fight?

The answer came two days later. There had been a long and tumultuous meeting of the City Council. It had finally terminated without action being taken on audience demands for renewed city control of Stearns Wharf and its closure to use by oil firms. After Mayor Firestone and other council members left the room, the crowd surged forward and occupied their seats.

Vernon Johnson was installed as "temporary mayor." He declared that the city government had broken down, but cautioned against rash acts, while urging his hearers to work for the election of a new mayor and councilmen.

But Bill Botwright, a prominent anti-oil fighter, jumped to the high counter before the council seats and urged the crowd, composed mostly of young people, to leave the room. "You're discrediting the entire anti-oil movement!" Botwright warned. Police appeared and the crowd dispersed.

Civic response went heavily against the extremists. GOO's leaders publicly disowned the City Hall disruptions. Civil disobedience went out of favor, at least for the time being. But the wharf had become an important symbol in the oil fight. A new militancy had been aroused that demanded outlet, and a number of citizens began daily picketing of the entrance to the wharf.

With the White House apparently unresponsive and their legal efforts apparently blocked by entrenched interests, Santa

Barbarans seemed to have no choice except to turn once more to Congress. Now the idea that "Congress may save us" was frequently expressed on State Street.

Senator Cranston had introduced a bill to terminate drilling on all of California's Outer Continental Shelf under jurisdiction of the federal government. A hearing on that bill had been set for mid-May. It would be held in Washington before the Senate Subcommittee on Minerals, Materials, and Fuels. As they prepared again to go to the national capital and present their case, Santa Barbarans looked around them and took stock.

On May 7—the one hundredth day of the spill— their view was mixed. On the positive side was the recent election of Mayor Firestone and two new City Council members. They gave the council a decidedly anti-oil cast. This had resulted in a council decision to study ways of regaining possession of Stearns Wharf for the city. Helping the decision along had been two weeks of peaceful picketing of the wharf by more than seventy citizens of both sexes and a variety of ages. They carried signs urging the public not to patronize the wharf's facilities as long as it served as a staging area for oil operations. Leading them was a prominent painting contractor, John Schaaf.

On another level, the District Attorney had warned the city to close its harbor to oil work boats or face the same criminal charges he was preparing against the channel's oil operators. He claimed that by letting the operators use the harbor, the city became an accessory to a misdemeanor.

Both city and county had joined in a civil suit seeking a permanent injunction against channel oil drilling. The joint suit alleged that drilling threatened irreparable damage to Santa Barbara's environment. In addition, it challenged the constitutionality of the Outer Continental Shelf Lands Act of 1953 on grounds that it delegated excessive power to the Secretary of the Interior, in matters of offshore drilling, by authorizing him to establish rules and regulations without holding public hearings.

These legal developments had received an unexpected assist when six independent companies holding leases on two channel tracts filed a $230 million damage suit against the federal government. They claimed the government's new regulations changed the terms of their leases and made it "economically and practically" impossible for them to continue operations. This was very good news to Santa Barbarans. The matter involved none other than Edwin W. Pauley, whose desire to "get out" had been rumored earlier. Suing with Pauley Petroleum were the J. M. Huber Corporation of Denver, Colorado; the Husky Oil Company of Delaware, with headquarters in Calgary, Alberta; Colorado Oil and Gas Corporation of Denver; Mesa Petroleum of Amarillo, Texas; and the McCulloch Oil Corporation of Los Angeles. The tracts concerned were 375 and 384 off Rincon, nearly at mid-channel.

The plaintiffs charged that Hickel's February 7 order halting drilling and a February 17 order imposing absolute liability for escaping oil—regardless of fault—constituted a taking of their interests. They charged that the government knew or should have known, when it leased its channel tracts, that the leases were in deep water in known fault areas subject to earthquake and tidal waves; that drilling would require operations reaching to the limits of existing technology; and that the tracts were in a channel heavily traveled by ships, adjacent to a densely populated coast.

The implication was that the government had invited the companies to operate in an area where risks were high. This was music to local ears. It sounded as though GOO had written the tune.

The plaintiffs claimed they were entitled to reimbursement for the "full value" of their leases: including $73,854,594 paid as bonus, plus the cost of exploitation, plus the value of oil discovered.

Questions immediately arose. No official announcement had been made of an oil discovery by the Pauley group. And weren't the plaintiffs aware of the risks when they offered their channel bid?

Though its purpose might have been, as some said, a cynical attempt to recover money lost in a bad gamble, the Pauley suit helped Santa Barbara's anti-oil effort in several ways. One member of the county's legal staff declared: "If we can get an expert to say in court what Pauley Petroleum has said in its complaint, we'll be well on our way toward securing an injunction."

In addition to these legal developments, a feeling was growing that regional and statewide planning were necessary, at once, if California's coastal environment was to be saved. A model for the idea was the San Francisco Bay Conservation and Development Commission which had successfully brought Bay Area cities and counties together in an effort to halt pollution and preserve natural resources. An assemblyman from the Los Angeles area now introduced a bill to create a Southern California Beach Study Commission. The SCBSC would study the coast from Santa Barbara to San Diego and produce a report by 1971. The report would be the basis for a regional shoreline authority, which could prevent pollution while preserving open space "for human pleasure and ecological survival."

Extending this idea to national level, W. H. Ferry, who had headed the April 6 citizens' meeting, told the U.S. Senate Subcommittee on Internal Affairs on April 24 that the deteriorating state of the American environment required the creation of a "National Ecological Authority." The authority would have power to prevent developments that might seriously disrupt the environment. Speaking as a Santa Barbaran who had seen what happened in the absence of such authority, Ferry affirmed: " 'Multiple-use' must be challenged sharply, since it has so often meant only equal opportunity to attack natural resources."

Walter Mead, the economist, joined the attack and said that national security would not be jeopardized by relying more heavily on foreign oil supplies. "Most of our imported oil comes from Venezuela, not from the Middle East as is commonly supposed. Moreover we have an eleven-year supply of domestic crude without using offshore reserves."

Hotly supporting Mead's contention was virtually all of New England. Senators Kennedy and Muskie, among others, wanted oil prices lowered there. Increased oil imports would do this, by reducing the price of a barrel of oil from about $3.50 to about $2.00. Kennedy was making the price of oil a number-one domestic issue in a campaign that many felt would lead to the Presidency.

There was also pressure from others in the Senate. A Senate antitrust investigation of the nation's oil import program had been launched. Additionally, a two-year moratorium on *all* U.S. offshore drilling, until problems raised by the Santa Barbara situation could be examined, was called for.

All this was a powerful entry on the positive side of Santa Barbara's one-hundredth-day ledger.

At this critical moment, Washington's offshore leasing authorities were revealed to have been acting largely in the dark when they leased the channel for drilling. The beleaguerd Interior Department released secret testimony given by Dr. Pecora, head of the Geological Survey, before the House Appropriations Committee on March 3. Pecora admitted that the government had not known the true value of what it was leasing. "It is a horrible situation to be placed in," Pecora said. The Department of the Interior had requested $450,000 to finance better advance study and supervision of offshore leases, but the Bureau of the Budget had vetoed the request. Consequently Interior was obliged to award bids by guesswork. "We have to arrive at fair market value from what is available in published reference, or do it from scuttlebutt."

This was tantamount to saying that the government had accepted nearly $603 million for oil leases in the Santa Barbara Channel without knowing the value of what it was selling.

Santa Barbarans had been aware of this startling truth for nearly two years, but now the whole country knew it.

A Santa Barbara scientist revealed another surprising fact. Alan Allen had made a detailed report to the annual meeting of the American Geophysical Union substantiating his findings that approximately 3,000,000 gallons of oil had been released into the Santa Barbara Channel. By the spill's hundredth day, Allen's estimate had become 3,250,000 gallons. Confirming it, Allen was given insight a few days later into a cloak-and-dagger aspect of the spill. A knock came on his hotel-room door in Washington, D.C. A man who identified himself as a member of a secret Interior Department team said: "Stick with your figures. Ours corroborate them." His team had been studying high-altitude photographs of the slick made by U-2 reconnaissance aircraft. The man was torn between loyalty to his government job and a desire to see truth prevail. Allen urged him to make a public statement; but he was afraid of losing his job. Later it was learned that the Interior Department was also using data supplied by satellites to study the depth, extent, and amount of the spill. This too substantiated Allen's figures rather than those Interior was publicly issuing.

Increasing public attention on oil spills, oil from the *Torrey Canyon* was coming ashore on the French coast more than two years after the wreck. It came in tarlike cakes identifiable by the detergents used by the British coastal defenders and by the sawdust used as coagulant by the French. And in California, the director of Scripps Institution of Oceanography at La Jolla, warned that tankers, particularly the new supertankers—much larger than the *Torrey Canyon*—posed a greater pollution threat to U.S. coasts than offshore drilling. This was interesting news for Santa Barbarans since the channel received heavy use by tankers and increased oil operations were bound to complicate their passage. By jeopardizing each other, the oil rigs, and the environment, the tankers might invite government curtailment of oil operations as well as of shipping.

Extending the influence of the spill into still further areas, the president of the American Medical Association said that national noise pollution had reached such a critical stage that it needed a Santa Barbara-type disaster to arouse people to its seriousness; while MTA, manufacturer of musical records, released a protest folksong, "Santa Barbara Gold," * sung by the radio-television personality, Arthur Godfrey. "Why did the Lord put gold in Santa Barbara?" Godfrey's husky voice intoned. This was unhistorical, since Santa Barbara had no true gold. More accurate was: "Men turned their bits and drills to the oil that lay/ just off the coast of Santa Barbara's hills/ but from the well there came a leak that men could not control/ and the oil shot up from the clear blue sea/ from an unseen man-made hole./ And the golden shores turned traitor dark/ and the white gulls were black with slime/ and Santa Barbara bore the scars of greed another time . . ."

Throughout all of this, Union at times preserved a public optimism. At a stockholders meeting in Los Angeles, where the chief topic was the sharp decline ($2.4 million) in company earnings for the first quarter of 1969, Fred Hartley declared that most of the cost of the spill was covered by insurance; and K. C. Vaughan, a Union vice president, told stockholders: "You will be pleasantly surprised with the condition of the shoreline next time you visit Santa Barbara." But Hartley and Vaughan had

* "Santa Barbara Gold" by Dick Feller and Clara Duraham, © 1969 Glaser Publications, Inc.

not reckoned on the channel's unpredictable ways. While they were talking, Santa Barbara's beaches were receiving their heaviest coating of oil in weeks.

Helpful as these developments were, the community's chief asset remained its human one. More than seventy thousand persons, nearly equivalent to the population of Santa Barbara, had signed anti-oil petitions.

Expressing this deep-rooted feeling in another way, Roderick Nash, a young professor of history and a wilderness expert, was putting the finishing touches to a lay sermon he would deliver Sunday, May 11, at All-Saints-by-the-Sea Episcopal Church.

Nash proposed "an Eleventh Commandment," an extension of Christian ethics to include man's relationship to his environment. *"Thou shalt not abuse the earth!"* was the Eleventh Commandment. Nash's sermon concluded with a prayer: "God of nature and God of man, temper our arrogance toward the natural world with humility and reverence. Rekindle in our hearts a sense of wonder and of awe in the presence of the earth and its myriad life forms. Help us to be responsible trustees of your creation. Open our eyes to the beauty of this world. Make us worthy of our environment."

On the negative side, the spill's hundredth day found oil stretching in windrows all the way from Platform A to shore, while fresh crude poured out at a rate Alan Allen estimated at 8,000 gallons daily. The stench hung over the beaches. Swimming, and even walking on the beach, were almost out of the question.

In addition to leakage that had no foreseeable end and a slick that had apparently become permanent, there was the threat of continued drilling. At the historical rate of 2.5 per thousand wells drilled, at least 10 more blowouts could be expected from the channel's projected 4,000 wells.

Also on the negative side, the oil industry had announced a massive counterattack against oil's enemies in general and Santa Barbara in particular. The industry had awakened to what its leaders were calling a dire threat, sparked by the Santa Barbara spill. The sixty-day crash counteroffensive would be aimed at preventing unfavorable changes in federal tax law, especially in the 27½ percent depletion allowance. It would focus on the House Ways and Means Committee which had begun to draft a new tax bill.

Coordinator L. Dan Jones, legal counsel for the Independent Petroleum Association of America, claimed that oil had many friends in Congress but that some of them had been shaken by the Santa Barbara spill. Other spokesmen said they were encouraged that President Nixon had, through a press secretary, reaffirmed his support of the depletion allowance—a support clearly enunciated during a campaign speech at Lubbock, Texas, in October, 1968. None of this promised well for Santa Barbara's effort at the approaching congressional hearing.

Neither did the phone call, early the morning of May 5, from the Interior Department to Dr. Robert Curry who had testified against oil companies and federal government at the Senate subcommittee hearing in February. Interior asked that Curry clear his testimony at the forthcoming hearing with them first. The call placed Curry, a part-time employee of Interior's Geological Survey and a full-time U.C. Santa Barbara faculty member, under considerable pressure. It outraged Santa Barbarans who learned of it. Curry obligingly cleared his testimony by a lengthy phone call, changing nothing he found essential but eliminating several points of questionable merit.

Locally oil's counteroffensive included the gift of $70,000 to the Santa Barbara Chamber of Commerce by the Platform A oil companies. The money was to finance an advertising campaign aimed at reviving Santa Barbara's slumping tourist trade. The advertisements were prepared by an advertising agency under direction of the Chamber of Commerce. The ads conveyed the impression that everything was all right on Santa Barbara's beaches. "Come play with us this summer!" they said, showing a boy and girl running happily on an inviting beach.

Local reaction was sharply divided. George Clyde denounced the advertisements as "false" and "misleading," and Bud Bottoms said their timing was evidently intended to hurt Santa Barbara at the approaching hearing. "Accepting money from the oil companies sullies the community's new image," Bottoms claimed. But others supported the chamber's move as necessary to the local economy; and chamber spokesmen argued that if Union could pay to clean up the beaches, it could pay to clean up Santa Barbara's image.

After a bitter disagreement which included picketing of the Chamber of Commerce by some citizens, the advertisements were changed so as not to convey the impression that the beaches were as clean as ever; and the promotional campaign continued. The civic rift remained. Maintaining anti-oil morale was a problem. Life had to go on. People tended to accept the status quo. As the sense of crisis following the blowout—and the oil ashore—and the renewed leakage—passed, a kind of oily despondency had settled in.

As Santa Barbara leaders prepared to go to Washington to appeal to Congress for help, they felt their base had been weakened. Their feelings of uncertainty were increased when they learned that a new presidential panel, designed to provide a new solution to the oil-leak problem, was meeting in secret at the Sheraton Hotel in Inglewood, California, adjacent to the Los Angeles International Airport from which they were about to take off.

The two-day hearing before the Senate Subcommittee on Minerals, Materials, and Fuels began on May 19. Petitions containing one hundred thousand anti-oil signatures were stacked at the end of the counter before the committeemen. The Chairman, Frank Moss, a Utah Democrat, said it was the most extensive exhibit of its kind he had ever seen.

Senator Cranston opened the proceedings with a defense of his bill. "I recognize that we need oil for our society and its security. I do not recognize that we need it from Santa Barbara." Santa Barbara, he said, "is a national treasure visited by people from all over the United States and from all over the world."

Congressman Teague told the committee he was drafting a bill that would exchange oil company interests in the channel's federal lands for similar interests in the Elk Hills Naval Petroleum Reserve. Teague also revealed that, regardless of what the Army Corps of Engineers thought about them, the Navy was finding the channel's drilling rigs a hindrance to its operations.

Harry Morrison, vice president of the Western Oil and Gas

Association, unlimbered the industry's big guns. His salvo was a broadside not only in the Battle of the Santa Barbara Channel but in what was fast becoming a national oil war.

"Petroleum supplies over 74 percent of the energy consumed in this country," Morrison said. The nation's total energy needs were expected to triple by the year 2000. In that same period, petroleum demands would more than double. Although requirements loomed large, exploratory drilling in the United States was sharply declining. At the end of 1958, there had been a thirteen-year supply of oil in reserve. By the end of 1967, this had dropped to a ten-year supply.

Morrison deprecated foreign oil as the solution to the problem of energy supplies. Foreign imports represented a constant outflow of dollars to the detriment of U.S. balance of payments. Imports also placed vital U.S. needs at the mercy of foreign governments. As for Santa Barbara: "Because it is virgin territory adjacent to long-prolific onshore oil fields, the industry regards continuous exploration in the Santa Barbara Channel, and all other Outer Continental Shelf areas of promising potential, as essential to maintaining a safe reserve-supply ratio."

But there was a larger principle involved. It was the one that Supervisor Dan Grant had already pointed out. Operations were being conducted off the shorelines of thirty-five nations. Fifteen more would soon be added to the list. U.S. oil companies owned or financed about 50 percent of this development. "If our government takes the position it cannot endorse offshore operations for the Santa Barbara Channel," Morrison said, "it may well encourage the taking of a similar position by foreign governments affecting offshore operations everywhere in the world."

The oil industry opposed Senator Cranston's bill; but it did not suggest how to stop Santa Barbara's oil leak or how to rid the channel of its polluting slick, which trailed away for miles from Platform A while the experts were talking in Washington.

Union Oil was conspicuous by its absence from the hearing. This appeared to confirm reports that the rest of the oil industry was angry with Union for getting it into a mess. As if to justify this feeling, a Union tanker was spilling six hundred gallons of crude oil into San Francisco Bay as the hearing progressed.

Humble, however, was conspicuous by its presence. As the

company with the largest investment in the channel ($217 million in lease bonuses, as a starter), it evidently wished to establish an independent position. While endorsing Morrison's stand, it dissociated itself from "the incident at Tract 402." Humble claimed its exploratory wells and pre-lease core holes extended the length of the channel and in none of them had any subsurface formations been encountered that presented unique problems in well control. It said that the Cranston bill, by banning channel drilling, would penalize Humble for an unfortunate accident not related to its operations.

Robert Curry challenged a statement by Dr. Pecora that state offshore wells had been producing for decades and there had been no problem there. "He is in fact technically correct," Curry said. "What he didn't say is that those wells had been producing from artificial islands at the ends of piers, in deeper capped structures under very, very different geologic conditions." In a subtle but bitter byplay, Senator Cranston had asked if Curry's testimony had been approved by the Department of the Interior. Pecora said it had not.

Again emphasizing earthquake threat, Curry said that Santa Barbara was the locus of the most damaging earthquakes ever recorded in the United States.

Morrison had testified that oil platforms were designed to withstand earthquakes of twice the magnitude expectable in the channel, but Curry rebutted: "We have had earthquakes in the Santa Barbara Channel of magnitude eight," or 100 times the magnitude designed for.

How to stop the leak? Curry proposed that a blanket of silt and fine sand, containing a cementing agent, be placed over the leakage area to a depth of "several tens of feet." This would, he said, increase pressure on the seeping oil and eventually overcome the slight amount of differential pressure allowing the leakage to move upward.

Such measures had reportedly been considered for use in seepage-control off Tasmania and in the North Sea. A similar cement blanket had been considered in detail by Lieutenant Brown and the Santa Barbara National Contingency Plan leaders. They had found that it could be constructed within two months. Rock could be hauled from Santa Catalina Island. It would be laid over the leakage area in three layers each about fifteen feet thick. Its interstices would be filled with cement and its cost was estimated at $1.5 million.

Another, more fanciful method of leakage control had been considered at the same time. According to Brown it originated with Fred Hartley and the Army Engineers. It consisted of a gigantic oval-shaped caisson, or ring of steel, extending from above the ocean surface down to the ocean floor and completely enclosing Platform A and the leakage area, thus preventing oil from escaping. Its cost was estimated at $15 million. Like the rock-cement blanket, it could have been emplaced in two to three months.

Brown had asked the Corps of Engineers to prepare a detailed presentation of both proposals. They were formally considered and rejected by the National Plan leaders, on the night of March 1, as too costly and time consuming. In the final outcome, both Union and USGS opposed them strongly as having a low probability of success.

Curry now warned that any attempt to stop the leak by depleting the shallow oil reservoir under Platform A would be ineffective, because of its connection with deeper oil-bearing sands.

The senators remained cool toward this and other aspects of the anti-oil position. Hansen of Wyoming and Allott of Colorado, both Republicans, were particularly sharp in their criticism of Curry. But it was Hollis M. Dole of the Interior Department who crushed Santa Barbara's hopes. The Assistant Secretary for Mineral Resources placed the Nixon Administration squarely against the Cranston bill. While admitting that programs being developed by the government "in response to the Santa Barbara accident" were serving as a model for "our future actions along the nation's entire coastline," Dole opposed additional legislation as "unnecessary."

Like the oil industry, the government did not say how or when it was going to stop the leak, though Dr. Pecora said it might take years to do so.

Plain-citizen witnesses had to wait until the last hour of the second day of the hearing. Finally Lois Sidenberg sent Chairman Moss a note asking that she and others be allowed to speak.

Perhaps exasperated by the long wait, Mrs. Sidenberg enunciated a major issue sharply. "We are entitled to a clean sea, a clean shoreline and beaches, and clean air. These are natural resources and they should be protected and respected by our government."

Fred Eissler drove her points home. "Not once was a public hearing scheduled prior to the sale of leases in February, 1968, nor were public hearings held before the recent adoption of new regulations."

When the hearings were over, Santa Barbarans returned home to share their disappointment with the rest of the anti-oil fighters. In contrast to the warm concern exhibited by members of Congress when visiting the beaches and seeing the pollution for themselves, the committee's hostility had been noticeable. Perhaps Washington insulated people from actuality. Perhaps hearings should be held on oil-soaked beaches.

Then suddenly from the White House came a note of hope. The President announced the establishment of a Cabinet-level council which would begin a "major attack on environmental pollution." The Environmental Quality Council would rank with the National Security Council and the Urban Affairs Council. It would "provide a focal point for the Administration's efforts to protect all natural resources." The President himself would head the new group.

The council was the result of the President's visit to Santa Barbara, according to Dr. Lee DuBridge, White House science advisor.

With Nixon showing renewed interest, there was hope that the special panel (also called the DuBridge panel because he had appointed it on behalf of the President), which had been meeting behind closed doors in Inglewood to study the oil-leak problem, would return a verdict favorable to Santa Barbara's cause. The panel was composed entirely of scientific and technical experts; it was chaired by Dr. John C. Calhoun, Jr., chairman of the earlier President's Panel on Oil Spills.

By June 2 the Inglewood panel's recommendations were ready. They called for intensive drilling and production of oil at Tract 402, at the very spot that had caused all the trouble. Up to fifty new wells were suggested for Platform A.

"Ten to twenty years might be required to deplete the oil deposits, reduce underlying pressures, and stop the leakage," Dr.

DuBridge said, in announcing the panel's findings. It was the precise solution warned against by Dr. Curry and other experts.

To Santa Barbarans, it sounded like the best way to keep their community and their environment in jeopardy while allowing Union and the government to have what they had wanted in the beginning: an offshore oil field at Tract 402.

15

"THE COURTS MAY SAVE US"

FIFTEEN HUNDRED concerned citizens held a community meeting Sunday afternoon, June 8, at La Playa Stadium overlooking Santa Barbara's harbor and beaches. Anti-oil sentiment had soared during the week since the announcement of the presidential panel's recommendations. "If you follow their logic, why not put a thousand wells out there?" Mayor Firestone had said.

George Clyde had labeled the recommendations "cheap and premature. They do not require the oil companies to try alternative methods, including some that are very expensive, before trying this ultimate solution of drilling." The Board of Supervisors had unanimously requested Hickel to try alternative measures.

Other citizens raised the question of conflict of interest and pointed out that nearly all the members of the panel had established their reputations through work with government or industry. Five had been members of the first presidential panel which had recommended the remedial pumping that had failed to stop the leak and had at first increased it.

Dr. Curry said it was impossible to make a competent judgment on the panel's decision unless he was in possession of the information available to the panel, and GOO's leaders demanded that the secret information used by the panel be made public and asked what assurances there were that the leakage would be stopped even after twenty years of drilling.

Congressman Teague failed to see why a technologically advanced nation could not develop the art of capping submarine oil leaks, rather than create an oil field to stop this leakage. Senator Muskie joined Senator Cranston in what was becoming a major bipartisan attack. Muskie said: "It is neither scientific nor professional to make recommendations based on testimony by proponents of one specific solution, especially when those proponents have a vested interest in continuing the drilling and are the same people who decided to do the drilling that led to the oil spill in the first place."

The Santa Barbarans who assembled in La Playa Stadium were in a mood to hear blunt truths. Facing them on a podium at approximately the fifty-yard line of their football field were their mayor, their supervisor, their senator, and their anti-oil leaders.

"I don't think Washington is going to get oil out of your channel's federal water until Sacramento gets it out of your state water," Cranston told them bluntly. He had found little support in Congress for his bill, or for any bill aimed at curtailing channel drilling, unless it was preceded by strong action at state level.

After nearly two hours of frank discussion and self-examination, the meeting ended in a decision to launch an all-out political offensive at state level and to reintensify efforts on the home front. It meant, in part, starting all over again, climbing a new political ladder, this time to Sacramento. At home it meant intensifying the civic split, symbolized by controversy over the wharf, between those determined to get oil out of the channel and those determined to accommodate or tolerate it. Many Santa Barbarans felt themselves the victims of a total, even a totalitarian, type of oppression. Disregarding their pleas and their distressed environment, Hickel had promptly begun implementing the presidential panel's recommendations. Drilling at Platform A was to get underway immediately.

When they learned that the President had also approved the recommendations, the Santa Barbarans were more than ever convinced that big government and big industry were riding rough-shod over them.

The Reagan Administration's attitude toward the spill had been unhelpful to the Santa Barbara position from the first. It had focused on what Santa Barbarans considered secondary issues. For example, the state was demanding the right to supervise oil operations in federal waters. Though unsuccessful, this demand had resulted in collaboration for the first time between state and federal officials in the formulation of new federal offshore drilling regulations. Reagan had taken a personal hand in naming the members of the two presidential panels (to be sure that they included Californians and even a Santa Barbaran, Dr. Gordon Mac-Donald), and he had helped make arrangements for their meetings. He had sent his director of natural resources to Washington to discuss offshore oil problems including the possibility of exchanging oil company rights in the channel for federal rights elsewhere. The State Lands Commission had, furthermore, suspended drilling and leasing in state waters, pending a review of the Santa Barbara Channel situation and a tightening of state offshore drilling regulations. And at legislative level, two committees of the Republican-dominated State Senate, those on Natural Resources and Government Efficiency, had held a joint hearing at which Union's John Fraser testified that "no prudent engineer" could guarantee against another spill. But Reagan had not thrown his great political weight behind the 150,000 citizens of the South Coast. He remained conspicuous by his absence from the oil spill scene, while at any moment his intervention could have tipped the scales in Santa Barbara's favor.

Complicating the political situation further was the rivalry between the Governor and Jesse M. Unruh, a leader in the Legislature and California's most powerful Democrat. Unruh had outspokenly advocated Santa Barbara's cause since his visit to the city in early February. He was virtually certain to be Reagan's opponent in the 1970 gubernatorial election. With other Democrats, Unruh was calling upon Reagan to take a stronger stand against channel drilling. Thus the city and its oil spill became the issue for a state as well as a national political contest.

In March the Santa Barbara Board of Supervisors had unanimously appealed to the Governor to support their demand for a permanent cessation of drilling. It was now June and they had had no reply. They appealed again, with the City Council joining in.

The new effort had bipartisan support in the Legislature. Unruh himself had introduced two bills. One required oil companies to pay all damages resulting from an oil spill. The other outlawed drilling in the channel after April 1, 1970. The first passed the Assembly by a vote of 60 to 4, but was defeated by a split vote of the Senate Committee on Governmental Efficiency.

"One word of support from the Governor could have made the difference!" Unruh charged. But Reagan denied responsibility, while declaring concern for channel oil problems.

The remaining Unruh bill outlawing drilling in the channel became a "must" for Santa Barbara's anti-oil forces. If it failed, the community's efforts in Congress must also fail, according to Senator Cranston's predictions.

The Unruh bill to ban drilling had passed the Assembly 66 to 0. When it also passed its first State Senate test—before the Committee on Natural Resources chaired by Senator Lagomarsino —the state seemed at last to be acting decisively and favorably. Of course, Santa Barbarans had been present at the committee hearings. By now they were probably the most traveled and the most testimony-prone citizens on record. By one estimate they had spent more than 100,000 man-hours and more than $100,000 in attending hearings. But they were up against stiff opposition in Sacramento. The oil lobby was present in force, led by the veteran attorney Albert J. Shults. State officials made the going harder for Santa Barbara and easier for Shults. They testified that a permanent ban on channel drilling in state waters would cost California $166 million in unrealized revenues, plus the "astronomical cost" of lawsuits brought by oil companies whose leases would be abrogated. To make matters harder still, the Deputy Director of Conservation revealed that a recent review of channel oil reserves showed there was more oil beneath the Santa Barbara Channel than in all the mainland oil fields of the state.

Then suddenly another obstacle came up. Frank Hortig, executive director of the State Lands Commission, announced that he and his technical staff would recommend to the commission that the temporary ban on drilling in state waters of the channel be lifted. To Santa Barbarans, this was nearly the last straw. It was sure to be construed, they argued, as state support of the federal government's new drilling proposals for Tract 402.

The two-edged crisis moved to a climax on the night of July 30. Shortly before midnight, the State Senate's Finance Committee killed the Unruh bill by a vote of 7 to 4. Voting for Santa Barbara were Lagomarsino and Donald Grunsky of the Monterey-Big Sur area, both Republicans, and Alan Short of Stockton and Walter Stiern of Bakersfield, both Democrats.

But next day the State Lands Commission, on a motion by Caspar Weinberger, Reagan's finance director and later chairman of the Federal Trade Commission, voted unanimously to reject the recommendation of its technical staff and to maintain the ban on drilling in state waters. The Lieutenant Governor and the State Controller supported Weinberger.

All was not quite lost, but all hope of help from Sacramento or Washington was dead until Legislature and Congress met next year.

In local anti-oil action stemming from the La Playa Stadium meeting, the Santa Barbara City Council killed a multimillion-dollar harbor expansion plan that would have provided additional slips for oil service boats. The council approved formation of an Environmental Quality Board of experts to advise it how to halt pollution of all types and "how to prepare for direct face-to-face talks between the city and the United States of America." It wired Hickel urging that he make public the data on which the presidential panel's decision had been based, and it backed an Assembly resolution urging Congress to ban channel drilling. It also established a Citizens Channel Oil Pollution Control Account so that members of the public could make tax-deductible contributions to the oil fight.

Following suit, the County Board of Supervisors refused to grant Sun Oil Company a right of way for a pipeline across county-controlled submerged lands. The pipeline was to service the platform Sun expected to erect soon in Tract 401 less than a mile from Platform A. City and county attorneys prepared to serve copies of an amended legal complaint on three federal officials (Hickel, Pecora, and Solanas), fourteen oil companies and two drilling firms. The complaint, seeking a permanent injunction against channel drilling, had been filed in Federal District Court in April but had been amended to include a new constitutional aspect. It now charged that channel oil operations violated the Ninth Amendment, in that they abridged the *civil* rights of the plaintiffs: "to wit, the fundamental right of the people to retain and enjoy the area's aesthetic beauty and natural resources reasonably free of pollution."

This was language of a kind not heard before in U.S. courts of law. The Ninth Amendment clause cited was the familiar one: "The enumeration in the Constitution, of certain rights, shall not be construed to deny or disparage others retained by the people."

At the complainants' request, a hearing by a three-judge federal court had been granted. This meant that an appeal could go directly to the U.S. Supreme Court.

Next, ordinary citizens organized their own legal effort. Seventeen Santa Barbara residents joined forces with the American Civil Liberties Union to demand release of the secret information used in decision making by the presidential panel. They also asked for public hearings on the panel's recommendations. Their action was an outgrowth of the efforts of Santa Barbara Citizens for Environmental Defense to develop a legal capability at local level —efforts which had led to contacts with the County Counsel's office and to an alliance of citizen and official talent, now bolstered by the ACLU.

The joint citizens–American Civil Liberties Union suit against the federal government and the Platform A oil companies charged that without a hearing Santa Barbarans had been deprived of personal and property rights. It cited the "due process" clause of the Fourteenth Amendment: "Nor shall any state deprive any person of life, liberty, or property, without due process of law." The complaint alleged: "The personal right is the right to live in, and enjoy, an environment free from improvident destruction or pollution; and the property right is the right to the ownership, use, and enjoyment of property free from improvident invasion or impairment."

This was further new legal language, announcing a new kind

of basic human right. It was also the ACLU's first venture into the environmental rights field.

The *Washington Post* bannered a head across the top of its Sunday Outlook page: OIL SPILL RADICALIZES STAID COAST CITY. It was true that once-conservative Santa Barbara was leading the way to a new kind of American radicalism based on environmental concern.

"If people everywhere realize their environment is in danger as ours is, they will rise up against the pollution that threatens every community," Norman Sanders told a meeting of the Citizens Planning Association. The somewhat listless association soon became a headquarters for action on environmental problems.

Young City Councilman Alan Eschenroeder, a scientist and engineer, went to Washington to try and obtain the secret data on which Hickel had based permission to resume the drilling at Platform A. Eschenroeder failed, but he made headlines that caused moviegoers to remember James Stewart's similar journey in the 1930s film, *Mr. Smith Goes to Washington.*

Out in Isla Vista, the predominantly student community adjacent to the University of California campus, black militants at a regional convention of the NAACP accused the oil industry of "keeping the people in slavery in Africa, in the Middle East— and here in the U.S." To see this for yourself, all you had to do was look out the window and see Platform A, one of them said.

In a novel protest, thirty to forty small boats circled Platform A for two hours, many of them bearing signs saying *Get Oil Out!* and *Union Means Pollution!* The sail-in was the idea of a local auditor, Paul Molitor, who said, "We've got to keep doing new things to keep resistance alive." Finally, after nearly six months of germination, local radicalism had become as real as the oil slick.

The new militancy was apparently getting results. Union had withdrawn from the Santa Barbara waterfront if not from Platform A. It had moved its waterfront staging and managerial operations to Ventura, but on Platform A it was sinking the first well suggested by the presidential panel. A second well was being drilled from Platform B. The Interior Department claimed both were aimed at stopping the leak by relieving pressure, but they were soon producing large quantities of oil for their owners.

As usual when a new drilling operation began, the oil slick increased. This time it was a spasmodic bubbling action that sent dirty water flying 6 feet in the air, over an area 25 feet wide adjacent to Platform A. A plugged hood was blamed. For several weeks Union had been employing a variety of plastic hoods, or "tents," to contain the escaping oil. Placed over the leaks, the tents conducted oil via a hose to the platform, where oil was separated from seawater and piped ashore. Some of the tents were 110 feet square. Together they covered about 40,000 square feet of ocean floor. But still things went wrong.

Sometimes the slick was twenty miles long and a mile wide. By mid-July five new wells had been authorized for Platform A and five for Platform B, making a total of fifteen for the Dos Cuadras field.

Then the government and oil company position on the withholding of secret information suddenly gave way. Union announced it had released for public inspection all data furnished by it to the presidential panel, and the Interior Department said it was preparing to publish a report that would contain all relevant material. Public pressure was telling on the oil forces in and out of government.

There were also new stirrings in the scientific community. Despite Deputy Attorney General O'Brien's charges that oil industry financial grants made it impossible for experts to maintain an honest point of view, experts connected with universities or research institutions were speaking out about oil pollution in substantial numbers. Dr. Wheeler J. North of Caltech found negligible biological damange to the channel's ecology, but said that "in the absence of proper technology" it was not "economically justifiable" to work the channel's oil deposits. At the Woods Hole Oceanographic Institution in Massachusetts, Dr. Max Blumer warned that oil might have subtle effects on the mating, homing, and foraging instincts of marine animals, with ultimately disastrous results on the sea's food chains. At Scripps Institution of Oceanography, Dr. Claude E. ZoBell said that although some species of marine bacteria oxidized oil, they were hardly a cure for oil spills, as some oil people were saying. And in Washington, Dr. Jerome B. Wiesner of MIT, science advisor to Presidents Kennedy and Johnson, had warned of the possibility of the inadvertent destruction of world life by man-made pollution: "We are engaged in a race between catastrophe and the intelligent use of technology, and it is not at all clear we are going to win." It was a first utterance of what was soon to become a commonplace.

But when GOO contacted all major U.S. science and engineering associations and asked for help in the specific problems confronting Santa Barbara, it got none. Locally, however, the response was more encouraging. Distinguished scientists and engineers agreed to serve on the Environmental Quality Advisory Board established by the City Council. The new board was headed by Dr. Howard Wilcox, former director of research at Santa Barbara's General Motors Defense Research Laboratory.

At their first meeting, the board members were informed of the case of Dr. Michael Neushul, a U.C. Santa Barbara scientist who had completed a contract report for the federal government and then been asked to suppress it. On July 1, Neushul had finished a study on the effects of the oil spill on shoreline plants and animals and forwarded the results to the Federal Water Pollution Control Administration. On July 28 he received a telephone call from the FWPCA asking him to suppress his report. Neushul wanted to release the report but the University of California, his employer and recipient of the federal funds with which he was paid, demurred because of what it called legal complications; and the report was not released.

But there was some encouraging news from Washington. On July 21 the House Ways and Means Committee recommended that the oil tax depletion allowance be reduced from $27\frac{1}{2}$ percent to 20 percent. It was the first reform action of its kind since the depletion allowance was established in 1926, and most observers cited the Santa Barbara Oil Spill as an important factor in the historic change.

Yet by the same date two new oil strikes had been confirmed in the channel. One was by Mobil four miles off Port Hueneme and one by Humble in the Tajiguas-Gaviota section. So the stakes in the controversy rose, as the value of channel lands increased. Humble's strike seemed particularly significant. Two of its discovery wells were in water 1,000 feet deep, requiring the use of more advanced technology—in more hazardous depths.

Against this, the County Board of Supervisors had voted $30,000 of the taxpayer's money to carry on the legal fight against oil, and said it was prepared to spend $60,000. The county's efforts seemed dwarfed by the fact that, on July 30, thirteen wells were producing 10,000 barrels of oil a day from Platforms A and B; and the floating rig *Wodeco IV* was sinking shallow holes nearby, through which cement slurry could be injected into the ocean floor in hopes it would help stop leaks. Santa Barbara's beaches were an oily mess, and the Oxnard *Press-Courier* reported that pollution "five times worse than at any time since the blowout" was spreading across a long stretch of beach, from Oxnard westward toward Ventura.

When this was added to the frustrating political news from Sacramento, where the Senate Finance Committee had just killed the Unruh bill, it brought Santa Barbara face to face with despair once again.

Would the community have the staying power to see the battle through? Again unforeseen events came to the citizens' aid.

As far back as April 8, the senior marine game warden for California in the channel area had stated that reports of oil damage to marine mammals on San Miguel Island were exaggerated. "It is not unusual to find dead seals in a colony of twenty thousand or more," he said, " and there are usually ten to twenty carcasses to be found along the sand. Those seen on the affected beach, covered with oil, are about the same number as has been found in the past."

This apparently contradicted the report of widespread damage made by two State Fish and Game Department biologists three days earlier.

Then on April 16 a group headed by a veterinarian specializing in horses, and including the president of the Humane Society of the United States and the chief ranger for the Channel Islands Monument, visited San Miguel and reported finding "fifteen to twenty" dead seals or sea lions, a number they described as normal. They also found a "thin coating" of oil on a limited beach area on the channel side of Point Bennett and no animals suffering discernible ill effects from oil pollution.

But on May 13 Ian McMillan, in company with the chief ranger, visited the affected area as an observer for the Defenders of Wildlife and counted 80 dead animals while walking a distance of a quarter of a mile. McMillan and his companion agreed that an estimate of 150 to 200 carcasses on half a mile of beach would be reasonable. Most of the dead were California sea lion pups. Although the pupping season was well along, McMillan observed more dead pups than live ones. On May 19, Dick Smith of the *News-Press* and the curator of mammalogy at the Santa Barbara Museum of Natural History confirmed McMillan's findings.

The differing reports, varying sharply over a period of a few days, were explained later by a Department of Fish and Game spokesman. Heavy wave action on a steeply sloping beach could transform appearances in a few hours. Also, the little-known fact that carcasses of dead seals sank readily to the bottom played a role in the sudden transformations.

On May 25, a team from *Life* magazine visited San Miguel. They saw mother and baby sea lions drenched in oil, pups lying like oil-soaked logs in tidal pools, an elephant seal with its nose in a pool of sludge. "At water's edge on the channel beaches the blight of oil extended in both directions as far as the eye could see, a slippery, stifling belt of tarry blackness the width of a tidal ebb," reported a *Life* senior editor. "Scattered through the mess were the living and dead creatures whose bright habitat this once had been." *Life*'s team counted more than a hundred dead sea lions and elephant seals in the immediate vicinity. A *Life* photographer said he had photographed disasters and battle scenes in many parts of the world, but that this was the most sickening sight he had ever witnessed. Entitled "Iridescent Gift of Death," *Life*'s findings appeared as the leading story in its issue of June 9.

Then a storm broke. No *Life* article of recent years had attracted so much attention. Animal lovers and oil companies were outraged, for opposite reasons. Local citizens claimed an infamous situation had been exposed. Oil companies claimed *Life* had grossly exaggerated. The companies threatened to remove their advertising from *Life*'s pages. They did so to the amount of $2.8 million, according to a *Life* staff member.

Throughout the controversy, the two men who had first reported the presence of oil on San Miguel and who probably knew more about the island's pinnipeds than anyone else, Dr. Peterson

Carcasses of elephant seals lie awash in the oily surf at
San Miguel Island. B. J. LE BOEUF

and Dr. Le Boeuf, remained silent about the two hundred young elephant seals they had found contaminated by oil and the seal pups that had had difficulty opening their oil-smeared eyes. Professional and political considerations were weighing heavily on Peterson and Le Boeuf. According to Le Boeuf, they had been threatened with revocation of their government research grants and other privileges.

Peterson's silence was soon total. He took his own life, for reasons, friends said, directly connected with the San Miguel controversy.

Stirring citizen indignation further, official reports on channel fishing—or the lack of it—were coming in. Fish and Game Department figures showed the total landing of commercial fish at Santa Barbara from December through March to be down a quarter of a million pounds from the previous year. Santa Barbara Fisheries, a leading firm, had received only 185 pounds of halibut from January 1 through April 30, compared to 9,050 pounds in the same period the previous year. Bonito were down from 14,779 to 46 pounds.

The report was not wholly dark. The catch of abalone, lobster, and red rock was up. But one fisherman, who had fished the channel commercially for half a century, said the overall take had never been so bad; and a leading fish spotter reported that his one-man airborne operation (he spotted commercial schools from his plane and radioed their location to the fishing fleet), which had grossed about $16,000 a year during the period January 1 through May 31 for the past four years, had grossed him $2,768.77 for the same period this year.

Frustrated in Sacramento and Washington, and infuriated by what had happened on San Miguel Island and in their channel fisheries, the citizens turned to the courts for help.

But the luster of legal solutions was already dimming. District Attorney David Minier's case had been crushed by the oil companies. After hearing arguments, a federal judge in Los Angeles enjoined Minier from bringing criminal action under the state's penal code against the channel operators and their subcontractors. Judge Albert Lee Stephens, Jr., ruled that Minier and his ally, the State of California, had no jurisdiction over operations in federal waters.

Critics pointed out that citizens might smother in pollution or have their rights and resources irreparably damaged while barristers debated who had jurisdiction; but this did not help Minier or his constituents.

On August 11, Judge Stephens also ruled against the seventeen Santa Barbara citizens in their civil suit seeking a temporary injunction against further drilling in the channel's federal water. Stephens "saw no urgency." He deferred any further consideration of channel oil problems until a three-judge federal court should meet in September to consider constitutional aspects of the citizens' suit.

The courtroom confrontation revealed some striking contrasts. Two attorneys appeared for Santa Barbara; fifteen for Santa Barbara's opponents.

The three autoloads and one planeload of citizens who were sitting in the courtroom felt themselves outgunned again. They also felt an urgency Judge Stephens did not. On August 2, Hickel had authorized drilling to deeper zones. Eight new wells at Platforms A and B would reach below the 1,200-foot range. Some would go to nearly 3,000 feet. The 10- to 25-year drilling and production program suggested by the presidential panel was apparently fully under way, though the Interior Department refused to admit that it was.

Adding to citizen apprehensions, Platform Hillhouse was looming. Hillhouse was the Sun Oil Company's model platform previously described. It had slots for sixty wells and Sun was asking permission to erect it less than a mile from Platform A.

Four days after Judge Stephens' ruling, Sun received permission from Hickel to erect Platform Hillhouse. Hickel justified his action on ground that Hillhouse's wells were needed to help reduce leakage in the Dos Cuadras field, of which Sun's Tract 401 was an integral part. Also within four days after Stephens' ruling, Humble and Shell applied to the Army Corps of Engineers for permits to drill exploratory wells in four channel lease tracts. Shell asked to drill in Tract 326, six miles off Point Conception; Humble in two tracts east of Shell's but not adjoining, and in Tract 380 near mid-channel. To most Santa Barbarans, the new permit requests were an arrogant disregard of their rights and protests.

Some of the new permit areas overlapped into commercial sea lanes. What about tankers colliding with drilling platforms or with each other? Local residents were reminded of a tanker, the *Cossatot,* which had collided head-on with a freighter, the *Copper State,* in the channel on a foggy night in June, 1968, at a point about ten miles seaward of Platform A. Fortunately none of the tanker's 5,000,000 gallons of jet fuel escaped. Both ships were equipped with the latest navigational aids and safety warning devices, but this had not kept them from smashing into each other. Suppose a tanker smashed into a platform, sheared off sixty wells, and ripped its own hull open?

Led by the voices of Mayor Firestone and George Clyde, the Santa Barbarans protested the new drilling applications. They demanded that public hearings be held by the Corps of Engineers before permits were granted and before Hillhouse was erected, and they protested the Department of Interior's decision to permit new and deeper drilling. In the hot, smoggy, late-summer days, the battle boiled up.

It was the local phase of a national battle. The House of Representatives had followed the recommendation of its Ways and Means Committee, and passed a tax reform bill that reduced the oil depletion allowance from $27\frac{1}{2}$ to 20 percent. In a surprising reversal, President Nixon had indicated he would accept the cut. He would go even further. Secretary of the Treasury David M. Kennedy urged a Senate committee to eliminate the existing one-year tax write-off of intangible drilling costs, a provision oilmen regarded as the blood-marrow of their profitable operations. By permitting them to deduct the entire cost of finding and developing a new well within a twelve-month period, it enabled them to save an estimated $750 million a year in taxes, whereas reduction of the depletion allowance to 20 percent would cost them only about $400 million.

The Santa Barbara spill had done many things, or helped to do them, but these were some of its most far-reaching effects. However they did little to alleviate the immediate channel crisis.

To bolster the city's effort as it prepared to challenge Army Engineers as well as Interior Department and oil industry, the City Council established not one but two funds for receiving financial contributions. The first was for tax-exempt contributions from the general public; the second for tax-exempt business-expense contributions "given for the economic betterment of local business through fighting oil pollution," as the council's resolution said, "a menace which most seriously threatens the commerce of the city."

Tourist spending was off an estimated $1 million for the first eight months of the spill.

The County Supervisors had established a similar fund and the Santa Barbara Citizens for Environmental Defense had channeled more than $4,000 to it. Most of the money had been raised locally by women of the Santa Barbara Audubon Society. Individuals were soon making contributions to all three funds. Some business firms contributed a fixed percentage of their monthly incomes. Arthur Godfrey piloted his own jet plane to Santa Barbara to assist in the resistance effort, and contributed $500.

Local labor unions maintained an official neutrality toward the spill, though jobs were at stake. Before the spill there had been 3,500 jobs connected with channel oil operations. Now there were about 1,500. Yet no voice was raised in labor meetings to oppose the oil resistance, and many union members, such as Bill Robinson, the Platform A worker, privately supported it. Some of them did so at considerable risk. They secretly kept anti-oil leaders and media representatives informed of what was actually happening on the platforms. Some lost their jobs for "talking too much." But labor's anti-oil underground continued.

On Thursday, August 21, Hickel announced that new offshore drilling regulations were in effect for U.S. federal waters. The new regulations authorized public hearings before the granting of offshore leases, but the hearings were not mandatory. However, consideration of environmental factors prior to leasing was made mandatory (but too late to affect the Santa Barbara Channel, where leasing had already occurred and where no more was scheduled). Oil companies were required to furnish more information to the government than heretofore, while the government was authorized to make more of this information public. Limited, rather than absolute, liability for oil spills was established. Under Hickel's earlier measures oil operators would have had to pay reparations for damages to third parties; but this requirement was replaced by a statement that an operator's responsibility to third parties would be governed by applicable law. In the Santa Barbara Channel, new drilling on existing leases was to proceed on a case-by-case basis, with additional safeguards and supervisions.

The new regulations reflected citizen pressure. In fact it seemed that Hickel was deliberately undermining the Santa Barbarans' suits against him by coming part way to meet their complaints. Unquestionably a new current of opinion was running. Speaking at the University of California at Berkeley, Wisconsin Senator Gaylord Nelson called for "a massive teach-in" to acquaint students and public with new environmental problems and values. The suggestion was to be implemented later at many campuses throughout the country. A conference on environmental law sponsored by The Conservation Foundation at Washington, D.C., encouraged Santa Barbara to think that the national legal fraternity might take decisive action, where the national scientific community had failed. The conferees were told that Santa

Barbara really had 115 million co-plaintiffs in its suits against the federal government. That was the number of people living in coastal states affected by federal offshore drilling regulations "from which they have no recourse and no right to public hearing." Ralph Nader, the founder and head of the Washington-based Center for the Study of Responsive Law, which had conducted penetrating investigations of the automobile and meat-packing industries, said he was turning his organization's attention to environmental problems. His "raiders"—young volunteer assistants —were already helping Santa Barbarans with information.

But despite these considerable efforts, on August 26 oil was so thick in Santa Barbara harbor that the harbor was closed as it had been in early February, and men in boats went around spreading straw on the water and picking it up again. On the two hundred eleventh day of the spill, this made Santa Barbarans feel they were back where they had started.

The Washington conference on environmental law showed the force of growing opinion favorable to the environment, but it was overshadowed by the growing power of oil. Sensational Alaskan oil leasings took place the same week, September 12. Lease bonuses paid the Alaska state government exceeded $900 million, setting a new record and posing a new series of problems.

Tankers streaming down the coast with Alaskan oil for oil-hungry Southern California would inevitably go through the Santa Barbara Channel, with its growing complex of platforms and floating drilling rigs. What had happened to the *Cossatot* and the *Copper State* would probably happen to other vessels, with less fortunate results.

Though some argued that the Alaskan discoveries made exploitation of channel oil less urgent, others responded that the proximity of the channel's supplies to Southern California's demands, plus the acknowledged shortage of national energy supplies, made exploitation as urgent as ever.

Then six days before the decisive September 23 hearing on their legal pleas, the citizens learned that "step six" of the controversial presidential panel recommendations—intensive drilling—had indeed been put into effect without their knowledge. An affidavit by John Fraser of Union Oil, filed in connection with the pending litigation, revealed that Union had received permission to implement all phases of the panel's recommendations, including "depletion" of "all" the oil reservoirs in Tract 402.

Depletion was the new and frightening word. The Department of the Interior had apparently tried to lull Santa Barbarans into thinking milder measures were being taken, while proceeding with all-out exploitation of the Dos Cuadras field. Challenged, Dr. Pecora, the head of the U.S. Geological Survey, took refuge in semantics; and Hickel said that drilling and pumping had been so successful in reducing the leakage that intensified operations were justified. The fact remained: Union and its government partner were rapidly exploiting a major field, while legal action to stop them was pending.

"When all the facts are in," Alvin Weingand told a Town Hall meeting of Los Angeles civic leaders at the Biltmore Hotel, "the Santa Barbara Oil Spill will rank in infamy with the Teapot Dome Scandal."

He called for a congressional investigation of the Interior Department's role in the leasing and the spill.

The Santa Barbarans hoped that a three-judge session succeeding the disappointing one-judge session of the Federal District Court in Los Angeles would grant them relief, but such was not the case. The enlarged court granted no injunctions, authorized no hearings, but took the constitutional questions raised by the seventeen citizens and their co-plaintiffs, the City and County of Santa Barbara, under study.

While the study was going on, Santa Barbara's television sets showed a veteran CBS reporter putting his hand in the water, at a point three miles from shore. It came out black.

Rallying for a renewed effort, anti-oil forces still hoped to block the erection of Platform Hillhouse and the granting of additional drilling permits. County and city joined citizen groups and the Sierra Club in asking the Army Corps of Engineers and the Department of the Interior to deny further permits until public hearings were held on questions of navigational hazards and environmental impact of new drilling.

By now there was powerful new support for such requests. In a notable statement in Washington, the President's First Santa Barbara Oil Spill Panel (appointed in February) issued a report that favored Santa Barbara's position. It recommended: (1) the placing in escrow of selected offshore mineral resources for fixed periods of time, rather than extracting them immediately; (2) the appointment of an independent board of experts to advise the Secretary of the Interior on matters pertaining to resources development; (3) a review of existing standards of construction for offshore structures.

The panel warned of tanker hazards, and it urged prompt and meaningful efforts "to incorporate the opinions, advice, and policies of state and local governments into plans for developing offshore resources."

With the President's advisors on their side, the Santa Barbarans could reasonably hope for relief. But the recommendations of the President's experts, so promptly accepted by the Administration in June, apparently carried little weight in October.

Convinced they were being given the runaround by the Corps of Engineers as well as by the Interior Department, the City and County of Santa Barbara and the seventeen citizens represented by the ACLU filed a new suit in the Federal District Court in Los Angeles. They asked for a temporary restraining order barring the Engineer Corps from issuing construction or drilling permits until public hearings were held. Judge Stephens again presided. Speaking for all the plaintiffs, A. L. Wirin, chief counsel for the Southern California American Civil Liberties Union, asked the court to set aside the permits issued since August 18 without a hearing. Wirin asked that hearings on future permits include evaluation of the effects of proposed drilling and construction on navigation, marine life, conservation, pollution, ecology, and the general public welfare as required by the regulations of the Corps.

Stephens did not act on the plaintiffs' urgent request until October 21. Then the petition for a restraining order against the Engineers was denied. Immediately the Santa Barbarans asked for a less urgent preliminary injunction. Stephens agreed to consider it, and this caused the Engineers to refrain temporarily from issuing permits for drilling or for the construction of Platform Hillhouse.

Then, when Senator Cranston revealed that the Engineers' parent department, Army, had urged that "full consideration be given to the question of public hearings" before permits were granted, it seemed that the monolithic progress of government and industry had finally been slowed, perhaps even stopped.

A drop of nearly $5 million in Union's third-quarter earnings even made it seem possible that oil companies might lose appetite for channel exploration. Three offshore earthquakes added to this feeling. One centered about forty miles off Point Conception at the channel's western end. It registered 5.3 on the Richter scale. The other centered near San Nicolas Island at the channel's eastern end. It registered 5.0. Coming a week after a 5.5 shock off Conception which had cracked plaster in onshore buildings, the new quakes made it seem as though natural forces were adding their comments to the legal argument.

But on Monday, November 3, Stephens denied Santa Barbara's request for a preliminary injunction. For some reason the plaintiffs were not informed of his decision. They learned about it by accident on Wednesday when a *News-Press* reporter telephoned the Corps of Engineers in a routine information check and was told of the Monday ruling. The Engineers, however, had been informed and were busily issuing permits—seven in all—to Union and to Humble. But the key permit for the construction of Platform Hillhouse had not yet been granted.

Amid accusations of collusion and foul play, the Santa Barbarans appealed Stephens' ruling to the Ninth Court of Appeals in San Francisco. But they were not able to file the necessary papers until Friday, November 7. On Friday the Corps issued its permit for the construction of Hillhouse.

The Santa Barbarans immediately amended their appeal to include nullification of the Hillhouse permit, as well as of all others issued by the Engineers during the preceding week; but Sun Oil announced that the platform's 1,500-ton structural steel base had been loaded on a barge at the Kaiser Steel works on the Oakland side of San Francisco Bay and would proceed down the coast in a few days.

The reaction in Santa Barbara to these events was one of outrage and disgust. It seemed that courts, government, and oil industry were working hand in hand against them. They resolved to impede the erection of Platform Hillhouse and block it totally if possible, in a protest that would be symbolic as well as physical. Through GOO, the Sierra Club, and numerous conservation groups with memberships along the California coast, they arranged to keep the platform under surveillance when it moved southward from San Francisco Bay, and they urged local citizens along the route to join in peaceful picketing of the platform as it passed.

On Wednesday, November 12, the Court of Appeals granted a temporary restraining order enjoining the Engineers from issuing drilling or construction permits. But did the order include the Hillhouse permit? The court was not saying, and nobody else could tell.

By now the State Lands Commission had offered to join in the legal fight against the Engineers, and Lieutenant Governor Reinecke had wired the Corps that he "strongly urged public hearings" before new drilling permits were issued. State Senator Lagomarsino as well as Cranston and Teague had pleaded with the Engineers to grant a hearing before the platform was emplaced. Even Governor Reagan had said: "We've got to stop this platform building."

Nonetheless on November 18, the Court of Appeals lifted its restraining order and next day the barge carrying Platform Hillhouse started moving down the coast, towed by the tug *Donna Foss*. At the same time, A. L. Wirin, accompanied by Marvin Levine, a Santa Barbara County deputy counsel, started flying toward Washington, D.C., to appeal to the Supreme Court.

While platform and lawyers raced against each other and against time, GOO was mustering a resistance fleet that ranged from rowboats to large-size yachts. GOO hoped to occupy the emplacement site and delay erection of the platform until the Supreme Court could rule.

On Thursday, November 20, the giant, 200-foot-long structure had rounded Point Conception and was in the channel, well publicized as it went, and Wirin and Levine were in Washington seeking Justice William O. Douglas' signature on a temporary restraining order.

Asked if the Coast Guard would prevent the "fish-in" that GOO had announced for the emplacement site, Lieutenant Brown said he did not have authority to order vessels out of the area. "International rules of the road must be observed by both sides," he said. The Navy, too, said it would not interfere.

Hillhouse arrived off Santa Barbara in the early morning darkness of Friday, the twenty-first. It found the 32-foot sloop *Don Lee,* skippered by a business executive, Donald McFarland and his wife, Lee, anchored over its emplacement site. The platform loomed up within 200 yards of the McFarlands but then withdrew. Oil company service boats harassed the *Don Lee* by racing close to its bow and stern, but the McFarlands held their position. At daybreak they were relieved by the *Galadriel,* skippered by another business executive, Harold Beveridge.

GOO's entire fleet soon gathered, many of them bearing *Get Oil Out!* signs. Hillhouse remained at bay on its barge, a quarter mile distant; while in Washington, Justice Douglas referred Santa Barbara's plea to the entire Supreme Court, which was expected to rule on Monday.

The race tightened shortly after noon on Friday when the platform was lifted from its barge by a huge floating crane and placed in the water. But instead of floating on its side as scheduled, Hillhouse flopped over on its head and floated bottom up, its eight elephantine legs protruding above the surface.

In Washington the well-known legal firm of Arnold and Porter, representing Sun Oil Company, engaged in an unusual procedure. It sent a letter to the Supreme Court saying that as of 3 P.M. Eastern Time of that day (Friday), the platform had already reached its site and was being emplanted into the ocean floor. The letter urged the Court to reject the Santa Barbarans' request for an injunction because of the *fait accompli* and the extreme expense necessary to remove the platform should the injunction be granted.

Neither the Court, Arnold and Porter, nor Levine and Wirin knew that the platform was in fact several hundred yards from its destination, floating in an embarrassing upside-down position. By the time Wirin and Levine learned of the falsity of Sun's allegation, it was Friday evening and there was no way to communicate a rebuttal to the Court. The two attorneys knew that an injunction's purpose is to maintain the status quo and that the Court would be loath to undo what it thought had already been done.

Divers went to work to right the capsized platform, while the nation watched on television.

On Saturday night the platform was still upside down. When

this continued next day, many people asked how Sun Oil could be trusted to drill sixty wells without blowouts or spills if they could not set their platform right side up.

The Supreme Court prolonged the drama further. On Monday it adjourned without acting on Santa Barbara's plea. Meanwhile a cable with which a huge crane was attempting to right Hillhouse broke, and the platform turned bottom-up again.

A vessel from GOO's resistance fleet was anchored day and night over the emplacement site, preventing any attempt by Sun to move the platform there. Twenty to thirty small boats manned by citizen volunteers supported the anchored vessel. As the opposing forces glared at each other there were several instances of near-collision or bodily contact. The oil company armada had been reinforced by the arrival of two more ocean-going tugs bringing two more large barges. One barge contained the steel pilings that were to be driven into the ocean floor through the platform's hollow legs. The other carried the first or lower deck for the platform's superstructure.

Sun was reported to be preparing to seek an injunction against the fish-in. But though Sun had mineral rights on the ocean's floor, it had no surface rights to the ocean's water, GOO spokesmen argued. "We'll stay until the Supreme Court rules," Alvin Weingand declared.

Lois Sidenberg had chartered a helicopter. Hovering thirty feet above the placement site, she dropped a fish line overboard. She was promptly christened "the Red Baroness."

On the water below, Norman Sanders rowed across the site in a 14-foot dory. "The fishing is lousy," he told newsmen who interviewed him from a passing boat. "But then it has been, ever since the spill." D. W. Solanas of the Geological Survey threatened the fishers with legal action by the federal government.

While the platform floated upside down on Tuesday, November 25, the Supreme Court rejected Santa Barbara's plea. The Court gave no explanation for its action and there was no indication of how individual judges voted. Justices Douglas and Harlan took no part in the decision. Whether or not the Court was influenced by Sun's letter giving erroneous information could not be ascertained.

"I'm extremely disappointed about the ruling," Mayor Firestone said, "but I don't think anyone is going to give up."

16

GOD HELPS THOSE
WHO HELP THEMSELVES

FLOATING IGNOMINIOUSLY with its feet in the air, Platform Hillhouse remained a symbol of government-industry ineptness and a focus of the people's will to resist despoliation of their environment.

But the resisters had exhausted nearly all their resources. The Hillhouse episode had used up what seemed final stores of energy. With President, Congress, Legislature, and courts apparently against them, where could people who had rejected extra-legal methods turn?

As in the past, new and unexpected sources of strength and knowledge appeared within the community when they were most needed. The city's new Environmental Quality Advisory Board was analyzing the at-last published Interior Department report on the blowout and spill, containing "all relevant data" used by the presidential panel in May. The Advisory Board was finding: (1) the instability and permeability of the caprock covering the Dos Cuadras oil field was unique in California; (2) escape routes for oil and gas might have been created by the driving of the pilings for Platform A; (3) earthquakes might "reopen cracks or reactivate leaks that originated from oil field exploitation"; (4) continued drilling might cause the sea floor to subside. These and similarly disturbing statements were set forth in the U.S. Geological Survey's own words. They were not the words to encourage instant channel oil development.

A retired drilling company executive with considerable experience in the channel, Robert Sharp, had come forward as an expert witness on Santa Barbara's side. He said he was motivated by a desire to see the opposing forces equalized in some degree. Sharp said that Union had been guilty of an error in judgment (among other errors) in not setting adequate casing in Well A-21. Before the earliest of the federal leases was awarded in the channel, Sharp's company, working under contract with Union Oil, had operated a core-drilling vessel near the area now occupied by Platform A. While drilling the first shallow core hole, they experienced a blowout of sufficient force to move the drilling ship off location. The blowout was fortunately all gas, and the hole "bridged itself" in a short time, so that no pollution of the sea resulted.

Sharp said now that given the present state of the art of offshore drilling, the Santa Barbara Channel was not a safe place to drill oil wells, particularly those drilled by floating rigs in deep water.

At a series of public meetings sponsored by Santa Barbara City College, citizens were educating themselves on oil problems, with the help of expert speakers and panelists. These included Dr. Lee DuBridge's assistant Dr. John Steinhart, who came from Washington to participate in a discussion. A man on the street could now distinguish a kelly from an Irishman and could talk intelligently of the effect of hydrostatic pressure on submarine oil seepage. Technical knowledge that had once seemed the exclusive possession of government and oil industry became common property. Thousands of laymen knew enough to form a reasonably competent opinion.

Broadening the community's resistance capability further was an influx of youthful leadership. Marc McGinnes was a twenty-eight-year-old attorney looking for a better quality of life. He had left a job with a San Francisco law firm to settle in Santa Barbara—only to find himself surrounded by record-breaking pollution. McGinnes had organized a group of young people, all under the age of thirty. Ecological Counter Offensive, they called themselves. With the encouragement of older leadership, they had established as their first project a commemorative program for the first anniversary of the spill, January 28, 1970. They had enlisted such widely diverse civic elements as the liberal Vietnam Moratorium Committee and the conservative Tuberculosis and Health Association. More than twenty citizens groups were cooperating, with the blessing of City Council and Board of Supervisors. Governor Reagan, former Secretary of the Interior Udall, and the heads of leading U.S. conservation organizations had been invited to attend.

January 28 was to mark a milestone in the city's history and in the nation's, if the multigroup citizens' effort had its way. Roderick Nash, the author and historian, had written the Santa Barbara Declaration of Environmental Rights, which articulated the community's larger purpose. It said in part: "We must find the courage to take upon ourselves as individuals responsibility for the welfare of the whole environment, treating our own back yards as if they were the world and the world as if it were our back yard." The new young leadership provided a needed lift at a critical time.

Ironically, Union Oil itself provided another lift. In a legal complaint, it charged its drilling contractor, Peter Bawden, with operating negligently and with violating federal regulations in the drilling of Well A-21. Union argued that Bawden, not Union, had been responsible for the damage caused by the blowout and spill; and Union claimed that itself and its partners at Platform A had been damaged by the blowout and its aftermath in amounts in excess of $25 million.

Santa Barbarans were delighted to learn of such fallings-out among their adversaries. Sometimes it seemed as if the enemy was making Freudian slips all over the world. Thousands of gallons of diesel fuel had leaked from a wrecked barge and polluted the shores of Cape Cod near Falmouth, Massachusetts. A fire in a blown-out gas well off northern Australia had finally been extinguished, the well's owner, Atlantic Richfield, announced. The blowout was believed caused by "an unusual series of mechanical failures." Panarctic said that a blowout on Melville Island off northern Canada was brought under control after Red Adair was summoned and special equipment flown to the site. The blowout was caused by gas escaping through a break in the well's casing.

The ice-breaking tanker *Manhattan* arrived in New York with a hole in its hull after its history-making cruise through the Northwest Passage. The hole would have spilled oil had the 800,000-barrel-capacity tanker been loaded. Prime Minister Trudeau came from Canada to New York to talk to the United Nations about the dangers of tankers like the *Manhattan* circling his country's shores with holes in their hulls. Another tanker, the *Marpessa*, owned by Shell, blew up and sank off the coast of West Africa. Luckily she had just discharged her cargo at Rotterdam. The *Marpessa*, 207,000 tons, was the largest vessel ever to sink.

Not only was the enemy vulnerable, invisible tides seemed to be rising higher against him every day. Secretary General U Thant had warned the United Nations that destruction of the human environment threatened the survival of mankind. Now, in Washington, Dr. DuBridge said that the smog-producing gasoline engine was "in a stiff race to survive." This voice from the White House would have seemed heretical a few months before but now sounded in keeping with the times.

Sometimes it seemed as if a milestone had been passed. There had been many indicative events: the death of Eisenhower in March, the resignation of De Gaulle in April, the landing of men on the moon in July. Now the happenings of a troubled environment were like messages from a new social order.

Philip Berry, a thirty-two-year-old San Francisco attorney, recently elected president of the Sierra Club, put it all together in a speech in Santa Barbara. "Progress can no longer be measured in terms of kilowatt hours, or barrels pumped, or board-feet-cut. Progress must be measured in terms of what we add to the quality of life. The ever-expanding economy is an outmoded concept. Americans must do away with the demand for more of everything."

A few years, even a few months, earlier and Berry's speech might have been mistaken for a radical manifesto. Now most people knew what he was talking about. Language itself was changing. Words like "ecology," "environmentalist," and "biosphere"—used only by specialists a few months before—were becoming part of everyday speech. In the minds of many, something irreversible had happened.

"You've become a symbol for the nation," William R. Ewald,

Jr., planning advisor to New York Governor Nelson Rockefeller, told Santa Barbara civic leaders. Like many observers, Ewald saw Santa Barbara as a catalyst in a profound change.

But catalysts are not supposed to be consumed in the reactions they encourage; and all legislation aimed at curbing channel oil operations was dead or stalled in committee, and all litigation aimed at the same objective was defeated or deferred; and Nixon and Reagan continued to remain aloof while oil polluted Santa Barbara's beaches as the wind and the tide determined.

Just when help was needed most, unforeseen forces intervened again.

Leon Durden, the veteran fish-spotter, saw the new slick first from his fish-spotting airplane. It extended easterly from Platform A for about ten miles and was about five miles wide. "It was a peculiar brown color, different from what I'd been seeing there regularly, and lots bigger."

Next day, December 17, federal officials announced there was an 8-inch-long break in the underwater pipeline carrying crude oil ashore from Platforms A and B. The break had occurred where the pipe was welded to a leg of Platform A. No automatic devices had detected the leak. No automatic equipment had shut it off. Oil had poured out for a time variously estimated at 30 minutes to 30 hours.

A U.S. Geological Survey inspector was reported to have been on the platform when the leak occurred. Divers went down to try and fix it, while Santa Barbarans wondered how many more disasters would be needed before channel drilling would come to an end.

The 16 wells on Platform A and the 14 on Platform B, which had been pumping a total of 22,000 barrels of oil per day, were shut down while work continued on the leaky pipe. But the shutting down of the 30 wells allegedly allowed pressure to increase in the underlying reservoir, which in turn allowed leakage from the ocean floor to increase, which made the slick bigger. Union Oil and USGS spokesmen alleged that the shutdown was the cause of the increased leakage. But an oil worker told Santa Barbara anti-oil leaders that the slick Leon Durden saw had been caused by the inadvertent closing of an onshore valve, which had backed up oil in the pipeline running to shore from Platform A, which in turn had caused the rupture of the pipe and the leakage. He and others said there had been no substantial increase in leakage after the shutting down of the wells, thus supporting the contention of anti-oil forces that the drilling and pumping recommended by the presidential panel were perhaps unnecessary. Heavy fog hindered accurate observation of what was really happening at or near Platform A. Whatever the reason, the channel was soon in the dirtiest mess since February.

Heavy surf began pounding the mess ashore. First it contaminated 10 miles of beach from Rincon to Ventura. Then 22 miles from Carpinteria to beyond Ventura. It lay in heavy black windrows on the sand when the tide was low, or splashed over the Highway 101 seawall onto passing cars when the tide was high.

The owner of a beach cottage counted 20 grebes in fatal trouble just offshore. As they came ashore, oil-soaked and helpless, he took them to the Child's Estate Rescue Station in Santa Barbara, or wrung their necks.

Protests exceeded in some ways anything so far. Speaking on the floor of the U.S. Senate, Alan Cranston told his colleagues: "I find it incredible that we are blindly plunging ahead into the Santa Barbara Channel before we have perfected techniques for safe drilling or adequate oil spill surveillance." And conservative Republican Senator George Murphy said the new leak might be a warning from God. "We ought to take the hint," Murphy said. "Maybe God doesn't want us to do any more poking around in the channel."

With God and Murphy on their side, the Santa Barbarans took new heart. Apparently siding with them too, Lieutenant Governor Ed Reinecke, Reagan's recently appointed anti-pollution coordinator, came and waded in the new muck on the beaches, and said he would tell the governor what he had seen.

Jesse Unruh came to Santa Barbara, did more wading, and announced: "If the Governor said 'no' often enough, loud enough, and long enough, the Nixon Administration—with its supposed concern for conservation—would go along." But Reagan remained silent and so did Nixon.

Lois Sidenberg, "the Red Baroness," lately named president of

GOO, successor to Alvin Weingand who had resigned "to resume making a living," wired President Nixon: "As a Christmas present to this and other Southern California coastal communities, won't you please take some personal interest in our plight and recommend to the Interior Department that all oil operations on the Outer Continental Shelf in the Santa Barbara Channel be halted until the recommendations made in the second report of your panel on oil spills are given thorough consideration and hopefully are adopted?"

Nearing seventy, GOO's new blonde leader looked—Marlene Dietrich-style—nearer forty, and acted accordingly. Her throaty voice had quickly become familiar on Washington telephones, including those of Teague, Cranston, Murphy, Pecora, and Hickel. But Nixon remained silent. It seemed as though he did not know the oil spill existed.

The new leakage blackened public beaches and the public mind during the week before Christmas. It became a kind of final insult, a last oil-soaked straw.

In Washington the new tax reform bill—in which the reduction of the oil depletion allowance was a central feature and Santa Barbara a silent one—lay on the President's desk. Would he sign or veto?

The national conflict over oil had come to a climax. Senator Russell Long of Louisiana, an oil-producing state, had tried to amend the tax bill to keep the depletion allowance at $27\frac{1}{2}$ percent. Senator John Williams of Delaware, a non-oil-producing state, had wanted the allowance reduced to 20 percent. The Senate had finally settled on 23 percent. It retained the one-year tax write-off of intangible expenses that oilmen considered essential. It did nothing about oil import quotas. But it closed the "ABC Loophole," the one used by Pauley and the University of California, and others who set up "straw" corporations to serve as middlemen in obtaining loans.

Under the provisions of the old law, oil and mineral companies could borrow money through a straw corporation and call it "income" and pay it back in another tax year and call the payment "expense." Operating to extend the effect of the $27\frac{1}{2}$ percent depletion allowance beyond the legal limit of 50 percent of net income, the loophole had cost the U.S. Treasury an estimated $300 to $400 million in tax revenues annually.

Senate-House conferees had finally settled on a 22 percent depletion allowance and had retained the closure of the "ABC Loophole" (so-called because of the three parties involved—oil company, straw corporation, and bank), and the Tax Reform Bill of 1969 had gone to the President.

As political tensions mounted, personalities had clashed. Senator William Proxmire, a leader in oil tax reform, had accused Michael L. Haider, former chairman of the Standard Oil Company of New Jersey (Essso), now head of the American Petroleum Institute, of exerting undue influence at the White House. Proxmire charged Haider with visiting Nixon privately and spending an hour with him. Independent sources confirmed the meeting. Esso, through its wholly owned subsidiary Humble, was the biggest operator in the Santa Barbara Channel.

Proxmire and Haider figured in the controversy in another way, this time via Southeast Asia and Santa Barbara. A Santa Barbaran named Eric W. Pollard had written a confidential report while employed by Haider's Esso organization in Saigon. Pollard's report asserted that about 50,000,000 gallons of military petroleum products were stolen annually from Esso installations in the Saigon area. Most of the material went to the Vietcong with the full knowledge of oil company and military officials, Pollard said. The arrangement between Esso personnel and the Vietcong was in his opinion the reason why petroleum installations at Nha Be, eight miles down the river from Saigon, had never been attacked by the Communists, though it would have been a simple matter for them to do so. Natives with highly questionable backgrounds held sensitive positions with Esso Vietnam. One of them was probably the chief of North Vietnamese intelligence in South Vietnam.

Pollard, who had been a captain in the Navy and served as attaché in several foreign countries before joining Esso, claimed his report had been suppressed. It had gone to top Esso management in New York, even to the White House where it reached Vice President Humphrey. But nothing happened.

Pollard then took his story to *Life*. After considering it for several months, *Life* declined to use it.

Meanwhile in January 1969, not long before the Santa Barbara Oil Spill, Senator Proxmire revealed that a Navy civilian inspector had been removed from his job in Thailand after starting an investigation that uncovered widespread thefts of petroleum products there. A few days later Helen Delich Bentley, soon to be U.S. Maritime Commissioner, charged in an article in the *Baltimore Sun* that the Thailand situation was being duplicated, with refinements, in Saigon. Pollard claimed that Mrs. Bentley had obtained a copy of his confidential report. Mrs. Bentley declined to reveal her sources but insisted Esso had never denied her story. On its part, Esso said it was aware there had been pilferage of its petroleum products being delivered to military installations in Vietnam, but that it had acted promptly in collaboration with Vietnamese national police to halt the thefts.

Proxmire joined Senator Joseph Montoya, the Democrat from New Mexico who had presided at the February 24 hearing of the Muskie subcommittee in Santa Barbara, in requesting that the U.S. General Accounting Office investigate distribution programs for petroleum products in Southeast Asia.

Now in December as the tax reform bill lay on the President's desk, insiders knew that the Proxmire-Montoya-GAO investigation was in progress. They also knew its findings would be detrimental to the oil industry. Notwithstanding any of this, or because of it, the President signed the Tax Reform Bill on December 30.

This was the furthest Nixon had turned away from the oil industry since becoming President. Would he turn further? There were indications that he might.

Nixon's first official act of 1970 was to sign a bill creating within the White House itself a "Council on Environmental Quality."

The bill, known as the National Environmental Policy Act, had been proposed by Senator Henry M. Jackson, a Washington Democrat, chairman of the Senate's powerful Interior and Insular Affairs Committee. It declared that every person "should enjoy a healthful environment" and directed federal agencies to analyze proposed legislation and administrative action in terms of their effect on the environment and to make such analyses public.

The President had reportedly opposed the Jackson bill as redundant, in view of the Environmental Quality Council created by his executive order in May; but when Senator Muskie introduced a bill to enlarge White House environmental functions, the President threw his support behind the Jackson measure and pointed up his rivalry with Muskie by asking Congress not to support the Muskie bill. All three measures had been largely inspired by the Santa Barbara spill, according to congressional aides.

In signing the National Environmental Policy Act on January 1 while at the San Clemente, California, White House, Nixon said: "I have become absolutely convinced that the 1970s must be the years when America pays its debt to the past by reclaiming the purity of its air, waters, and our living environment. It is literally now or never."

He had been motoring through the San Clemente-Laguna Beach area he had known as a young man. He said he could not help thinking that within a few years the region might become unlivable due to pollution.

Perhaps helping his thinking along, an officer of the Matson luxury liner *Lurline* claimed that while passing northward through the channel the *Lurline* had been obliged to change course to avoid hitting the drilling rig *Bluewater II,* anchored near Point Conception. The *Lurline* was carrying some 600 passengers returning from a Caribbean cruise.

As a former tanker officer, now a Santa Barbara anti-oil partisan, said: "All it takes is one mistake by one deck officer on one foggy night, and this channel will have an oil bath that will make the present oil spill look like a shower."

Congressman Teague promptly asked that Santa Barbara Channel oil problems be given top priority by the new Council on Environmental Quality. Teague had visited Nixon at San Clemente in August, and Nixon had told him that the best way to curtail channel oil operations was to make rules so strict that oil companies would not want to operate under them. But now Nixon seemed to be thinking about more affirmative action.

GOO chose this moment to try and gain the President's attention. Like Congressman Teague, it hoped to encourage him to select the channel as the place to demonstrate his new environmental concern. GOO also wanted to present him with 150,000 anti-oil petition signatures. When they found there was no way to contact the executive offices at the San Clemente White House by telephone or in any other fashion, GOO's leaders improvised.

When Nixon looked seaward on January 4, he might have seen a 16-foot Boston whaler bobbing a mile and a half off shore, beyond security limits. The whaler displayed an orange and blue banner with one large word: *GOO!* Aboard it in charge of 150,000 anti-oil signatures were Paul Molitor, Bill Botwright, and Bud Bottoms. But the Coast Guard refused to let the three go ashore and see the President, and declined to carry their petitions to him.

There was hidden unfairness in this. Had it not been for the channel spill, Nixon might have had a steel platform to look at as well as a Boston whaler. The spill had caused the cancellation of a Shell Oil Company drilling permit off San Clemente.

Even if the President didn't see GOO's boat, he was probably aware of some of the things GOO wanted to tell him. By now it was generally known that six billion tons of fossil fuel, chiefly petroleum products, were being burned annually in the world. The temperature of the earth's surface was slowly rising. Polar ice caps were melting. The oxygen balance was changing. All life was being affected. As James Reston said in the *New York Times:* "It is only in the past year that Nixon, like many other Americans, has come to realize that a population increasing by more than two million a year and an indifferent industry expanding even faster are poisoning the atmosphere of the nation."

On January 6 came a major breakthrough. Ronald Reagan urged the federal government to ban further drilling for oil in the channel's federal waters. Reagan's statement, contained in a State of the State message to a joint session of the California Legislature, echoed Nixon's San Clemente remarks of five days earlier. "A booming economy and 'the good life' will be no good at all if our air is too dirty to breathe, our water too polluted to use, our surroundings too noisy and our land too cluttered and littered to allow us to live decently," the Governor said. It was his first decisive move against oil, against pollution in general, and in aid of Santa Barbara.

The new Sacramento-Washington posture brought immediate response at other levels. The Army Corps of Engineers announced that if the State of California objected to offshore structures, the

Corps was likely to view them differently than if only the City and County of Santa Barbara objected. The Interior Department announced it was not lifting its ban against the emplacement of Platform C westerly from Platform A, an emplacement announced by Fred Hartley on December 31 as imminent.

In a simultaneous but unrelated action, the National Academy of Sciences prepared recommendations calling for the establishment of a "quick alert" research team. Scientific experts would make "quick explorations" into environmental crises, and they would investigate suspicious rises in pollution levels. It seemed that NAS was at last responding to GOO's appeal for help of six months earlier.

Even the Western Oil and Gas Association was undergoing an apparent change of heart. A spokesman said the association might have been too highhanded in its approach to channel leasing problems in the pressurized days before federal leasing began. The public had perhaps been unnecessarily antagonized. "If we had it to do over, we'd do it differently."

WOGA's members were taking steps to police their own oil spills, be more concerned about pollution, and present a new public image.

On January 19, in a major address to the U.S. Senate, Senator Nelson of Wisconsin proposed an environmental amendment to the U.S. Constitution. In language resembling that of Santa Barbara's legal complaints and recently published Declaration of Environmental Rights, Nelson's amendment read: "Every person has an inalienable right to a decent environment. The United States and every State shall guarantee this right."

Quoting from the recent report of the President's Panel on Oil Spills, Nelson said: "We can expect a Santa Barbara-scale pollution incident once a year by 1980 if offshore oil development continues at the present rate." Although New York State had added a similar amendment to its constitution in November, Nelson's amendment was a historic first suggestion at national level.

Other signs of change followed rapidly. On January 20, Hickel told Lois Sidenberg, Fred Eissler, Norman Sanders, and Philip Berry, meeting in his office in Washington, that the Interior Department "would probably hold public hearings" on any future applications for permanent oil platforms in the Santa Barbara

Channel. Dr. Pecora went further. He said he would make available all data used by the special presidential panel in formulating its recommendations for remedial pumping and drilling in Tract 402. Making good his promise, Pecora sent Santa Barbara's Environmental Quality Advisory Board a 77-page blue book containing the data.

On January 21 Hickel went further still. In an exclusive interview in Washington with Robert H. Sollen of the *News-Press,* he proposed a federal marine sanctuary extending from the outer limit of the existing state sanctuary across the channel to the state waters bordering the islands. It might be possible, Hickel thought, to phase out permanent platforms in the proposed area, including those in Tract 402. Undeveloped leases would have to be negotiated or legislated out. The project would require congressional action. But Hickel saw possibilities in legislation introduced by Teague and Murphy making the federal area of the channel an undeveloped reserve in exchange for rights to development in the Elk Hills Reserve.

The Nixon Administration was at last proposing to get at least some oil operations out of the channel. It was the second major breakthrough in three weeks. Coming from Secretary Hickel, whose appointment had been regarded by conservationists as a disaster and who had been regarded by many Santa Barbarans as their chief adversary, it was astonishing.

Then in his State of the Union Message to Congress on January 22, Nixon made pollution control a number-one national priority. He asked for $10 billion to fight pollution over a five-year period. "Clean air, clean water, open spaces—these once again should be the birthright of every American."

The President's proposals were the most comprehensive and costly of their kind in the nation's history. They were further evidence that a turning point had been reached in public attitudes toward environment.

Next day Senator Muskie announced his own comprehensive program for fighting pollution. Muskie's program called for spending more money more quickly: $2 billion in fiscal 1971, $3.5 billion in 1972. Unlike Nixon's message, Muskie's program specifically mentioned Santa Barbara Channel oil problems, and it went a good deal further toward solving them than did the proposals

advanced by Hickel. Muskie proposed that the federal government: (1) reacquire *all* its oil leases in the Santa Barbara Channel,
less costs and damages to lessees; (2) do what was necessary to
abate the leakage; (3) provide for removal of platforms as soon as
possible; (4) set the channel's oil aside as a national reserve to be
tapped only in an emergency, or by act of Congress.

Santa Barbarans felt as if they had been drinking heady wine
when they learned that leaders of both political parties were
proposing specific plans for getting oil out of the channel. It was
a consummation they had wished for so long that now it was happening they could hardly believe it. Three decades of effort seemed
to be coming to fruition at last.

The first anniversary of the oil spill, January 28, 1970, dawned
bright and clear. There had been rains. The foothills were green
again. The islands were clearly visible and so were Platforms A,
B, and Hillhouse, looming like three aircraft carriers advancing
abreast toward shore.

Shortly after dawn Harold Beveridge's sloop, *Galadriel,* the flag-
ship of GOO's fleet, placed a commemorative marker buoy on the
spot about 800 feet east of Platform A where the "big bubble" had
broken the surface a year before.

Ashore there was a new atmosphere. Throughout the city, schoolchildren had put aside their regular work to discuss environmental
problems and to listen to environmentalist speakers. Service club
members prepared to do likewise at their noon meetings. The news
media that approximately a year before had carried news of disaster
were devoting time and space to programs for environmental improvement, such as the proposed Community Ecology Center—
citizen staffed and citizen financed—where all types of environmental projects would be coordinated. The new aim was to make
Santa Barbara an environmental model for the future, rather than
a disastrous example of the past.

At 9:15 A.M. in the auditorium of the City College Student
Union Building, Mayor Firestone opened the first Santa Barbara
Environmental Rights Conference.

Appropriately the building was located on the mesa overlooking
harbor and beaches, with a long view southward down the coast
past Carpinteria and Rincon, Ventura and Oxnard, and on to

the blue Malibu Mountains. It was the stretch of shoreline that had suffered most during the spill. Appropriately, too, the conference site was located within a stone's throw of the old Mesa Oil Field where Santa Barbara's resistance to oil development had begun.

Seaward the platforms were clearly visible through the tall solar-glass windows of the auditorium or from its sunlit decks—where the overflow crowd was listening to loudspeakers. A thousand people had come.

Roderick Nash, the wilderness expert who had proposed the "Eleventh Commandment" to extend Christian ethics to include man's relationship to his environment, provided the keynote. Reading from the Santa Barbara Declaration of Environmental Rights, Nash called for "a revolution in conduct toward an environment which is rising in revolt against us."

Dr. Paul Ehrlich, Stanford biologist and author of *The Population Bomb*, speaking next, pointed toward the oil platforms. "They are symptomatic of nearly everything that is wrong with our society." But far more dangerous were the subtle poisons affecting food chains and life itself. "Man is now an endangered species."

Alan Cranston announced a new bipartisan effort in the U.S. Senate. With Senator Murphy, he had "today" introduced a bill to establish a federal oil sanctuary seaward of the state sanctuary and extending across the channel. The Cranston-Murphy bill formalized the proposal made by Hickel the week before. Though anti-oil leaders were to attack it as an inadequate solution, it was a step in what most citizens agreed was the right direction.

Charles Teague said he had received assurances from both Defense and Interior Departments that they would not oppose his bill for making the channel into an oil reserve in exchange for development of the Elk Hills Reserve. This was a clean breakthrough, since congressional committees seldom reported favorably on bills that were opposed by executive departments.

A university student, who was a member of the Interior Department's Student Advisory Board and of Santa Barbara's Environmental Rights Day Steering Committee, was skeptical. He noted that talk of saving the environment had become "an additive, giving politicians more mileage." Relating it to the drug problem, he said: "As you drive away in your cars, remember that you are doing your bit for your pushers, the oil platforms."

But Philip Berry of the Sierra Club enlarged on Senator Nelson's idea for a constitutional amendment. He said the United States needed an Environmental Bill of Rights against which all major legislation could be checked for its constitutionality.

A United Automobile Workers representative asked for ideas he could take to the negotiating table. Ellen Stern Harris, the citizens' representative on the Los Angeles Regional Water Quality Board, shot back from the speakers' platform: "Tell them you won't work on any product that exceeds minimum criteria for air pollution!" The United Automobile Workers had paid for the printing of 10,000 copies of the Santa Barbara Declaration of Environmental Rights and circulated them widely among its membership.

Lieutenant Governor Reinecke promised that the moratorium on drilling in the channel's state waters would continue indefinitely, as far as he was concerned; while an assemblyman from San Francisco proposed that the oil industry be nationalized. "There are times when I'd like to get a machine gun and head for the hills too," he told militants, "but you won't win that way. Organize. We'll change the system."

At noon a group of clergymen, led by Episcopal Bishop Edward Crowther, who had been deported from South Africa because of his opposition to apartheid, went down to the beach and held a communion service by the oily water. Platforms A and B were producing about 30,000 barrels of oil a day as a result of the government's remedial drilling program. It was worth about $115,000.

Union Oil's presence was felt again during the afternoon of the conference. A copy of the *News-Press* was brought in disclosing that County Petroleum Engineer David Bickmore had signed two trust deeds and a promissory note in Union's favor, to secure an old debt. Bickmore had the exclusive power to grant oil drilling permits in Santa Barbara County. He had recently granted Union a controversial permit to drill on Santa Cruz Island.

Bickmore was temporarily suspended from his duties but was reinstated, when cleared of wrongdoing, by county attorneys and Board of Supervisors. He later resigned when it was learned that he owned oil wells in the county and did private consulting work which he had failed to disclose to his public employers.

In the evening younger people gathered for a box supper, with rock music and speakers, on the City College grounds; while their elders moved to El Paseo Restaurant in the city's historic heart. There Deputy Attorney General O'Brien told them of the "governmental-industrial-academic complex" that, he said, was still blocking the state's efforts to obtain expert witnesses and technical data needed in its suits against government and oil industry. The University of California, tied to government and industry by financial and political bonds, had been less than cooperative. "This partnership between official secrecy and pollution provides unique protection for the polluter and silently handicaps government agencies fighting him."

Former Secretary of Interior Udall said: "Looking back on my term in office I have two chief regrets: one is that we didn't do more for the American Indian, the other is the Santa Barbara Oil Spill."

Young Marc McGinnes presided, as he had done all day. To many of those present, it had felt like a young day, perhaps even the dawn of a new one.

An aspect of its newness broke out while the El Paseo speakers were talking. About five hundred people, most of them young, marched to Stearns Wharf and blockaded its entrance. They were protesting its continued use by oil companies and oil service firms. George Castagnola, the franchise holder, invited the protesters onto the wharf. When he attempted to speak to them and was cut off by jeers, Lefty Bryant, a black militant, told the crowd to shut up and give Castagnola a chance.

Castagnola told of years of work and hundreds of thousands of dollars spent in developing the wharf from a rundown failure into a productive economic enterprise including restaurants, tourists' shops, and fisheries as well as offshore service facilities. His ease and affability kept the situation under control. But the blockade lasted all night. At one point firemen were called to extinguish smouldering asphalt caused by demonstrators starting a fire.

There were no arrests. Next morning when police told them

they had made their point and were now breaking the law, the demonstrators left the wharf.

Though on the whole peaceful, the wharf blockade reflected feelings surging near the surface once again. One young man had told police officers early in the evening: "You can move us if you like, but you'll have to lift us off this wharf, like the tar has had to be lifted off the beaches."

Moderates accused extremists of trying to take over what had begun as a peaceful commemorative march on the wharf, participated in by many age groups, and turn it into a springboard for radical student activity at the University of California campus and nearby Isla Vista.

Santa Barbara's first Environmental Rights Day had commemorated a new kind of thinking, a new kind of personal concern, a new kind of political action, and a new series of social problems.

The blowout of Well A-21 had indeed been heard around the world.

III

CONSEQUENCES

17

HOW DID THE
BLOWOUT HAPPEN?

RECRIMINATIONS were well advanced by the end of the spill's first
year. Chief among these was the question: how did the blowout
happen? An unpublished U.S. Geological Survey Report ("Report
on Lease OCS-P 0241") prepared in June, 1969, by the Survey's
Pacific Region and made available by one of Ralph Nader's raiders
(who copied it in the office of the USGS in Washington, where it
was open to public inspection) said that the "primary cause" of
the blowout was "the pulling of a balled bit."

A balled drilling bit is generally understood to be one so caked
with mud and cuttings that it plugs the well bore.

"Contributory causes were twofold," the little-known report
continued, " (a) the use of a mud weight that provided too little
differential above the probable formation pressure, and (b) the
existence of mud characteristics that did not follow good drilling
practice."

Point (a) implies a need for closer inspection of drilling mud.
Point (b) may mean that mud of improper viscosity was being
used, with consequent loss of sealing potential.

The report also said that a lost-circulation-of-drilling-mud condition existed in Well A-21 "for at least 48 hours before the blow-out" and that "this alone should have been a warning of pending trouble."

This suggests that mud was seeping from the well bore into porous formations surrounding the hole during a two-day period prior to the accident.

Were there other warnings? The general area of Tract 402 was evidently blowout prone, judging from the gas blowout that lifted a drilling vessel out of position, and from a similar blowout that caused an eruption of seawater, reported by a U.C. Santa Barbara geologist as having taken place about two years before the drilling of Well A-21.

Before the erection of Platform A, "a fairly large oil slick with some gas bubbles" was reported by a Union Oil official at a point identified later as 960 feet west of Platform A. Such natural seep-age is evidence that an uncontrolled flow of hydrocarbons may result if a well is drilled, says the Geological Survey.

There were other warnings. During 1968, eight shallow core holes were drilled to provide information for the emplacement of Platforms A, B, and C. Evidence of fluid oil was reported in all three core holes at the Platform A site; none at the other sites. During the emplacement of Platform A, oil was released by the driving of the pilings, and gas was bubbling from the ocean floor as the platform was erected. Some of the gas caught fire. During the drilling of each of the wells preceding A-21, there was a loss of mud circulation. Well A-25, for example, which penetrated to a depth of 4,550 feet, experienced a "kicking" or upsurge of mud at 4,034 feet, at approximately the same structural depth reached later by Well A-21. The kicking indicated gas pressure of about 1,700 pounds per square inch. Heavier mud was used to control the pressure as Well A-25 went deeper.

According to the Geological Survey, these and other data showed that hydrocarbons under Platform A, from a depth of about 3,400 feet to about 4,000 feet, were under higher pressure than normally encountered at such depth, and that problems of mud circulation existed.

Against this can be set the fact that the blowout was the first mishap of its kind reported to have occurred in the Pacific Coast waters of the United States. Approximately one thousand production wells had been drilled in California waters without disastrous blowouts. Additional exploratory wells had been sunk off Oregon and Washington. Scores of test holes and more than two dozen wells had been drilled in the federal water of the Santa Barbara Channel without major mishap. Finally, the four wells drilled from Platform A prior to Well A-21 had penetrated geological structures similar to those penetrated by the blowout well. They had been completed or were nearly so (including casing throughout their entire lengths) and were waiting to be placed in production when their companion blew.

What happened to make Well A-21 unique? Union Oil and Peter Bawden Drilling have declined to discuss the question in detail, citing pending lawsuits as their reason, but independent experts say that a balled bit "swabbing the hole," (pulling mud up as the drill string was being removed) probably caused the loss of mud pressure resulting in the blowout. Seepage of drilling mud into porous structures surrounding the uncased hole may have been a contributing factor. And the mud may have been too light in weight, as the little-known USGS report suggests.

Was there any infraction of rules? Secretary Hickel and other Interior Department spokesmen insisted repeatedly that no rules had been broken. They were positive that the blowout was an unavoidable accident. But in December, 1970, Dr. Pecora said that the blowout was caused by "loss of well control" and that that in itself was an infraction of rules.

What about the controversial waiver of casing regulations? Before the drilling of Well A-21, Union requested and received the waiver permitting it to place initial casing to a depth of 239 feet below the ocean floor, rather than down to the 880 feet required by regulations. But such waivers were authorized by regulations "when necessary for proper well control," and the drilling plan for Well A-21, including the waiver, was approved by the Geological Survey. The plan resembled those of some of the four preceding Platform A wells. Though the granting of the waiver may have been an error in judgment, it was not an infraction of rules.

But why was the waiver thought necessary? D. W. Solanas said the reason was the lack of competent formation to cement a casing to. After the blowout, John Fraser contradicted this by saying there were competent formations at about 1,200 and 1,800 feet. But Solanas defended his position by saying that since Union could not guarantee that it could cement initial casing at depths lower than 239 feet, the safest procedure was to drill to total depth as rapidly as possible and completely case the hole, as had allegedly been done with the preceding wells; yet later evidence showed that several of the preceding wells were left uncased for hours and even days while core samples were taken and other tests made.

Post-blowout Platform A wells reportedly were cased to 1,000 feet, or more, before being drilled to completion.

Some observers say the controversial waiver reflected Union's desire to produce oil from a shallow sand, and it could not readily do so through a casing cemented in place. Still others say the company did not want to spend the money necessary to stop drilling, remove the drill string, and case the hole to an ocean-floor depth greater than 239 feet, before drilling further.

Did the granting of the waiver in fact reflect an error in judgment? Apparently it did. If something went wrong at deep levels, high pressures seeking to escape up a largely uncased hole might find paths of least resistance through the near-surface formation of known instability. "Union and USGS apparently agreed to take a shortcut," a member of Santa Barbara's Environmental Quality Advisory Board said, "and it backfired."

Other questions the courts may find it necessary to decide include the length of time that gas roared out of Well A-21. The official record says it was thirteen minutes. Three eyewitnesses agree it was thirty minutes and perhaps as much as an hour. The question may have bearing on the wisdom of the measures taken to control the blowout, and on the amount of oil released. The eyewitnesses' statements seem irreconcilable with the record. Either the well was sealed by the closing of the blind rams or it was not. One possible explanation: gas escaped from the well outside the sealed-off casing.

There is a similar disagreement over the length of time between the closing of the rams and the appearance of the first large boils of gas and oil on the surface of the ocean. USGS field reports say it was "soon" after the closing of the rams. *U.S. Geological Professional Paper 679* says it was one and a half to two hours. Eyewitnesses say it was less than an hour. A Battelle Memorial Institute report says the first large boil appeared within fourteen to twenty-five minutes. Other investigators found that "about seven minutes" after the rams were closed "the sea about 200 yards from the northeast corner of the platform began to boil."

Accounts agree that the eruptions appeared in a line running easterly and westerly through Platform A and that the first one was located 600 to 800 feet east of the platform. It was probably situated above the highest part of the anticlinal geologic structure toward which highly pressurized oil and gas migrated, after escaping from the well bore. The later location of another major boil at the northeast corner of the platform may have resulted from slightly greater penetrations there by two of the foundation pilings.

After the blowout occurred, were effective measures taken to control it? The decision to drop the drill string and close the rams was made against a background of extreme fire and explosion hazard. The decision may have saved Platform A from destruction, while paving the way for a rupture of the ocean floor and for the spill that followed. Some experts say the rams should not have been closed, though one of them says in defense of the closure: "It's a miracle the platform didn't catch fire or blow up. Luckily no gravel was blowing up the hole to make a spark."

Once the rams were closed and the drill string was dropped back into the hole, control measures followed expectable patterns. But they met with unexpected difficulties. When the lost "fish" was reconnected with the platform, the drill string was found to be stuck and the bit "plugged" (its apertures clogged with mud and earth). Pressures of 5,000 pounds per square inch could not unclog the bit. Attempts to withdraw the entire string and replace it with another failed, probably, said John Fraser, because dropping it had caused caving of the hole, which stuck the pipe fast.

With the plugged bit preventing mud circulation and with the caved hole preventing removal of the drill string, it was necessary to remove the safety valve located in the first joint of pipe snubbed onto the fish, so that a perforating gun could be lowered. The gun would make holes in the drill pipe through which mud could circulate out into the annulus and up the well. But each attempt to disengage the joint containing the valve resulted in unscrewing the string *above* the joint. Thus precious time was lost, and the additional effort of milling through the valve was required.

When the valve was milled through, the perforating gun lowered, and ninety-seven holes a third of an inch in diameter blasted in the drill pipe at a depth of approximately 2,870 feet, circulation of drilling fluid was regained. This was on Monday, February 3, six days after the blowout occurred.

During the six-day interval, nearly forty-eight hours of working time had been lost by enforced evacuation of the platform due to fire and explosion hazard; but on February 3 Union mounted its massive well-killing effort. Five days later Well A-21 was choked with cement. By then the unneeded relief well had reached a depth of 1,990 feet, reportedly cased throughout its entirety.

In terms of volume, the blowout of Well A-21 was rated "medium." A "large" one would probably have caused cratering of the ocean floor and possible collapse and disappearance of Platform A. The largest blowout on record, onshore or offshore, is also attributable to Union. It occurred near Taft in the southern San Joaquin Valley, some one hundred miles from the later site of Platform A. Beginning in 1910, Lake View Number 1 gushed an estimated nine million barrels of oil, and untold volumes of gas, during an eighteen-month period. Thus Union could still claim the blowout record.

Was the blowout preventable? Apparently it was. Dr. Pecora said so emphatically. The fact that a total of more than one hundred wells were drilled afterward without mishap from Platforms A, B, and Hillhouse is further evidence that the blowout was not only preventable but was perhaps an isolated incident.

That makes the more uncanny the reverberations of an event that need not have happened at all, or that might happen again at any time.

18

REPERCUSSIONS IN THE OIL INDUSTRY

As THE spill entered its second year, it seemed as if the oil industry's Freudian slips might continue indefinitely. On February 4, 1970, the Liberian tanker *Arrow* ran aground off Nova Scotia and began spewing its 6,000 tons of oil into the Atlantic. On February 10 a Chevron (Standard Oil Company of California) drilling platform off the Louisiana coast caught fire and burned for seven weeks, spilling 30,000 gallons of oil into the Gulf of Mexico. On February 13 a Greek tanker chartered by Humble polluted Tampa Bay. On February 20 fire swept a Mobil drilling pier at Rincon 18 miles from Santa Barbara and caused $1 million damage, and on March 4 officials were puzzling over the source of an Alaskan slick that fouled 200 miles of Kodiak Island shoreline and killed more than 1,000 birds. On March 29 the federal government shut down a Shell platform in the Gulf of Mexico for violating safety regulations. On May 29 an explosion and oil spill at an offshore platform near Galveston, Texas, killed 9 men and injured 15. And on September 4 fire swept Standard of California's Platform Hazel, a few miles from Platform A in state waters, causing $1 million damage and sending oily debris ashore. On October 24 two tankers, the

Pacific Glory and the *Allegro,* collided in the English Channel and 70,000 tons of Libyan crude began seeping into the sea near the resort beaches of the Isle of Wight. On December 1 came the Shell blowout, fire, and spill off Louisiana, which was to continue for more than three months. On December 2 Humble was fined $300,-000 in federal court in New Orleans for failing to provide safety devices in 33 wells off the Louisiana coast, and Union was fined $24,000 for similar violations. These fines brought to $1,566,000 the amount levied against oil firms in the Louisiana area since the Chevron fire and spill of early February. The amount promised to grow larger on December 23 when Gulf and Mobil, two Platform A firms, were among companies charged with failure to obey safety regulations in Gulf of Mexico operations. And on January 18, 1971, two Standard tankers collided head-on in San Francisco Bay.

This extraordinary series of mishaps was merely representative. In 1969, the Coast Guard reported a total of 1,007 oil spills in U.S. waters alone. The 1970 rate was four times higher. This may have been due partly to increased offshore drilling and transport activity. Nearly 1,000 new wells were drilled in U.S. waters in 1970, and nearly 1.5 billion tons of oil were moved worldwide in tankers. But it may also have been due partly to other causes.

The Platform A spill shook the oil industry. It blackened its image, perhaps permanently. It cost it scores of millions in extra expenses and lost or deferred income. It deprived it of tax advantages worth hundreds of millions. It weakened its political influence, at least temporarily. It threatened its offshore operations everywhere with restrictions and prohibitions. People began to watch it and to report its malfeasances and accidents. The industry was revealed to be the chief polluter of the environment and thus the chief enemy of the new environmental revolution. In addition and perhaps most importantly, the spill destroyed the myth of oil's infallibility and political invulnerability, a myth that had grown up around U.S. industry generally since the industrial revolution of the nineteenth century.

Old and new revolutions, those of the nineteenth and twentieth centuries, met head-on in the channel controversy. It was their first clear-cut confrontation.

The environmental revolution thrived on Platform A oil. The industrial revolution nearly foundered in it. Conflict-of-interest issues were a major factor in this classic meeting. Conflicts of interest were revealed by the spill to run through government and industry and to have deep roots.

Back in 1941–1945, for example, Edwin W. Pauley was treasurer of the Democratic National Committee and a generous contributor to Democratic campaigns. In 1946 he was nominated by President Truman to be Undersecretary of the Navy. This was generally regarded as a first step toward Pauley's becoming Navy Secretary. But Harold Ickes, Truman's Secretary of the Interior, resigned in protest over Pauley's nomination. Ickes warned of possible scandals of the Teapot Dome-Elk Hills variety if Pauley were given a Cabinet post. In the resulting furore, Pauley's nomination was withdrawn.

A conflict-of-interest precedent had been established for the Santa Barbara Channel where Pauley and other oilmen had interests and Ickes was deeply enmeshed on behalf of federal ownership claims.

The precedent was apparently continued by President Johnson who, according to sources within the oil industry, ruled against channel marine sanctuaries in favor of channel oil development, in order to reduce an unfavorable balance of trade. Money spent in the channel would not be spent in foreign oil ventures. Linking the President directly to the channel-leasing decision, Budget Director Charles Shultz sent a letter to Secretary of the Interior Udall a few days before the decision was reached in November, 1967, reminding him of the President's feelings on the subject: "As you know, the President has on several recent occasions instructed us to make every attempt to produce additional revenue from Federal sources . . . he specifically asked me what might be done to increase revenues from offshore leasing."

The conflict-of-interest precedent was certainly continued by Secretary Udall, a known conservationist, who, alone or with Johnson's urging, made the decision to lease the channel's federal lands for oil; and it continued into the early days of the spill, when the Geological Survey established offices with Union Oil on the Santa Barbara waterfront. For four days USGS representatives made no contact with the National Contingency Plan command group headed by Lieutenant Brown. This convinced Brown and other observers that the USGS was too little concerned with pollution and too intimate with the people it was supposed to supervise. But D. W. Solanas, the regional supervisor for the USGS Oil and Gas Division, defended the close association. "In any regulatory operation, whether it be city, county, state, or federal, there must be professional contacts and exchanges of data. This is required by law and regulation. If this type of 'professional intimacy' were foul, I believe the entire system would have been changed long ago."

A later statement attributed to Udall qualified Solanas' view. "I know nothing that would indicate there was any kind of corrupt relationship. But they [the U.S. Geological Survey Oil and Gas Division] regarded themselves as doing a good thing for the country by promoting more oil and gas exploration. In that sense, I think that they saw a common identity of interest with the oil companies that wanted exploration. . . . It's the sort of thing you get in the federal government, in state government. . . . You get a slack attitude toward enforcement."

As he inspected the polluted Santa Barbara beaches on March 21, 1969, President Nixon may have thought of the $278,962 reportedly donated by the Mellons of Gulf Oil (and Platform A) to Republican efforts in the 1968 election campaign, or of the $41,000 reportedly donated by the Pew family of Sun Oil, or the $103,000 donated by Max Fisher of Marathon Oil, Sun's partner in Tract 401. Linking Nixon, Reagan, and Santa Barbara oil was the fact that Henry Salvatori, the drilling company executive and a leading Reagan backer, was listed as the third-largest contributor to Nixon's 1968 campaign, with $83,000. Nixon may also have recalled the $18,000 campaign fund—drawn largely from oilmen including Herbert Hoover, Jr., of Union Oil, who later became the White House advisor on oil matters—of which he was the beneficiary during his 1952 campaign for the Vice Presidency; and he may have remembered the strong support received from oilmen during his 1968 presidential campaign and his campaign promise to uphold the 27½ percent tax depletion allowance.

Thus conflicts of interest, apparent or real, entered the oil spill scene. They permeated its later background as well.

In April, 1969, Peter M. Flanigan resigned as president of Barracuda Tanker Corporation to become Nixon's special White House aide and top assistant for oil matters. But Flanigan retained

$20,000 worth of stock in Barracuda. He was also a partner in Dillon, Read and Company, the New York investment banking firm, which had formed Barracuda Corporation for the benefit of the Union Oil Company's tanker program. The ill-fated *Torrey Canyon* had belonged to Barracuda and been leased to Union.

Flanigan's stock in Barracuda Corporation was sold to other Barracuda company officers (all of them Dillon, Read officials) on February 25, 1970, five days after Flanigan announced Nixon's decision to make no changes in the national oil import program, a controversial decision highly beneficial to the oil industry. Five days after the stock sale, Secretary of the Treasury David M. Kennedy issued a special order permitting Barracuda's 70,000-ton tanker *Sansinena*, which sailed under the Liberian flag, to carry oil for the Union Oil Company in U.S. waters. Union wanted the *Sansinena* to transport Alaskan oil through the Santa Barbara Channel to Los Angeles refineries.

The permit issued by Kennedy, however, was a direct exception to the Jones Act of 1920 which forbade vessels sailing under foreign flags from carrying cargoes between U.S. ports. The Jones Act had been passed to protect the U.S. shipping and shipbuilding industries from foreign competition. Though exceptions were sometimes granted in the interest of national defense, they were made on recommendation of the Defense Department. No such recommendation had been made in the case of the *Sansinena*.

In a speech on the floor of the Senate, Senator Joseph Tydings, a Maryland Democrat, charged that U.S. shipbuilding companies had invested heavily to build new tankers in U.S. yards, and that if exception was made for the *Sansinena* it could establish a principle that would imperil U.S. shipbuilding and shipping interests. Tydings claimed the value of the *Sansinena* rose from $4.5 million to $11 million as result of the Jones Act waiver granted Union by Secretary Kennedy.

The waiver was immediately revoked, under the glare of publicity and Senate scrutiny; and Tydings asked for a congressional investigation of the part played in securing it by Flanigan and by Union Oil President Fred Hartley. Even the President's special oil-spill panel was not above suspicion. Conflict-of-interest charges flourished following the June, 1969, announcement by the White House of the panel's recommendations for increasing drilling and production at Platform A. Dr. DuBridge, the President's science advisor, who had appointed the panel, was accused of possible bias because of his previous connection with Caltech, where he had served as president and where Fred Hartley was a trustee and Union a financial donor. DuBridge gave the accusations substance by saying that "none of the members of the panel are employed by oil companies or derive any of their income from oil companies," only to have the *Los Angeles Times* reveal that quite the opposite was true.

Five of the eleven panelists depended on Union for partial support of their businesses or professions. Ross A. McClintock was president of Fluor Drilling Services which held contracts with Union before, during, and after the initial phases of the spill, and his firm drilled the relief well intended to stop the blowout. Carl H. Savit was vice president of Western Geophysical Company, a Houston firm that did hundreds of thousands of dollars worth of business with Union. The panel chairman, John C. Calhoun, Jr., of Texas A&M University, and two other panel members—Hamilton M. Johnson of Tulane and Murray Hawkins, Jr., of Louisiana State—were officers or department heads of institutions that shared in grants from Union, Gulf, Mobil, and Texaco totaling $179,000 during the five years preceding the spill. The six other panelists disclaimed any connection with the Platform A consortium; however, some of them said they had dealt with other oil companies.

Defenders of the panel claimed it was almost impossible to find experts on drilling, geology, or oceanography who were not associated in some way with oil industry or government. They pointed out that the recommendations of the panel were unanimous and that no alternate recommendations were presented, apparently overlooking the fact that three months earlier a rock-and-cement blanket had received serious consideration by the on-scene command group. Though Dr. DuBridge may not have known of the connection of a number of panelists with the oil industry when he said that none of them had any, the impression of conflict of interest remained strong.

The impression grew stronger in December, 1970, when Dr. Pecora, head of the U.S. Geological Survey, revealed that Union had broken government regulations by losing control of Well A-21, though official spokesmen for a year and a half had been saying that Union had abided fully by regulations.

Had Governor Reagan come to Santa Barbara to inspect its polluted beaches, he might have remembered Henry Salvatori's contributions to his own and Nixon's campaigns. Or had G. Ray Arnett, Reagan's newly appointed head of the State Fish and Game Department, visited Santa Barbara to inspect oil spill damage to wildlife, he might have been asked to discuss his recent employ-ment with Atlantic Richfield.

There was a strong impression locally that state authorities, like federal, were dodging issues, covering up, or not telling the truth fully. Their failure to appear, their failure to announce the presence of spilled oil on San Miguel or San Nicolas islands, the discrepancy between their official accounts of the oil's damage to marine mammals, their minimizing of the spill's damage and potential damage, all seemed proof of this impression.

Secretary Hickel's personal involvement with the Dos Cuadras field oil companies was not forgotten. The Anchorage National Gas Corporation, of which he once was chairman, had held a twenty-year contract with Union and with Marathon Oil, Sun's partner in Tract 401. The two companies had agreed to furnish Anchorage with natural gas from their fields on nearby Kenai Peninsula.

There were conflicts, too, at local level. Santa Barbara County Oil Well Inspector David Bickmore resigned because of his inti-mate financial relations with Union and other oil companies. Bickmore was quoted as saying that he was afraid oil's power with local politicians would remove him from his job, should he dis-please the companies he was supposed to supervise. Bickmore's misfortunes raised the crucial question of the integrity of super-visors at all levels of the channel oil bureaucracy, subject as they were to monolithic forces.

When anti-oil forces turned to the federal courts for help, they seemed to find conflict of interest there as well. District Attorney Minier demanded that Federal District Judge Albert Lee Stephens, Jr., disqualify himself as judge of the Platform A consortium cases because Stephens' wife owned 300 shares of Atlantic Rich-

field and 266 shares of Texaco stock. Though Stephens had publicly disclosed his wife's ownership of the stock and invited comments from attorneys involved in channel cases, he made no public reply to Minier's charges. But on November 27, 1970, Stephens suddenly vacated jurisdiction over all suits involving Santa Barbara Channel oil matters, giving as reason the fact that he had been appointed chief judge of the Southern California federal judiciary, and additional administrative duties required reduction of his case load.

This de facto self-disqualification by Stephens, in company with his overt lack of sympathy with the anti-oil position, supported the belief that the federal courts were too involved with the status quo in government and industry and that conflicts of interest might result.

Then there was the case of the University of California. The State Assembly had pressed the investigation of the $10.7 million arrangement between Edwin Pauley and the university whereby U.C. officials formed a straw corporation that acted as middleman in securing a loan for Regent Pauley, in return for financial gain to the university. The amount involved had nearly doubled since it was first reported. The Assembly investigation found that: (1) the arrangement might have cost more in administrative and legal costs than the $24,000 gained by the university, (2) millions in university funds placed in the First National Bank of Chicago might have been placed there to assure the deal's success, (3) the arrangement gave Pauley needed working capital he might otherwise have been unable to raise (Pauley Petroleum reported a net loss of $648,308 for the first nine months of fiscal 1970 and a $1,504,200 loss for the same period of 1969), (4) the deal might have resulted in a tax benefit to Pauley of more than $2 million, and (5) an adverse ruling by the Internal Revenue Service might mean that the university's holding company and Pauley would owe the IRS "significant sums for tax avoidance." The Assembly investigators also found that "impropriety" might have been involved in the deal.

Oil-covered lined shorecrab. One of many creatures affected by oil spill from Platform A. DICK SMITH PHOTO.

University authorities cooperated in the investigation and defended their actions, but the Assembly decided that a new policy should be developed to guide the regents in future business transactions.

Deputy Attorney General Charles O'Brien meanwhile reiterated his charges that fear made University of California faculty and administration reluctant to cooperate with the state in its suits against oil companies and federal government. His charges were supported by the experiences of Dr. Burney Le Boeuf and Dr. Richard Peterson after they disclosed the presence of oil on San Miguel Island, and by Dr. Robert Curry after he testified against government and oil companies at congressional hearings. O'Brien was still having difficulty finding experts willing to testify against oil companies and government; and he accused the university administration of reluctance to furnish him with scientific information contained in the long-sequestered report on the spill, sponsored jointly by the university and the Federal Water Pollution Control Administration. The Neushul Report was finally made public in mid-1970, a year after it was completed.

In a development related to situations such as that represented by the Pauley and Neushul affairs, Lee Metcalf, the Democratic Senator from Montana, said that "universities and faculty members who are too closely tied to corporations tend to behave like public servants who get into that kind of a box. They don't ask and answer the questions that need frank answers."

Metcalf was making a survey of the finances of fifty-three leading universities. He found that they held 1,774,130 shares of Jersey Standard (Humble, Esso) stock valued at about $130 million. They also held more than 2,000,000 shares of Gulf and more than 2,000,000 shares of Mobil, two Platform A companies. Thus U.S. universities were chief investors in channel oil development.

The University of Southern California, which declined to reveal the sources of its income to this writer but which is known to be the recipient of substantial gifts from oil interests, sponsored the $240,000 post-spill study of the channel paid for by the Western Oil and Gas Association. USC's Allan Hancock Foundation, which conducted the survey, was established by an oilman. Thus there was the appearance of possible conflict of interest in the scientific study even if none existed.

"The spill was the turning point," said Henry Wright of the Western Oil and Gas Association. "Before it, environmental concern in the oil industry was all talk. Now it is all money and action."

Wright's estimate was too sweeping, but by early 1970 Standard of California was leading an industry-wide movement to shape a more responsible attitude in environmental affairs and a new public image generally. In the channel, this took the form of a program participated in by fourteen major operators called Clean Seas Incorporated. Clean Seas' purpose was to develop an anti-pollution strike force capable of coping with massive spills quickly and effectively. It began by preparing emergency plans, establishing liaison with government agencies and organizations interested in oil-spill control, and training personnel. Its headquarters was at Santa Barbara and its working base at the deep-water harbor of Port Hueneme. Its president was Humble's engineering director for Southern California. Its field manager was a former district superintendent for Standard.

Though criticized by anti-oil forces as mere eyewash for continued channel exploitation, Clean Seas was a step forward from the industry's virtually nonexistent pre-spill contingency measures. Similar organizations were planned for coastal regions north and south of the channel, and for elsewhere in the United States.

The Union Oil Company, traditionally a maverick, traditionally wary of its larger colleagues, at first refused to participate in the industry's cooperative moves. But by April, 1970, Fred Hartley was telling his stockholders: "Santa Barbara may become a symbol, an awakening."

Hartley even took credit for helping the environmental revolution along. "When Well A-21 blew out," he said, "it created a symbol that did more to rally public concern than almost any other peacetime incident."

By January, 1971, Union had spent some $3 million in pollution-prevention equipment at its Los Angeles Harbor refinery and had joined the Clean Seas program.

Did the spill really hurt the industry financially, or was it merely a flea bite to an elephant? Oil-stock values plummeted in 1969, faster and to greater relative depth than other industrial stocks. They dropped faster and deeper than might have been the case had there been merely an economic recession and no channel spill. Union's stock was quoted at 57⅞ on the New York Stock Exchange on the day of the blowout. On July 28 it was 52; on December 31, 38¼.

Oil stocks generally reached their nadir in the fall and winter of 1969 during the height of public and congressional feeling roused by the spill. On December 31 most of them, like Union's, were within a few points of recently set market lows. Standard of California had fallen from 75 to 48½. Texaco had descended to 28, its lowest in eight years.

But during 1970 oil stocks began to rise in value, particularly those of companies with foreign outlets and with tanker fleets. Foreign demand for petroleum products was outpacing that of the United States and there was an acute shortage of tankers. On January 28, 1971, the spill's second anniversary, Standard of California stock was quoted at 52⅛ on the New York Stock Exchange and Texaco at 35⅝. Union's stock remained comparatively depressed. At 37¾, it was lower than it had been at the end of 1969.

Earnings were another matter. Oil industry earnings were affected by inflation and other economic factors in such a way as to make oil-spill effects perhaps indistinguishable. Most oil company earnings, however, were down sharply in 1969, the year of the spill. They continued so in 1970. Union's were down 23 percent for the first nine months of 1970. Many others were down, but not so sharply. Mobil showed a record profit. Perhaps Union's declining profits were in part a reflection of the spill's effects.

Certainly a $100 million loss attributable to the spill would be significant, as would an increase in insurance costs of several tens of millions, and a $600 million annual increase in tax burden caused in many respects by the spill. But these burdens seemed likely to be relieved by increases in the prices of petroleum products. The consumer would eventually pay them; and crude oil prices had already advanced by twenty-five cents per barrel.

Oil's political influence suffered as result of the spill, but here, too, there were signs of recovery. Proposed restrictions on the oil import program (a program worth about $6 billion a year to the industry) failed to materialize; and John B. Connally, a former Texas governor and close friend of the oil industry, was appointed Secretary of the Treasury, succeeding David M. Kennedy who had been willing not only to reduce oil's tax depletion allowance but to abolish its precious one-year tax write-off of intangible drilling expenses which often included 60 to 70 percent of the cost of a well. In California, a bill to reduce oil's state income tax depletion allowance died in the Legislature, thus permitting an annual tax subsidy estimated at $26 million to continue.

Oil's public image was blackened by the spill, but it received immediate brightenings when Union, Mobil, Texaco, Humble, and other channel operators launched extensive advertising campaigns with intensive environmental responsibility slants. The American Petroleum Institute allocated $9.4 million for advertising in the two-year period, 1971–1972, compared to about $1.7 million annually in pre-spill years. Oil executives joined other business leaders in the President's new National Industrial Pollution Control Council designed to open wider channels of communication on environmental matters between the U.S. business community and the White House and to establish a national industrial action front on pollution. The no-strings-attached gift of $240,000 for the scientific study of the channel was a further step in the new direction. So supercharged was the new atmosphere that when Henry Ford, II, in the most significant pronouncement yet made by a U.S. business leader on an environmental issue, called upon the oil industry to get the lead out of its gasoline, the industry promptly began doing so.

Given the public's short memory and an end to offshore disasters, oil's image promised to mend.

Then why was the spill a disaster to the oilmen? Because it showed that aroused citizens were stronger than oil. Marching under the banner of environmental revolution, they had brought channel development nearly to a standstill and had completely blocked similar development in Puget Sound and nearby Georgia Strait, and were threatening it elsewhere. Their representatives in Congress had curbed oil's tax privileges for the first time in history, and the executive branch had been forced to take unprecedented restrictive and punitive measures against the federal government's close business associate. It was rather like publicly chastising a permanent house guest. Oil's position, offshore or onshore, would never be quite the same.

19

SOCIO-POLITICAL REPERCUSSIONS I: TO THE PRESIDENT'S MESSAGE

THE SPILL changed people as well as institutions. It transformed a quiet, conservative resort and residential community into the militant spearhead of a national movement. It ignited the smoldering thirty-year conflict between Santa Barbarans and the oil industry into a full-scale war that spread across the United States and to other parts of the world. But though it created bitter divisions, the spill united human beings in a way that nothing before had done. It cut across economic, ethnic, age-group, and political distinctions, thus providing a new kind of social hope.

Setting and following a national example, Santa Barbara's anti-oil movement grew, in 1970, into a general environmental movement, concerned with a variety of ecological problems, while focusing on the oil spill.

The January 28 Committee which had brought thirty-two disparate groups together to create the community's first annual Environmental Rights Day, reorganized itself into a Community Environmental Council. City Council and Board of Supervisors appointed liaison members to the new group. F. W. Woolworth Company provided housing at reduced rent. Labor union members painted the interior without charge. A local foundation gave $4,000 toward operating expenses. Soon the Santa Barbara Community Ecology Center, one of the first in the nation, had a citizens' reading room, citizens' conference room, reference library, and bookstore. It provided free informational and educational services to the public and to the Santa Barbara school system. It furnished speakers, slide and photographic exhibits wherever needed, and coordinated the community-wide collection of solid wastes for recycling—while operating an organic garden in a nearby vacant lot provided by a cooperative realtor. It had its own publication, *The Survival Times*. But more importantly it became the locus for a generalized environmental effort.

Oil pollution remained the community's primary concern, however. GOO's membership and influence expanded steadily. During April, 1970, GOO processed more than 2,500 requests for information. They came from 34 states, 217 cities, and 3 foreign countries. In addition, GOO provided speakers for schools, colleges, and universities and for public meetings locally and regionally, and information and exhibits for libraries and environmental fairs; and it continued to lobby in Sacramento and Washington against channel oil development. Regionally and nationally it encouraged the formation of organizations similar to itself. GOO TWO sprang up in Los Angeles to fight oil development in the city's harbor area. KOO (Keep Oil Out) was formed at Freeport, Maine, in Senator Muskie's home territory, aimed at blocking a proposed free-trade-in-oil area at Machiasport, where national import quotas would not apply. NO (No Oil) appeared at Pacific Palisades, California, to oppose oil development in the Los Angeles coastal area. STOP (Stamp Out Pollution) sprang up in New Orleans to fight unbridled Gulf Coast oil development, and GOO Northwest at Seattle opposed oil drilling in Puget Sound. Other groups were formed to fight water pollution in the Lake Erie area, in Maryland, and at Grosse Point, Michigan.

GOO's staff, composed mostly of women volunteers led at first by Mrs. Alvin Weingand and later by colorful Lois Sidenberg and her imperturbable daughter-in-law Ellen, worked at night to keep pace with the growing demands for assistance against not only oil pollution but pollution of many kinds. Thousands of people had found a place to turn in their search for help in combatting a common problem.

But GOO's survival was painful. It seldom had more than $1,000 in the bank and often lacked money to pay its office rent while its opponents had billions. Apathy threatened it with adaptation to pollution, while violence threatened to undermine and destroy the entire oil-resistance effort. Soon after the January 28, 1970, occupation of Stearns Wharf by anti-oil militants, there was a riot in the nearby student community of Isla Vista. The riot was followed by the burning of the Bank of America there and the death of a student by shooting. Within six months there were three disastrous riots in Isla Vista, resulting in more than 500 arrests and some $550,000 in law-enforcement costs alone. The Santa Barbara Citizens Commission on Civil Disorders found the oil spill to be a root cause of these disturbances.

"The damage inflicted upon the young's belief in the system—in this instance of real crisis—has been incalculable," the citizens commission said.

GOO successfully maintained a militant but nonviolent posture, striving patiently to work "within the system." But GOO's petitions never reached President Nixon. Bearing two hundred thousand signatures, they traveled to Washington twice, were delivered to the White House once, were sent from there to Secretary Hickel at the Department of the Interior who sent them to Dr. Pecora at the U.S. Geological Survey, who put them in his closet, where they were finally found and sent back to Santa Barbara—all without acknowledgment from anyone in the federal government that they had been received.

Nevertheless, on January 28, 1971, nearly two years after James Bottoms and Marvin Stuart conceived of a citizens movement that would get oil out of the channel, the President and congressional leaders of both parties were trying to get at least some of it out. The issue was no longer whether but how much. The oil escaping from under Platform A had brought the American System up for questioning in a way that nothing before it had done. The chief questions it raised were: Who is responsible for the environment? How can government be made more responsive to the will of the people? The Santa Barbarans thought they were finding an answer.

A community in revolt against intolerable conditions became a microcosm for a society in revolt against similar conditions.

Platform Hillhouse floating upside down had become a symbol for the upside-downness of some U.S. values and priorities and the willingness of some citizens to work to set them right.

The environmental movement triggered by the spill swept across the country following the Environmental Rights Day observances in Santa Barbara. The movement culminated on April 22, 1970, with Earth Day, a day devoted to nationwide concern for the environment.

Speaking at the University of California at Berkeley, Senator Gaylord Nelson, originator of the Earth Day idea, said: "To restore man to his proper place in the environment will require a commitment beyond anything we have done before." Nelson proposed national policies on land use, pesticides and herbicides, and a ban on all offshore drilling "until we can extract oil without fear of ecological disaster." Representative Paul McCloskey, a California Republican (who later strongly challenged President Nixon's conduct of the Vietnam War), joined Senator Nelson in sponsoring the Earth Day idea; and Congress recessed to observe it.

There were observances in more than 2,000 communities and in more than 5,000 high schools, colleges, and universities. The National Education Association estimated that 10 million public school children participated. Action was the order of the day. Five tons of garbage were picked up along a five-mile stretch of U.S. Highway 50 and dumped on the Harrison County Courthouse steps in Clarksburg, West Virginia. In New York, Mayor John V. Lindsay drove to Earth Day events in an exhaustless electric bus. Former Interior Secretary Udall, speaking at Kent State University in Ohio, said the United States was a nation of "environmental slobs" and called the gasoline-powered automobile the nation's worst pollution machine.

At Santa Barbara, Dr. Roderick Nash announced plans to develop the University of California's Santa Barbara campus into a center for environmental studies. Like the community, the university intended to become a focal point for ecological understanding. "Man has discovered the moon," Nash said. "When are we going to discover the earth?"

There were parallels in foreign countries. The year 1970 had been proclaimed "European Conservation Year." The Rhine, Europe's central river, was virtually an open sewer. Smog in Paris was nearly as bad as in Los Angeles or New York. Italy was surrounded by oily refuse from its dozens of refineries, and tanker disasters such as that of the *Torrey Canyon* were a threat to every coastal nation. The Council of Europe organized a series of national and international environmental conferences. Twenty-two non-Soviet-bloc nations initiated anti-pollution programs.

In Russia, meanwhile, somebody had inadvertently tossed a burning cigarette into the polluted Iset River near Sverdlovsk and set it on fire. Lake Baikal in Siberia was nearly as dead as Lake Erie. The Soviet government announced an all-out attack on pollution.

Heavily industrialized Japan was suffering so acutely from air pollution that forty-eight schoolchildren died of it, or became seriously ill, and the Japanese Diet passed stricter anti-pollution laws. In Communist China, the "spring patriotic sanitation movement" focused on cleaning up local waters and recycling solid wastes. Regardless of geography and ideology, 1970 became the year of the environment almost everywhere in the world.

Some said it had all begun with the publication of Rachel Carson's *Silent Spring*. Most agreed that the Santa Barbara Oil Spill had triggered its current explosion.

The explosion impelled politicians to act as well as talk. On the day following Santa Barbara's first Environmental Rights Day, January 29, 1970, President Nixon named the three members of the Council on Environmental Quality established by the National Environmental Policy Act. They were Russell E. Train, the lawyer who had been Nixon's campaign advisor on environmental matters and more recently Undersecretary of the Interior; Robert Cahn, a Pulitzer Prize-winning Washington correspondent for the *Christian Science Monitor;* and Dr. Gordon J. F. MacDonald, the Santa Barbaran and the council's only scientist. They were to implement an act that had been passed largely as result of the spill. Nixon had signed the NEPA into law at the San Clemente White House as his first official action of the New Year and the new decade. Few people had heard of the NEPA when the President signed it, though environmentalists quickly recognized its importance. It required that environmental impact studies be made and publicized *before* federal projects affecting the environment could be initiated. It took the public into the federal decision-making process in a new way. Had it been in effect before channel leasing started, there might never have been any leasing. Despite the great significance of the act—and the broad powers inherent in the Environmental Quality Council it created—there was nevertheless a widespread belief that nothing was really going to happen politically to stop pollution in the Santa Barbara Channel or across the country.

On February 4, however, Nixon followed up by describing the federal government as "one of the nation's worst polluters." He ordered all federal agencies to cease polluting air and water. Compliance date was December 31, 1972. Nixon also directed that $359 million be spent during the next three years to implement his order and to "provide government leadership in the national antipollution effort."

Coming hard on the heels of the Administration's sudden willingness to cancel at least some of the channel's federal leases and create a cross-channel oil-free sanctuary, this encouraged Senator Cranston to renew effort on behalf of his dormant bill to terminate all the federal leases except the three productive ones. The Democratic Senator from Utah, Frank Moss, chairman of the Subcommittee on Minerals, Materials, and Fuels, agreed to conduct new hearings.

There was simultaneous movement at state level. Santa Barbara anti-oil leaders met for the first time in a long-deferred conference with Governor Reagan. The Sacramento meeting was indecisive, but Reagan listened sympathetically to the views of Lois Sidenberg and George Clyde. Then on February 6, a high-level state-government advisory group warned that California was in "severe danger of being destroyed as a desirable place to live." The bipartisan Environmental Quality Study Council had been appointed jointly by Reagan and the Legislature. It included businessmen, lawyers, professors, and local and state officials. They announced that the time had come to "scrap the idea of growth at any cost." They detected a "public clamor in favor of the environment" and said there was every indication that the clamor would grow louder. "It might even become violent. Immediate and drastic steps are imperative."

With such urging, it seemed that Reagan might act decisively to solve the state's most pressing environmental problem: the channel spill. But though he had devoted more than half his State of the State address to the environment only a few weeks before, only one-fifth of 1 percent ($12.6 million) of the governor's new state budget for 1970–1971 ($6.48 billion) was devoted to environmental programs, and he made no move at all in Santa Barbara's direction.

By contrast, Nixon moved swiftly. On February 6, touring the nation's heartland and taking a firsthand look at Chicago's air and water pollution, the President said he would soon announce details of his $10 billion program "to bring pure water back to the people." Three days later, the federal government filed suit against eleven Chicago firms, including the Pure Oil Company, a subsidiary of Union Oil, charging them with polluting the waters of the Chicago area.

It was the most dramatic anti-pollution action of the Nixon Administration. The President was clearly riding the groundswell of public opinion generated by the national environmental movement and the channel spill.

His attorney general and closest advisor, John N. Mitchell, announced the filing of the suits against Pure Oil, the Penn Central Railroad, Procter and Gamble, International Harvester, Olin Corporation, National Sheet Metal Works, and General American Transportation, among others. The Pure Oil Company's superintendent of oil storage was charged separately with violating federal anti-pollution statutes. This seemed to come close to Fred Hartley and Platform A.

On the next day, February 10, Nixon sent Congress a special message dealing with the environment. As promised in his State of the Union Message of January, it spelled out the most costly and comprehensive anti-pollution programs ever proposed by a President. At their heart were regulations calling for tough federal standards on auto emissions by 1975, and a $10,000 a day fine for water polluters.

Senator Muskie, not to be outdone, still planned to introduce legislation providing $12.5 billion over a five-year period for waste treatment grants, with states and cities matching for a total of $25 billion. Muskie, still the President's prime rival on environmental issues, was also seeking $325 million a year for three years for clean air programs.

The nation's leading political adversaries seemed to be raising their bets in the environmental game. The channel seemed likely to benefit.

On February 20 in Washington, however, a sharply divided Cabinet committee recommended to the President that the nation's oil import program be revised. It was the latest flareup in the national oil controversy sparked by the spill. The Cabinet committee found the quota system unreasonable and inefficient. It proposed a tariff of $1.45 per barrel on imported oil and a lowering of the tariff at regular intervals, thus permitting a steady inflow from foreign nations. Oil from Canada and Mexico would be exempted from the tariff if a satisfactory alternative policy could be negotiated with them. Oil from Venezuela, the major foreign supplier for the United States, would be given a special lower tariff. All of these measures would have worked against Santa Barbara Channel oil development by providing less expensive sources of oil.

But the President took no action on his Cabinet committee's report. Instead he appointed a new, permanent Oil Policy Committee to study the import program and make new recommendations.

The *New York Times* expressed what was probably the prevailing opinion. "President Nixon has bowed to the oil industry in shelving the recommendations of the majority of his cabinet-level task force on oil import quotas."

Now two events combined to change the political atmosphere decisively. On February 13, the Greek tanker chartered by Humble Oil ran aground and began spilling 10,000 gallons of crude oil into Tampa Bay, Florida. On February 26 a Danish freighter was blamed for ramming a barge that spilled oil into the St. Johns River near Jacksonville on Florida's east coast. Florida's citizens and representatives in Congress began to talk and act like Santa Barbarans, while Florida sued the owners of the freighter for $1 million and the owners of the tanker for $2 million damages.

As a consequence, House-Senate conferees approved a tough new water-quality bill. Senator Muskie and Representative William C. Cramer, a Florida Republican, credited the approval largely to the Santa Barbara and Florida spills.

The new bill, known as the Water Quality Act of 1970, was signed by the President on April 3. Indicative of the new national feeling, it was passed unanimously by both Senate and House. It provided for: (1) evidence of financial responsibility, by shipowners, of $100 per gross ship ton, or $14,000,000, whichever was the larger, to meet possible liability for spillage of oil; (2) criminal penalties for failure to give notice of such spillage [the prompt giving of notice had become a major issue since the question of the lack of it arose at the time of the Santa Barbara spill]; (3) immediate federal action if necessary to clean up spills; (4) federally funded research to develop new containment and cleanup measures; (5) presidential authority to determine the quantity of oil discharge that might be harmful to human health and to marine life; (6) presidential authority to remove or destroy a vessel causing oil pollution; (7) a new National Plan for protecting U.S. shores and waters against oil spills; (8) an Office of Environmental Quality in the White House to provide administrative support to the new Council on Environmental Quality.

The Water Quality Act of 1970 changed the name of the FWPCA to Federal Water Quality Administration, and concluded with the statement that: "The Congress declares that there is a national policy for the environment which provides for the enhancement of environmental quality."

Perhaps the bill's most important provision from the viewpoint of Santa Barbara, and from that of any coastal or inland waterway city, was the provision for a new national contingency plan to cope with oil spills. National strike forces were established at various locations, on call in case of pollution incidents. Regional strike forces were also established, as were emergency reaction teams of trained personnel located at major U.S. ports. The forces and teams were for use primarily in cases where responsibilty for spills could not be fixed and the federal government was therefore empowered to act. Regional plans assured coordination of federal action with state and local agencies. The entire effort was supervised by a National Response Center in Washington.

Overall authority for administering the new plan was given to the Department of Interior's recently named Federal Water Quality Administration. But as under the old plan, on-site command responsibility for coping with pollution incidents rested with the Department of Transportation's Coast Guard.

The old plan had worked better at Santa Barbara than might have been expected under the circumstances, but it had proved wholly ineffective in stopping the channel spill or in containing it. If Union had not voluntarily assumed cleanup responsibility, a serious problem could have resulted. And Brown, De Falco, and Biglane had more than once found themselves without power or money to do what might have to be done. The new plan benefited from their findings and was immensely strengthened by having statutory, rather than executive order, authority.

Meanwhile, on March 13 and 14, Senator Moss's Subcommittee on Minerals, Materials, and Fuels met in Santa Barbara to hear testimony on five bills dealing with the channel oil controversy.

One was Cranston's original bill. It had been modified to suspend drilling and leasing in the channel's federal waters pending a study to determine whether they could be resumed without threat to the environment or should be terminated.

A second bill, authored jointly by Cranston and Murphy, created a cross-channel sanctuary adjacent to the existing state sanctuary.

A third bill established federal marine sanctuaries off the California coast seaward of all existing state sanctuaries (such as now existed off much of Southern California and nearly all of Central and Northern California, as well as at Santa Barbara); it was a bipartisan measure introduced by Cranston, Murphy, Muskie, and Nelson of Wisconsin.

A fourth bill, authored by Murphy, was identical to one introduced in the House by Teague. It set aside the channel's federal lands as a naval petroleum reserve and terminated all oil development there except for operations in the leakage area; under the Murphy bill, the channel would become Naval Petroleum Reserve No. 5; in exchange, Reserve No. 1 at Elk Hills would be opened up for commercial development; the Murphy bill transferred mineral administration in the federal waters of the channel from the Interior to the Navy Department, and it authorized the state to lease part of the Elk Hills Reserve for commercial development should the state set aside all of its waters in the channel as a petroleum reserve; oil companies vacating their channel leases would be reimbursed in a lump sum or given credit on a competitive basis for leases at Elk Hills.

The fifth bill was authorized by Muskie. It ended all oil activity in the channel's federal waters except that necessary to cope with continued leakage; such operations, however, would be removed from oil company hands and given to the Interior Department; the channel's federal leases would be purchased by the federal government and existing production and platforms phased out; the federal waters of the channel would become an ecological preserve with oil development prohibited.

Citizen testimony supported all these measures in varying degrees. Oil company interests opposed them.

Thanks substantially to state Democratic leader Jesse Unruh,

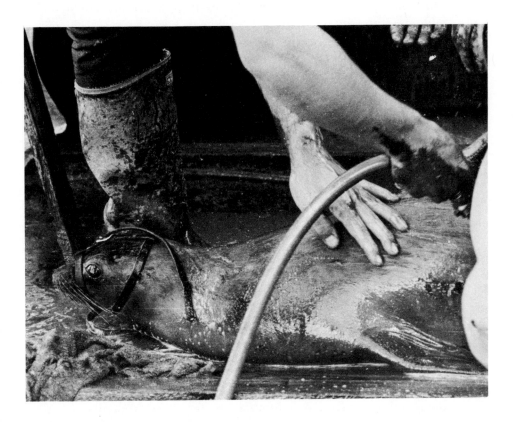

A California sea lion undergoes oil-removal treatment at a wildlife rescue station. SANTA BARBARA NEWS-PRESS.

the State Legislature had unanimously adopted a resolution urging that the federal waters of the channel be made an oil-free sanctuary. On March 18 a committee of California Assembly leaders announced a 10-year multimillion-dollar program designed to "save California's environment." Describing its program as "urgent and drastic" the committee proposed: (1) a constitutional amendment establishing a legal basis for laws controlling where people lived and how they used their land, (2) an immediate tax on automobiles and cigarets to produce at least $100 million annually to be spent in the next two years on a crash anti-pollution program, (3) rewriting of charters of cities, towns, and special districts to permit coordination of state-wide environmental control policies, (4) immediate establishment of local and regional planning agencies, (5) a halt to all state projects [including oil development in Santa Barbara Channel state waters] that might harm the environment until such projects could be reevaluated, (6) a $15 million state-wide environmental monitoring system to keep track of changes in the environment, (7) immediate control of public and private coastal development to prevent destruction of resources, (8) a $300 million 5-year program to bring a quick end to dumping of sewage and other wastes into rivers; (9) a $250 million 5-year program to buy open spaces and undeveloped beaches. The committee hoped and believed that Governor Reagan would support their program.

California's leaders were being indirectly pressured by the example of their neighboring state, Washington. Washington was outstripping California in terms of environmental action. The Washington Legislature had completed a special thirty-two-day "environmental session" and enacted six major bills. These environmental reform measures included holding oil companies and tanker owners absolutely liable for cleanup and damage from oil spills, establishing a council to evaluate nuclear power sites, and regulating water-polluting effluents at their sources.

Washington citizens groups opposing offshore oil development had been working closely with Santa Barbara anti-oil forces, and Washington soon banned offshore drilling in Puget Sound.

When the Canadian government followed suit by banning oil exploration in the Strait of Georgia between Vancouver Island and the mainland of British Columbia, the channel spill became truly international in its effects. Santa Barbara Citizens for Environmental Defense and GOO representatives had worked with Vancouver citizens anti-oil groups.

The spill was soon to have further international repercussions. On March 21 in the United Nations, Christian A. Herter, Jr., and Shirley Temple Black disagreed with former U.S. ambassador to Russia George F. Kennan's statement that the United Nations was too large and diffuse a body to police international pollution. Herter, until recently a Mobil Oil (Platform A) vice president, was speaking as director of the State Department's new Office of Environmental Affairs and as special assistant to the Secretary of State. Mrs. Black was speaking as Herter's deputy. They supported proposals made earlier, on March 10, by Sweden's ambassador to the United Nations, Sverker Astrom. Astrom, originator of the idea of a world conference on environment at Stockholm in 1972, had proposed immediate worldwide monitoring of air and sea pollution by the entire U.N. membership. He had also urged that the world community take speedy action to discuss a series of agreements that would prohibit emission of oil into the oceans, prohibit or reduce the manufacture or use of persistent environmental poisons such as certain pesticides, identify and control additives harmful to the environment such as tetraethyl lead from no-knock gasolines, and protect the world environment in other ways.

Astrom, whose convictions had been strengthened by a visit to Santa Barbara during the spill, urged U.N. members to explore these subjects immediately in order to determine whether some of them should be included in pollution-control treaties that might be ready for signature at the time of the June, 1972, Stockholm conference sponsored by the United Nations. But his first priority was for the worldwide pollution monitoring system participated in by the entire U.N. membership; and this was where former ambassador Kennan disagreed with him, arguing that a new group of nations—those most highly industrialized and hence most pollution-prone—should be formed to deal with world pollution.

In supporting Astrom's broader view, U.N. Secretary General U Thant touched on an aspect of pollution that Santa Barbarans had already found to be a true one. "I would hope," U Thant said, "that in saving ourselves by preserving our environment, we might also find a new solidarity and a new spirit among the governments and peoples of the earth, and so look to the future with greater courage and confidence."

On June 1, Secretary Hickel announced the first public hearings ever to be held on proposed leasing of federal offshore lands for oil development. They were scheduled for July 14 in New Orleans and were a direct result of the much-criticized absence of such hearings prior to Santa Barbara Channel leasing. In announcing them, Hickel said: "I want to stress that no further federal offshore oil lease offers will be made unless I am satisfied that oil and gas development in the area is fully compatible with the protection of all resources."

This was taken by some as evidence that "a new Hickel" was continuing to emerge, one more favorably inclined toward environmental causes.

In inviting public participation in the forthcoming hearings, Hickel asked that written comment consider: (1) the environmental impact of the leases, (2) any adverse environmental effects that could not be avoided if the leases were made, (3) alternatives to leasing, (4) the relationship between the local short-term use of man's environment and the maintenance and enhancement of long-term productivity, (5) any irreversible and irretrievable commitment of resources which would be involved if the leasing took place.

All of this was a completely new departure and so was what followed.

On June 11, the President asked Congress to buy back twenty federal oil leases in the Santa Barbara Channel and thus create an oil-drilling-free sanctuary adjacent to the existing state sanctuary and extending across the channel. It was implementation of the proposal made in January by Hickel and embodied in legislation introduced in the Senate by Murphy and in the House by Teague. Under the Administration's plan, Tract 402 (the Platform A lease) and Tract 401 (the Platform Hillhouse lease) would not be affected. Pumping and drilling would continue there in order, the President said, "to bleed off the high pressure" which would otherwise cause the channel floor, damaged by the blowout, to leak oil profusely.

The twenty leases to be cancelled covered 109,800 acres. A total of $178 million in bonus bids had been paid for them. No oil had been found on them and prospects for future discoveries were not considered good. Five of the leases were owned by Humble alone; six by Humble in combination with Standard of California and Atlantic Richfield; seven by the Platform A consortium; one by Union alone; and one by Humble and Standard of California. The companies would be compensated for their interests by the sale of oil from the Elk Hills Naval Reserve.

The proposed legislation would terminate the leases and give the companies one year in which to file suit should they so desire. In addition to the twenty leases, unleased tracts totaling 27,700 acres would be added to make the proposed cross-channel sanctuary.

The President termed his proposal an illustration "of our strong commitment to use offshore lands in a balanced responsible fashion."

Lois Sidenberg, GOO's president, called the plan "meaningless and deceptive. It does nothing about the three operating platforms in front of Santa Barbara, as well as the two others opposite Carpinteria. Besides, you could have as damaging an accident or blowout outside the proposed sanctuary as within it." Mrs. Sidenberg also charged that in making compensation for nonproducing leases, the government would be paying oil companies for oil that did not exist and for money lost in a bad gamble.

In addition to exempting Tracts 401 and 402, the President's proposal allowed other leaseholders, chiefly Humble, to retain a most promising section of the channel, its western end—where six major discovery wells had revealed reserves estimated at a billion barrels.

Nevertheless the Nixon Plan represented an advance from no plan at all. It was a drastic change from the Administration's previous position that drilling in the channel's federal waters was quite safe as result of tightened regulations and increased supervision. And despite Mrs. Sidenberg's charges, it contained safeguards against paying leaseholders something for nothing. Courts would determine the exact amount payable by the government for each rescinded lease.

But the plan promised to please few people outside the Administration. The President's new and newly powerful Council on Environmental Quality had recommended a much larger area for inclusion in the proposed sanctuary. Train, Cahn, and MacDonald had recommended the inclusion of eleven leases north of San Miguel Island, citing their threat to the island's seal herds and to other marine life. In a letter to Nixon, the council had called the spill "an international symbol for the environmental movement" and had urged the President to announce the proposed sanctuary in April, on Earth Day. But details could not be worked out in time.

The channel spill now became entangled with Secretary Hickel's political fate. The Secretary was pointedly not invited to the White House press conference where the channel-lease-cancellation plan which he had conceived was made public. This was the first clear evidence of a rift between Hickel and Nixon. The rift stemmed from a letter Hickel had written the President on May 6, at a time of keen public concern for the environment following the Earth Day observances, and of keen public concern for national policy following the invasion of Cambodia by U.S. forces. These concerns were particularly prevalent among young people, and Hickel's letter had urged the President to give greater attention to the views of the young. The letter was leaked to the press and caused a sensation.

The political action continued on July 1 when Senator Cranston introduced a bill to create a Channel Islands National Park. Four similar bills were pending in the House. The Democrats seemed determined to match the Republicans in every move concerning the channel and the larger game of national environmental politics it represented.

On July 9, President Nixon went one up on his opponents by an order creating two new agencies: the Environmental Protection Agency and the National Oceanic and Atmospheric Administration.

The Environmental Protection Agency (EPA) became the enforcement arm of the federal government's anti-pollution effort. It was formed partly from the existing bureaucratic structure, partly from new material. From Hickel's Department of the Interior, it took the Federal Water Quality Administration with broad authority to combat water pollution. From the Department of

Health, Education, and Welfare the new agency acquired the National Air Pollution Control Administration, plus certain solid waste, water hygiene, and radiation safety functions, as well as the pesticides program of the Food and Drug Administration. From the Department of Agriculture, EPA acquired pesticide control activities. From the Atomic Energy Commission, it took the Federal Radiation Council and general radiation protection activities; from the Council on Environmental Quality, ecological research functions. EPA was assigned a budget estimated at $1.4 billion and 5,650 employees.

The National Oceanic and Atmospheric Administration (NOAA), the second agency created by the President's order was also partly formed from existing agencies. It became the federal government's chief means for: (1) collecting information about the nation's marine and air environments, (2) developing programs of research and development in these areas, and (3) providing services concerning them to other government agencies, industry, and individuals. NOAA was to have a budget of some $270 million and about 12,000 employees.

These far-reaching reforms revealed the inadequacy of previous systems for coping with environmental crises and for determining their ecological effects. They also revealed a serious intention on the part of the President to act on environmental issues, and they placed the Democrats in the position of having to do more.

Upvaluing both party positions in regard to the channel, a recent estimate by the National Petroleum Council showed that the channel's oil reserves totaled 10 billion barrels, nearly twice what had been thought.

Again the stakes were increased and decisions were worth additional billions.

The President's reforms were an additional slap at Secretary Hickel, since they reduced the power and substance of the Interior Department, which Hickel was saying should dominate the U.S. environmental protection effort.

On July 21, Senator Moss's Subcommittee on Minerals, Materials, and Fuels held a hearing in Washington on the Nixon Administration's proposal to cancel twenty channel oil leases. Moss criticized the proposal as likely to cost "many hundreds of millions if not billions." Santa Barbara anti-oil leaders opposed it as offering insufficient protection against future spills. Major oil company spokesmen opposed it as "impeding the proper and orderly development of our nation's natural resources." Assistant Secretary of the Navy Frank P. Sanders testified that should compensation for the cancelled leases come from Elk Hills production, depletion of reserves there would cost about $200 million, would take three to nine years to accomplish, and would require subsequent production to restore equilibrium in the field.

But eleven smaller companies led by the so-called Pauley Group said they would support the Administration proposal if they could be compensated adequately for their channel interests. The pressure seemed to be telling on those less able to bear it.

Congressman Tunney, now the Democratic candidate for the U.S. Senate seat held by George Murphy, was among those belittling oil company arguments that cancellation of the leases represented a national security risk. Tunney urged support for the Cranston bill which called for cancellation of all but currently producing leases.

The Administration proposal was thus left with only Hickel and its congressional sponsors behind it, and Teague was saying publicly he would try to expand its scope once it reached the floor of the House.

At state level there was similar backsliding. On July 23 Unruh's reintroduced bill to ban drilling permanently in the state waters of the Santa Barbara Channel lost by one vote in the State Assembly. Thus it failed to reach the Senate where it had been killed in committee the previous year.

Unruh, now the Democratic nominee for governor against Reagan in the November, 1970, election, charged that an oil-dominated Reagan Administration had killed the bill. But he himself had been absent during the crucial vote.

On August 2, the long-awaited General Accounting Office Report requested by Senators Proxmire and Montoya in connection with the alleged thefts of petroleum products from military installations in South Vietnam and Thailand appeared. Coloring its appearance was the fact that leading channel operators such as Jersey Standard and Mobil were negotiating with the Republic of South Vietnam for offshore drilling rights, and voices were being raised against this as a significant element in the continuing U.S. presence in Southeast Asia. Titled *Investigations of the Handling and Control of Petroleum Products in Southeast Asia,* the GAO report confirmed the essentials of Eric Pollard's charges in Santa Barbara and of those made in Baltimore by Helen Delich Bentley, now U.S. Maritime Commissioner. "In Vietnam, control over Government-owned products in the hands of contractors and products delivered by tank trucks was inadequate . . . ," the report said, "fragmentation of responsibilities for fuel activities caused confusion, and deliveries were not verified. . . ." Many truck drivers were found to have employed hidden compartments, false calibration devices, stolen official seals, sandbags and water in attempts to steal the product they transported. Faulty application of temperature conversion scales possibly allowed the delivery of less oil products by ship than called for in contracts with private oil corporations. In some regions of South Vietnam, "commendable efforts" had been made to avoid "losses" of petroleum products, but in the Saigon area such efforts had not been satisfactory.

The investigators concluded that it was impossible to determine exactly the quantity of the petroleum products that had disappeared, but that "to effectively reduce the extraordinary losses by theft experienced in Thailand and Vietnam, it is necessary to seek additional cooperation from the foreign governments concerned."

The investigators were handicapped by the fact that "individuals knowledgeable of petroleum, oil, and lubricants operations before July 1966" and "pertinent records" were "no longer available."

In October, 1968, however, the Defense Contract Audit Agency had evaluated Esso, Shell, and Caltex policies and concluded that the three major oil contractors in South Vietnam had good accountability and management controls.

Eric Pollard's view was somewhat different. "They respond only to pressure," he told Santa Barbarans. "They will treat your channel spill as a mere incident, and they have more power than can be imagined."

Asked why her story in the *Baltimore Sun* concerning Esso's operations in Vietnam had not received wider attention (it had appeared nowhere else) and if there had been an attempt to suppress it, Helen Bentley said she did not know why the story had received so little attention.

Senator Proxmire found the GAO report "shocking," but it created scarcely a ripple in congressional circles and passed virtually unnoticed by the public, as Captain Pollard had predicted would be the case.

However, on the home front, on August 3, Hickel blocked development of oil shale deposits in the Rocky Mountain area until the oil industry showed that it could develop them without despoiling the environment. And on August 10, Nixon made a historic environmental report to the nation, the first ever made by a U.S. President. It was in fulfillment of a requirement established by the National Environmental Policy Act.

In sending his report to Congress, Nixon urged that "areas of special ecological significance" be preserved. He urged direct federal grants for open-space acquisitions and worldwide monitoring of the environment.

"This first report to the Congress on the state of the Nation's environment is an historic milestone," the President declared. "It represents the first time in the history of nations that a people has paused, consciously and systematically, to take comprehensive stock of the quality of its surroundings."

The President's message took special note of the fact that on June 11 he had asked Congress for legislation cancelling twenty oil leases in the Santa Barbara Channel and creating a marine sanctuary there.

Thus the spill continued to hold its place among the nation's chief environmental concerns.

20

SOCIO-POLITICAL REPERCUSSIONS II: TO TWO MORE PLATFORMS

PREDICTIONS WERE that local and national environmental issues would get their first big test at the November 3, 1970, general election. But by late October environmental concerns seemed to have receded. Looming in their place were economic recession, law and order, and the Indochina War.

In California, however, Unruh tied his campaign for governor to attacks on the oil industry, environmental pollution generally, and the despoliation of the Santa Barbara Channel in particular. Reagan tended to mute environmental issues but in the California contest for a U.S. Senate seat, environment was a major issue in the campaign of John Tunney to unseat George Murphy. Tunney emphasized Murphy's allegedly weak record of environmental defense at Santa Barbara and elsewhere. Murphy avoided environmental issues.

Reagan defeated Unruh by a vote of 3,439,664 to 2,938,607. Tunney beat Murphy, 3,496,558 to 2,887,617.

Proposition 18, a referendum measure, the only major environmental issue on the California ballot, lost narrowly. Known as "the antismog bill," it would have allowed local voters to decide

whether 25 percent of their share of state gasoline tax revenues
should be diverted to smog control and to the development of
rapid transit systems. Proposition 18 was supported by most of
California's environmentalists and opinion media and by many
political leaders including Governor Reagan, and opposed by most
of the state's oil companies, transportation firms, and others associated with the automobile industry and highway development.
Two Platform A companies, Union and Texaco, reported contributing $20,000 each against the measure. Shell and Standard of
California, also channel operators, reported contributing $30,000
each.

In the Santa Barbara area, Assemblyman MacGillivray barely
won reelection over a Democratic opponent who attacked him for
a wobbly anti-oil effort and a weak environmental record generally.
State Senator Lagomarsino, now substantially anti-oil, won easily
as did Congressman Teague. Reagan carried the area over Unruh,
who had strongly espoused the local anti-oil cause. But in a special
kind of triumph, local anti-oil forces joined other environmentalists in a referendum victory reminiscent of the onshore facilities
oil referendum of two years earlier. This new referendum of 1970
compelled a South Coast land developer, Jules Berman, to abandon
plans for intensive residential development at El Capitan west of
Santa Barbara. In a related result, a veteran county supervisor,
Joe J. Callahan, who had favored the development, was unseated
by a relative unknown running on a strongly environmentalist
program opposing the development. The South Coast election
results reflected a mixed national trend, but with overtones of the
new radicalization on environmental matters.

Nationally, Governor Rockefeller of New York, who like
Reagan had been attacked as weak on environmental issues, easily
defeated his Democratic opponent, the former U.S. ambassador
to the United Nations, Arthur Goldberg. Republican Governor
Don Samuelson of Idaho, however, who contended that a molyb-
denum deposit in the central Idaho wilderness should be exploited,
lost to former governor Cecil Andrus, a Democrat, who made a
major issue of the mining venture.

Down in Florida, Lawton Chiles walked his way to a U.S. Senate
seat, in somewhat the same way Tunney had dived to one in the
Santa Barbara Channel. Chiles tramped the length of his long

state. He found people deeply concerned about environmental pollution, and he advocated a National Space Agency-type development to combat it.

Up in Maine, Edmund Muskie, recognized regionally and nationally as an environmental candidate par excellence, won reelection easily.

A presidential voter poll taken shortly after the election showed Muskie leading Nixon by 46 percent to 40 percent, pointing up the rivalry between the two men that had been publicly apparent since the Santa Barbara spill began.

However, the President continued to strengthen his position on the environmental front. Three days after the election Nixon appointed an assistant U.S. Attorney General, William D. Ruckelshaus, to head the Environmental Protection Agency created by Nixon's reorganizational order in July. Ruckelshaus, a former Republican leader in the Indiana Legislature, said he would use "all available laws" in prosecuting polluters. Appearing with Ruckelshaus at his first press conference was Chairman Russell Train of the Council on Environmental Quality. Both men spoke against an Internal Revenue Service proposal to eliminate tax-exempt gifts to private organizations who filed lawsuits against polluters. Prominent among these organizations were the Sierra Club, the government's longtime opponent in the channel controversy; the Wilderness Society, engaged in litigation against the government over a proposed oil pipeline across Alaska; and the American Civil Liberties Union, some of whose attorneys were conducting Santa Barbara's cases against government and oil companies. The Internal Revenue Service proposal was later withdrawn.

On November 26, the President took another step affecting the channel and the entire U.S. environmental scene. He fired Hickel as his Secretary of the Interior.

Many conservationists expressed regret at Hickel's dismissal. They said he had developed tendencies favorable to the environment, since his baptism in the channel controversy. Hickel had halted construction of a jet airport threatening Florida's Everglades; defended alligators, condors, and bald eagles; hauled Chevron Oil into court on nine hundred counts of violating the Outer Continental Shelf Act; challenged U.S. industry to make the fight against pollution one of its own major interests; and begun to take a sympathetic view of Santa Barbara's position in the channel oil fight.

Senator Nelson, who had voted against Hickel's confirmation, said: "It turns out he had a great instinct for what was right and the guts to act on his convictions. . . . Conservationists have lost a great fighter and a great friend." And Lois Sidenberg wired the ex-Secretary on behalf of GOO: "We felt you were sympathetic to our problems and would have done more to alleviate them had circumstances permitted."

On the day Hickel was fired, however, the President's Council on Environmental Quality disapproved Hickel's plan for resuming oil and gas leasing in the Gulf of Mexico. In an apparent political move, Hickel had announced the leasing, with almost no prior notice, early in October during a political rally in Houston attended largely by oilmen. The council now urged that the scheduled December 15 lease sale be postponed because of unanswered environmental questions. Among these was the unknown long-range effect of another large oil spill, such as the Chevron spill of the preceding spring. The lease sale would, furthermore, break the nineteen-month moratorium on federal offshore leasing begun during the Santa Barbara Spill's early days. Revealing a cleavage between federal agencies charged with responsibility for the environment, Interior disregarded the council's recommendations, and the Louisiana leases were sold as scheduled. They brought the federal government $850 million in bonus payments.

Money, oil, and politics seemed to be developing insurmountable power when, on December 4, the *Los Angeles Times* revealed that four anonymous donors, and a number of oil companies, had contributed most of the $333,445.69 spent in defeating Proposition 18, the California-ballot anti-smog referendum measure. The backers of the measure, by contrast, had spent $22,721.

In the Louisiana sales and in the Los Angeles revelations, channel oil operators figured prominently. In addition to previous contributions by Union, Texaco, and others, Shell was now reported to have given $20,000 in opposition to Proposition 18, Phillips $15,000, Humble $12,000, Sun Oil $2,000, and Marathon (Sun's partner in Tract 401) $1,000.

The four anonymous donations against the proposition totaled

$100,000. Of course keen interest was aroused as to the identity of the anonymous donors.

The interest was heightened by the disclosure that carbon monoxide levels in the Los Angeles area might be responsible for 100 to 500 human deaths annually, according to Dr. John R. Goldsmith of the State Health Department.

Santa Barbara anti-oil leaders charged that channel oil was being turned into Los Angeles smog with a cynical disregard for public health, and that the federal government was abetting this process. And they saw the Louisiana sales as part of a movement that would reopen channel exploitation on a large scale.

Then on December 14, William T. Pecora, head of the U.S. Geological Survey and often the federal government's spokesman on channel oil matters, arrived in Santa Barbara and declared that "the die is cast" and Santa Barbara "should face the facts." Continued pumping and drilling in Tracts 402 and 401 was necessary to stop the leakage, Pecora said. Though the two tracts were producing oil at the rate of nearly 75,000 barrels a day to stop a leakage Pecora estimated at 5 to 10 barrels, two additional platforms would be necessary for proper leakage control. One of the two new platforms, Platform C, would be located westerly from Platform B. The other, designated Platform Henry, would be located easterly from Platform Hillhouse.

Pecora later explained that Platform Henry would not drain the Dos Cuadras structure but would be tapping the adjacent Carpinteria offshore field. In other words it would simply be a step toward business as usual. The implications of the Louisiana leasing were apparently coming true, despite a statement by the President's Council on Environmental Quality that the United States was three years away from successful techniques and equipment for coping with massive offshore spills and despite the refusal of the State of California to lift its drilling moratorium for this very reason.

On the day that Pecora announced the new platforms, Mobil Oil, one of the Platform A companies, admitted it was one of the anonymous donors to the defeat of Proposition 18. Mobil had given $30,000, considerably more than the 2,684,287 voters backing the proposition had given to support it.

Pecora next defined the rationale behind the federal government's newest position on channel oil development. The government based its position on the fact that the state had historically encouraged oil development on either side of its sixteen-mile-long sanctuary. Pecora said this meant that the federal government could justifiably encourage development on either side of its proposed cross-channel sanctuary. Though Pecora's argument was weakened by the fact that the state had imposed—and maintained—a drilling moratorium in its channel waters, the importance of state policy was clear: until the state banned oil development from the channel, Washington could say that federal policy there reflected "the will of the people of California."

As 1971 began, the future of the channel seemed to be more in Reagan's hands than in Nixon's. But in sharp contrast to his State of the State Message of a year before, Reagan's inaugural address of January 4 almost dismissed the environment. "Much remains to be done, of course," the governor said, "but we are meeting the challenge."

In fact the Republican-dominated Legislature had failed to act on some three hundred environmental bills, including the urgent proposals of the citizen and legislative committees of the previous spring, and the Governor had provided very little leadership on environmental issues.

Nevertheless, the Sacramento lawmakers had passed the State Environmental Quality Act of 1970. Patterned after the NEPA, the California EQA could also be said to have stemmed from the channel spill. It required state and local agencies using state or federal money to submit reports to the State Office of Planning and Research on projects having "significant" environmental impact. The planning office was directed to formulate a statewide land use policy, a program to protect land and water resources, an environmental monitoring system, and to formulate a state environmental goals and policy report. The planning office was allowed a staff of nine and an annual budget of $177,000. Offshore lands use was almost certain to come within its purview. Coupled with a tough new water-quality law, the Porter-Cologne Act, passed as result of the spill, this gave the state significant new power in the environmental field.

The beginning of the end or the end of the beginning of the spill's political history came on January 13, 1971, when the

Interior Department began a two-day hearing in Santa Barbara on the subject of the two new platforms described by Dr. Pecora. Santa Barbarans protested the suddenness with which the hearing was held. It had not been publicly announced until January 1. This seriously handicapped anti-oil forces in preparing their testimony. They also protested the apparent prejudging of the hearing's outcome as evidenced by Pecora's "the die is cast" statement of a few weeks earlier; and they invoked the National Environmental Policy Act which the spill itself had helped create. They demanded that an environmental impact study, as required by the NEPA, be made by Interior before action was taken on the new platforms.

Spokesmen from all elective levels of government opposed the platforms. Lieutenant Governor Reinecke frankly accused the Interior Department of prejudging the issue. County Supervisor George Clyde said the spill's most tragic effect had been the erosion of public trust in the federal government.

Senator Cranston announced that he and Senator Tunney were preparing new legislation, in consultation with city and county authorities and representatives of GOO. The Cranston-Tunney bill would terminate 38 leases in which no oil had been found, including 23 leases in the area covered by the Nixon Administration's cross-channel sanctuary plan, 13 leases north of San Miguel and Santa Rosa islands, and 2 leases near Anacapa; leaseholders would be entitled to a fair market value of their leases on the date of termination. The bill would also provide: (1) a moratorium of five years on 29 leases including 18 leases west of Santa Barbara where there had been the substantial discovery by Humble, and 11 leases off Ventura County, where Standard of California was engaged in exploratory drilling; (2) a termination of the Union and Sun leases in Tracts 402 and 401, as soon as operations to stop leakage were no longer necessary; (3) removal of the two platforms on the Phillips lease off Carpinteria, if and when the State of California terminated drilling into the same formation; and (4) replacement of existing platforms by underwater drilling and production equipment as soon as possible.

Cranston would seek an indefinite moratorium from the Interior Department until the new bill could be considered by

Congress. Teague would do likewise with the President. Teague was preparing a bill similar to Cranston's and Tunney's.

At the conclusion of the hearing, the Interior Department announced it would conduct an environmental impact study before action was taken on the proposed platforms, but there was a widespread feeling that this was a mere gesture to appease "the natives" and that the hearing itself was much the same. These fears seemed justified a few months later when William D. Ruckelshaus' Environmental Protection Agency sharply criticized Interior's impact study and recommended that the Department disapprove the proposed new platforms and halt all exploratory drilling in the channel.

As usual, the January hearing had been conducted against a background of offshore disaster. Blowing out of control since December 1, a group of fiery wells owned by Shell had killed four men and released thousands of gallons of oil into the Gulf of Mexico. And three days after the hearing, two Standard of California tankers collided in Golden Gate at the entrance to San Francisco Bay, releasing 875,000 gallons of oil into the bay's waters.

Perhaps even more significant for the channel's future, Senator Henry M. Jackson, chairman of the Senate's powerful Interior and Insular Affairs Committee, expressed dissatisfaction with the way Interior had conducted the hearing and said that he and his committee would investigate the circumstances. This was nearly equivalent to the investigation of the Department of the Interior's role in the spill that Santa Barbarans had long requested.

Jackson's committee would also hold hearings on the general subjects of offshore drilling and oil-spill containment and cleanup.

The intervention of Jackson was an important new element. He was one of the most influential men in Washington, a prominent conservationist, and a potential candidate for the Democratic nomination for the Presidency.

Now Nixon reentered the scene, with words that seemed ready-made to fit it. In his second State of the Union message on January 23, the President announced "a new American Revolution" that would "turn power back to the people—in which government at all levels" would be refreshed and renewed and made truly responsive.

As a reminder of another power, on January 28, the spill's second anniversary, Gulf Oil, one of the Platform A companies, was revealed to have made an anonymous gift of $20,000 to the defeat of Proposition 18. Gulf's check was drawn on the Mellon National Bank in Pittsburgh, Gulf's headquarters and bastion of the Mellon family interests. Also on January 28, the State Lands Commission lifted its long moratorium on drilling in state waters by permitting Standard of California to drill a well from a man-made island off the Los Angeles coast.

Ambivalence characterized all facets of the oil spill. People were responsible for the steadily increasing demand for oil, yet they opposed oil development designed to satisfy their demand. The government, the proprietor of the offshore lands where most untapped oil sources lay, tried to satisfy both the popular demand for oil and the popular demand for a clean environment. The oil companies depended on the people, who were their customers, for their livelihood, yet engaged in activities apparently inimical to the public welfare. The spill was the embodiment of this deep-rooted conflict.

The federal government's role was perhaps most ambivalent. Its exploitive authority clashed with its protective authority from the beginning of the spill. The early conflict of Standley, Acuff, and Solanas—the Platform A triumvirate—with Brown and his onshore command group was not a minor bureaucratic tangle. It was fundamental. It exposed a vein of division that ran deep through the federal structure and into the White House (witness the President's zigzag course) and on into the national mind.

Sacramento's role in the spill resembled in lesser degree that of Washington. Caught in a dilemma between exploitation and protection, it asked Washington to do what it was unwilling to do itself. If it would permanently ban offshore oil development in its channel waters, it would set an example that the federal government would be almost bound to follow.

As for the people, the nation as a whole is being asked, through Congress, to make a decision about the channel, a decision that may express a new national will toward our offshore resources as a whole. The exploitive Outer Continental Shelf Lands Act of 1953 was an extension of the national will at that time. Until it is repealed or modified, it remains the definitive expression of what Americans want done with their offshore lands.

Nixon and Reagan continue to play key roles. It is interesting to speculate on what might have happened had Nixon taken a strong stand against channel drilling during his visit to Santa Barbara, or what might have happened had Reagan met him there for a Republican environmental summit conference. A good portion of the world could have been changed.

Yet 1969 was the year of the political turning. It saw politicians and people begin to move decisively toward the side of the environment. By contrast, 1970 was the year of defining environmental problems and discovering their political implications. In the channel, this led to frustration and stalemate. Oil development edged steadily forward. Ten billion barrels were a powerful incentive. But aroused public opinion was a powerful brake. And the physical and ecological consequences of the spill were, it appeared, serious enough to warrant continued public concern.

21

PHYSICAL AND ECOLOGICAL CONSEQUENCES

ACCORDING TO Alan A. Allen's estimate, 2,300,000 gallons of oil escaped into the channel during the spill's first ten and a half days. By the spill's hundredth day Allen's figure had grown to 3,250,000 gallons. By January, 1971, it reached 3,330,000. Allen insisted that his estimate was conservative and that the actual amount of spillage was probably much larger.

The Geological Survey estimated the total amount of the spill during the period of major leakage to be 760,000 gallons. But it hedged its figure. One Survey spokesman gave an upper estimate for the initial ten and a half days of uncontrolled spill of 1,250 barrels (52,500 gallons) and a lower limit of 500 barrels (21,000 gallons) per day. Another spokesman made estimates for the same period ranging from 5,000 to 500 barrels per day, the former figure agreeing with Allen and the latter with Union Oil Company estimates. Union's estimates of the total amount of the spill during its first two years were in the neighborhood of 250,-000 gallons.

Allen's figures became widely accepted. They were substantiated in part by the President's Panel on Oil Spills, which estimated the total amount of the spill as of mid-1969 at between 1,000,000 and 3,000,000 gallons, and by the study conducted by Dr. Michael Neushul for the Federal Water Pollution Control Administration and for the University of California, which measured onshore dosages during the early days of the spill that tended (as will be seen) to confirm Allen's emission figures. A study by the University of Southern California added further confirmation.

Whatever the total amount of the spill, attempts to control it were at first inadequate and have never wholly succeeded. Two and a half years after the blowout, the Platform A slick was still a feature of Santa Barbara's seascape.

Leakage is believed to originate at depths ranging from near the ocean floor to at least 2,000 feet below it. Oil emerging near Platform A has been found to have an API gravity ranging from 18 to 24 degrees; that emerging 800 feet east of the platform ranged from 19 to 28 degrees. At both locations the oil has varied from a low-density greenish brown to a high-density brownish black. It has been accompanied by colorless gas, and sometimes by lumps of heavy black tarry material.

Approximately fifty acres of caprock were damaged by the blowout. This is the still-active seepage area. Exactly how many channels outside the well bore were opened and how deeply into the ocean floor they extended is not known.

Initial efforts to control the spill elsewhere than at its source met with limited success, as has been seen, and later ones fared little better. Chemical dispersants were the first of these controls applied. They included nearly the full range of commercially available brands: Corexit, Polycomplex A-11, Ara Chem, Unico, Crane OD-2, and Chem Treat. Some, such as Unico and Crane OD-2, were applied in very small, or test, amounts. Ara Chem, developed for use by the Navy in San Diego Harbor, was used regularly from Platform A at a rate of 1 to 3 barrels a day dropping through a hose directly into the oil-gas bubble at the platform's northeast leg. Later a rainbird sprayed it onto the bubble. According to the Federal Water Quality Administration, 1,616 drums of chemicals, or approximately 89,000 gallons, were applied to the spill during its first year. Ara Chem, Corexit, and Polycomplex A-11 were used predominantly.

The conclusion reached by most observers was that chemicals were ineffective in controlling large amounts of spillage.

Mechanical devices used in an attempt to control the spill at sea were ineffective. Surface devices included booms (wooden, air-inflatable, and foam-rubber), skimming devices, and suction pumps. Booms proved almost wholly ineffective. They broke up in even moderate seas, failed to conform to rough ocean surfaces, and maneuvering them posed continual problems.

Except at Santa Barbara, harbor defenses were successful in reducing the impact of the oil on shore. At Ventura, log booms arranged in a series of three repelled oil successfully, as did an inflatable boom at Channel Islands Harbor. At Port Hueneme two log booms supplemented by straw between them proved effective, as did two rows of log booms plus an inflatable boom at Point Mugu. Success in all instances depended on the constant presence of work crews who removed accumulated oil and debris and made repairs. In none was there a direct onslaught of oil in large quantity driven by high wind as at Santa Barbara.

Later defense efforts at Santa Barbara, against much smaller amounts of oil, aided by more favorable weather conditions, succeeded. Notable among these was an underwater air curtain or bubble barrier. Compressed air emerged from a pipe laid on the harbor bottom and created an upwelling of water that was sufficient to bar the entrance of oil if surface current was not excessive and if debris did not accumulate sufficiently to break the force of the bubble barrier. The chief advantage of the air curtain was that it permitted surface vessels to come and go through it freely.

Efforts to clean up the spilled oil after it reached shore were relatively successful. Limited amounts of such absorbents as talc and perlite were used, but straw proved most effective. In addition to pressurized hot and cold water and steam cleaning, some detergents were used in rocky areas. Sandblasting eventually proved the only satisfactory method of cleaning oil-stained rocks.

Union was commended for its work as were government agencies involved. At the peak of the cleanup, 1,000 men, 125 vehicles, 55 boats, and 3,000 tons of straw were being used. Beach cleanup costs were estimated at $5,000 per mile, or about $1 per linear foot.

Despite Union's commendable cleanup job, the evidence was overwhelming: the channel coast, and the nation's shorelines generally, were virtually defenseless against a major oil spill. Nearly three years later this was still true. Plans and organizations existed, but effective equipment—booms, skimmers, floating barriers—was simply not available.

Except for birds, the spill's effects on the channel's marine ecology appeared negligible at first. Injury was most extensive in the tidal zone where oil was deposited in large amounts. Suffering most were barnacles and surf grass. Immediate injury to organisms was the result of smothering. Some colonies of acorn and goose-necked barnacles were virtually wiped out. Some varieties of alga also suffered, according to State Fish and Game Department reports. Anemones survived surprisingly well as did mussels, limpets, and starfish. Common amphipods and bloodworms escaped serious injury by digging into the sand.

In the near-shore zone, abalone suffered no apparent harm. California spiny lobsters also escaped as long as they remained below the surface. When brought to the surface in traps and contaminated with oil, the lobsters soon died. Lobster eggs and larva may also have been damaged by the slick. The giant kelp survived without apparent harm. It secreted a mucous-like substance called fucosan which prevented oil from adhering to the kelp's leaves and stems.

Bottom studies revealed no major damage to plant or animal life attributable to the spill, but University of Southern California researchers found that vast quantities of Platform A oil—perhaps most of it—had adhered to the grains of silt washed into the sea by record pre-spill floods and were lying on the channel's floor, presenting a pollution hazard of significant nature.

Later studies of the water column did not confirm the possible damage to plankton noted by the *David Starr Jordan* during the spill's first days. The initial low plankton count may have been due to a local condition caused by foraging of fish or crustaceans, or later investigations may have been inadequate. Similarly, the locally observed decrease of dissolved oxygen may have been caused by a concentration of bacteria feeding on the oil. Meaningful conclusions in either case were limited by lack of pre-spill data

for use as comparison and by lack of extensive simultaneous observations throughout the slick.

Damage to fish and shellfish remained debatable. Two years
after the spill began, Gene Hall, proprietor of the Smoke House
on Stearns Wharf, claimed to have pulled up 500 lobster traps
from various bottom sites in the channel and netted 41 pounds
of lobster, a record low for his thirty years in the fishery. Hall
said his seasonal catch was down 50 percent from pre-spill years
when 300 traps sometimes brought him 3,000 pounds a week. And
Leon Durden, the fish-spotter, who had overflown the channel day
and night for seventeen years and knew its fish perhaps as well
as anyone, said that though his income for the first six months
of 1970 was three times better than during the first six months
of the spill, it was still only half that of pre-spill years. Fishing-boat
operators confirmed Durden's figures. But statistical surveys conducted by federal, state, and academic investigators showed no
significant damage to fish populations attributable to the spill.
California Fish and Game Department statistics even revealed a
slight increase in commercial fish taken from the channel's eastern
end, during the six-month period between February and July,
1969, while the spill was at its height. But Herbert W. Frey, the
department's senior marine biologist, called such statistics misleading. "I can use statistics to show that the spill was beneficial,
which is of course fictitious," Frey said. He believes that the spill's
impact on the channel's fish population was masked by the little-
known movements of its migratory fish. Large numbers of anchovy,
mackerel, and bonito entered and left the channel during the
spill's early months, but no one knows how their numbers compared to those of other years or how they were affected by the oil.
"We have detected no impairment of numbers, reproduction, or
feeding activities attributable to oil pollution," Frey said. "That's
not saying that five years from now we won't find something
different."

Dr. Dale Straughan of the University of Southern California
agreed with Frey's statement. She headed the $240,000 study of
the spill's effects on the channel's ecology conducted by USC and
financed by the Western Oil and Gas Association. Her twelve-
month-long field study, completed in the fall of 1970, found the
spill's effects on marine life negligible; but the study was primarily

visual and qualitative and made little or no attempt to examine subtle toxic effects, or long-range effects generally. It was sharply challenged by Dr. Max Blumer, a senior scientist at the Woods Hole, Massachusetts, Oceanographic Institution. In a report prepared for the Maine Environmental Improvement Commission, Blumer pointed out that oil is a chemical that has severe biological effects and that to be meaningful oil-pollution research should combine chemical with biological studies. For chemical characterization of the oil in sediments and organisms, gas chromatography and mass spectrometry are commonly used. But in the WOGA-sponsored studies at Santa Barbara their use was extremely limited. Where used on ocean-bottom sediments, gas chromatography showed oil pollution persisting nearly two years after the spill began; and the burrowing organisms usually found in ocean floor soil had not reappeared in these sediments. Blumer also faulted the WOGA study for not scrutinizing carefully the smaller, lesser-known organisms of the ocean floor, such as polychaetous annelids and amphipod crustaceans. Off Massachusetts, these important members of the food chain had suffered severely from the impact of an oil spill. No chemical analysis of the Santa Barbara oil was made, showing its composition, boiling range, the presence or absence of persistent poisons, and other important information. Dr. J. H. Connell, a U.C. Santa Barbara zoologist, joined Blumer in faulting the WOGA study. In a report prepared for the Australian Royal Commission on Oil Exploitation on the Great Barrier Reef, Connell said Dr. Straughan and her colleagues had employed imprecise methods involving no replications, no control observation of unpolluted or undisturbed beaches, and line transects that entirely missed animal populations familiar to Connell and his students. He found their work so imprecise that almost no valid conclusions could be drawn from it.

Damage to sea mammals remained as debatable as damage to fish and other life forms. Despite earlier conflicting claims, the State Fish and Game Department's official report of the spill found that "some elephant seals may have been lost" as result of oil washing ashore on San Miguel Island. Seventy-four animals were involved to some extent, the department found; but there was no conclusive evidence that any of them died. Dr. Burney Le Boeuf, who with Dr. Richard Peterson conducted the survey of the San Miguel elephant seals and later continued their work alone, found no evidence linking oil with seal deaths. "However, my results do not show that the oil had no effect on elephant seal mortality. That would be proving a negative and would be virtually impossible to do," Le Boeuf told this writer.

As for California sea lions—the "trained seals" of circuses—the Fish and Game Department found that "losses as a direct result of the oil" occurred but "were difficult to assess," and that "approximately seventy-five sea lion pups were contaminated." Dr. Connell showed that in a sample of 881 living and dead sea lion pups observed on San Miguel Island, slightly less than half were oily but about two-thirds of all dead pups were oily, indicating that many more dead pups were oiled than would be expected by chance.

Three dead dolphins were found on channel beaches during the early days of the spill. A field autopsy performed on one of them by Fish and Game authorities showed no evidence linking its death with oil. But eyewitnesses said its breathing hole was clogged with oil and its lungs were ruptured. This raised a new issue: the efficacy of autopsies as a measure of the spill's effects on marine animals.

Of the five dead whales washed ashore on the California coast during February and March, 1969, three were gray whales, one was a sperm and one a pilot whale. The total was almost exactly representative of other years. An autopsy performed on one of the gray whales under the auspices of the Interior Department failed, as has been seen, to link its death with oil. But critics such as Clark T. Cameron, president of the American Cetacean Society, argued that this proved little or nothing: "If I hit you over the head and you die, an autopsy may show you died of a fractured skull." Cameron claimed that the central issue was that whales and other sea mammals were highly susceptible to respiratory ailments and that interference with their respiratory systems could result in death from a number of causes, pneumonia for one. Supporting Cameron, Dr. Blumer said that the method used in the Department of Interior's whale autopsy, sensitive in the

50–100 parts per million level, was not sensitive enough. He cited the case of the shellfish containing as little as four parts per million of oil that suffered biological damage.

Most experts were convinced that several factors mitigated the spill's effects on marine life. First, in the intertidal zone there was wide variation in the amount of oil reaching shore during the first days of the spill, the period of heaviest dosage. Variation in dose ranged from approximately 12 pounds per square yard of beach at Santa Barbara to about one-fiftieth of that amount at Ellwood and El Capitan on the west. Easterly, the Summerland and the Ventura-Port Hueneme coasts received doses nearly as heavy as Santa Barbara's. Approximately 390,000 gallons of oil came ashore along a 7-mile stretch centered on the Santa Barbara waterfront. A total of 1.3 million gallons reached shore along 55 miles of seriously contaminated coast between El Capitan and Port Hueneme. Smaller amounts polluted some 25 miles of channel island coast.

These estimates were based on the study conducted by Dr. Michael Neushul of the University of California at Santa Barbara in conjunction with the FWPCA. Neushul's was the only systematic study of spill-to-shore dosage, and it showed that in most cases damage to intertidal life was directly related to dose. Besides supporting Alan Allen's estimates of leakage rate and total oil released during the spill's first days, Neushul's findings showed that about one-third as much oil reached the channel's mainland coast as reached the English coast during the *Torrey Canyon* spill.

Another factor that may have mitigated the spill's effects on marine life was the relatively extended period that most of the oil remained at sea. It probably lost some of its more toxic fractions through atmospheric and bacterial action. There was also evidence that channel crude oil was less soluble in seawater than other crudes, and this may have decreased its contamination of the water column. Limited use of chemicals was definitely an ameliorating factor. And there were seasonal factors such as the dormant state of most plant and animal species. Red alga, for instance, might have been heavily damaged had it been in bloom. Injury to intertidal zone animals might have been much greater had they been caught at breeding season by the black tide. Fortunately most of the contamination occurred during midwinter when plant and animal activity was at low ebb. One exception was that of the California sea lions who were caught during their May-June pupping season by the oil on San Miguel Island. Sea lions on San Nicolas Island, seaward of the channel's eastern end, may have been similarly caught by oil that came ashore there, or so Richard Peterson reported shortly before his death. He had found a number of oil-stained animals on San Nicolas.

Straughan and others believed that continued exposure to oil from natural seeps could have conditioned the channel's marine life against the adverse effects of an oil spill. But Dr. Neushul found that intertidal zone life was sparse where oil from natural seeps reached shore and that species were fewer there.

"It appears obvious that these seeps, and others that may result from further drilling, may drastically reduce the availability of intertidal surfaces that would otherwise be occupied by intertidal organisms," Neushul said. In his opinion, a "subtle and gradual erosion" of a natural resource had begun.

Several unique factors may have made the spill's effect on marine life impossible to determine accurately. These factors were: (1) the unseasonably low temperature of the channel's water —2 degrees F. colder than a ten-year average—at the time of the spill; (2) unusually high runoff from the January, 1969, floods which decreased the salinity and increased the sediment content in the channel's water mass and which may have carried large quantities of pesticides into it from recently sprayed crops and citrus groves; (3) the unpredictable movements of pelagic fish which may have masked the effects of the spill on fish populations; (4) lack of pre-spill data to serve as a basis for comparison.

There were, however, glaring deficiencies in the study of the spill's ecological effects. No investigation was made of atmospheric effects, which may in turn have influenced the channel's biosphere and, cumulatively, that of the entire earth. Floating oil affects the interface between sea and air. It prevents evaporation, inhibits gaseous interchange between the atmosphere and the sea, changes the reflective quality of the sea's surface, and modifies the amount of solar radiation entering seawater. "These effects require study and some of them may be of considerable importance," according to Dr. Robert W. Holmes, director of the University of California at Santa Barbara Marine Science Institute.

Similarly, no systematic laboratory studies were made of the possible toxic effects of the spill on marine organisms. "Therefore, we cannot know the ecological effects of the spill," Dr. Bruce Halstead of the World Life Research Institute at Colton, California, insisted.

Woods Hole Oceanographic Institution scientists agreed in principle with Halstead. Dr. Blumer found that certain toxic hydrocarbons from the September, 1969, spill of fuel oil at West Falmouth on Buzzards Bay, Massachusetts, were as plentiful six months later in sediments and in marine organisms as at the time of the spill. These hydrocarbons were like chlorinated pesticides in their persistence, and their effects were not fully understood. The most dangerous were believed to be the aromatics, such as benzene, toluene, and xylene, which did not dissipate in seawater as rapidly as had been thought. But all hydrocarbons should be considered a potential menace to animal and human health, according to Dr. Blumer. Some might cause cancer. Others might cause cell damage. When ingested they tended to concentrate in the fatty tissue of organisms where they remained almost unchanged by metabolic processes. By transfer from one organism to another they moved up the food chain, becoming more concentrated as they went.

After the West Falmouth spill, they passed into fish and shellfish normally eaten by humans. Though the Falmouth spill differed from that of the channel in that it consisted of refined rather than crude oil and in that it reached shore quickly, before its more toxic fractions were exposed to long-term biological and atmospheric degradation, if Blumer's findings were correct they applied in essence to the Santa Barbara spill.

Dr. Richard Backus, also a Woods Hole scientist, described another way in which oil entered the food chain. Small lumps of floating tar resulting from the eight to ten million tons of oil dumped or spilled into the sea each year were eaten by fish. The fish were eaten by people. Oil was thus taken into the human body, with results as yet unknown. Confirming Backus' description, California Fish and Game Department diver-biologists working offshore near Anacapa Island during the early days of the spill saw fish swim up to the "oil canopy" and nibble at its lower surface.]

"Everything to do with the long-term effects of oil spills is superficially known," Dr. Howard Sanders, another member of the Woods Hole group, said. "We need to look at the subject very critically."

Birds suffered severely from the spill. The California Fish and Game Department listed 3,686 known dead during the spill's first four months. Questioned about the rigor of its count, the department admitted it had no way of knowing how many birds died at sea or on remote stretches of island and mainland shore.

The ornithological curator of the Santa Barbara Museum of Natural History, Waldo Abbott, estimated that a minimum of 6,000 birds died as result of the spill. Abbott had made regular surveys and was in a position to comment on the accuracy of official counts. "Furthermore, the museum received reports of oiled birds sick or dying for hundreds of miles north and south of Santa Barbara that I'm sure were never accounted for in the Fish and Game Department's total," he insisted.

Some experts believe that the number of dead birds that can be accounted for after an oil spill represents about one-fifth of the total dead. Thus the number of birds that died as result of the Santa Barbara spill can be reasonably estimated at between 6,000 and 15,000.

Diving birds such as grebes, loons, murres, and cormorants suffered most. Sea gulls were affected least. Several brown pelicans, their survival already threatened by DDT, died of the oil. Death was caused in a variety of ways: by smothering (nostrils and throats clogged with oil); by starvation due to inability to fly, swim, and feed; by loss of body heat caused by destruction of natural insulation; and—in all probability—by chemical poisoning due to ingesting oil. Of 200 dead birds autopsied by the Fish and Game Department during later stages of the spill, none was found to have ingested oil. But dozens of birds treated during the early days of heaviest contamination were found to have nostrils, tongues, and throats clogged with the black goo. Unfortunately no professional autopsies were performed on-scene during the hectic early days. But informal visual autopsies conducted by Dr. Barbara

Drinkwater, U.C. Santa Barbara research physiologist, revealed oil in the intestinal tracts of many birds.

About 1,575 birds were treated at rescue centers during the first four months of the spill. Many died from the stress of handling. Of fifteen types of treatment used, that with Polycomplex A-11 proved most successful. Organic cleansers such as Nutriclean and Basic H were also effective. Severely oiled birds required repeated washings and even scrubbing. Many required mouth-and-throat swabbing with butter- or margarine-soaked cotton on the end of a stick. Certain species were found to need water support. Grebes and loons are not land birds and injured themselves unless supported by water. But no wholly satisfactory treatment was discovered. In conjunction with an efficient oil-removal method, the application of a substitute oil or wax to compensate for lost natural body oil seemed to provide immediate protection against heat loss. And some promise was seen in the use of corn meal and mineral oil, or in fuller's earth, as absorbents in preference to the more severe treatment of rinsing in Polycomplex A-11. A prolonged rehabilitation period extending through a complete moult appeared necessary in order to allow clean feathers to replace oily ones. Yet a quick return to a natural habitat seemed desirable, even before birds were spotlessly clean.

The State Fish and Game Department reported that four and a half months after the spill began, 162 birds treated at rescue centers had survived. This was about 11 percent of the total treated. It appeared to compare favorably to a 5 to 6 percent survival rate first reported for the 5,800 birds treated following the *Torrey Canyon* disaster. But *Torrey Canyon* victims finally released to wildness were estimated at 1 percent or less of those treated. At Santa Barbara, the total eventually released to wildness was about 100. The survival rate after release was impossible to determine. Some banded birds were found dead. Of twenty released in the Santa Barbara Bird Refuge, all were believed to have died. Thus the final survival rate may have approached zero, a figure analogous to that of the *Torrey Canyon* disaster. Some rescue-center workers felt it was more merciful to let oiled birds die than to try to save them.

The waterfowl population of the channel at the time of the spill was estimated at the quite low figure of 12,000 due to heavy

22

FINANCIAL AND LEGAL CONSEQUENCES

THE COSTS of the spill were perhaps incalculable in terms of dollars, but courts of law were asked to calculate them that way, to compensate a multitude of private individuals, business firms, and public entities claiming monetary loss. The courts would thus help determine the spill's actual dollar costs.

But there were dollar costs of another kind. Two oil economists, Dr. Walter J. Mead of U.C. Santa Barbara and Dr. Philip E. Sorensen of Florida State University, attempted to measure the spill's "social cost." They defined "social cost" as the net dollar cost to U.S. society of: (1) resources lost in the spill; (2) resources used in its control and cleanup; (3) the value of recreational and property services foregone because of the spill, such as the loss of opportunities to boat or swim or the decline in sale value of beachfront property; and (4) damage to the channel's marine life.

In determining social costs, Mead and Sorensen argued that because the spill diverted tourists to other areas, the resulting economic loss to Santa Barbara was offset by gains in other areas, and so there was no significant "social cost" (loss of tourist dollars to society generally) as result of the spill. Emphasizing that their findings were tentative, minimal, and subject to revision upwards, the two economists found the social cost of the spill to be $16.4 million.

They assigned Union's onshore cleanup a social cost of $4,-887,000. Union's well-control efforts were similarly estimated at $3,600,000; its oil-collection efforts at $2,000,000.

The federal government's involvement in the spill was estimated to have cost society $382,000; that of the State of California $200,000; that of the County of Santa Barbara $57,200. Costs to the City of Santa Barbara were rated as socially negligible, as were damage to tourism, fish life, and sea mammals.

Damage to commercial fishing was estimated by Mead and Sorensen at $804,250; damage to property owners at $1,197,000; to bird life $7,400. Intertidal life loss estimates ranged from $1,000 to $25,000.

The value of the lost oil was placed at $130,000 (using Allen's estimate of 3.3 million gallons for total oil escaped), and the value of lost recreation was estimated at $3,150,000.

These figures were quickly labeled unrealistic by other critics. The fact that many thousands of tourists went elsewhere during the early days of the spill may have mitigated social costs, these critics argued, but it did not compensate Santa Barbara businessmen for money lost. Convention visitors (a key measurement of tourist trade) were down 22 percent during 1969 compared to 1968. Convention tourists spent an estimated $500,000 less in Santa Barbara than in 1968. Allowing for the effect of the 1969 economic recession, a substantial portion of the decline could nevertheless be attributed to the spill. The exact amount was probably impossible to determine.

As a beginning measurement of other actual costs, Union reported spending a total of $10,600,000 on well control, containment of oil at sea, and shoreline cleanup; but this did not include the cost of the time of salaried personnel diverted from other work to the spill effort. Union also expended more than $150,000 in settlement of some of the damage claims arising from the spill, and would probably spend much more.

According to the Western Oil and Gas Association, the channel oil operators, exclusive of the Platform A group, had lost approximately $45 million by January, 1970, as result of the drilling moratoriums in federal and state waters. This actual loss continued as the state's moratorium continued and as controversy arising from the spill slowed or prevented oil development in the channel's federal water.

Following the spill, Humble abandoned a costly lease, immediately seaward of ill-fated Tract 402, for which it had paid a nonreturnable bonus of $45,262,080; and Signal abandoned a tract off Ventura for which it had paid $225,558. Humble cited unpromising tests as its reason for vacating, while Signal mentioned unpromising geophysical data. However, Signal's abandonment of its leases within Santa Barbara's city limits was attributed directly to the spill. The company decided that the city's will to maintain its charter amendment against oil drilling was firm. Thus an estimated 60 million barrels of oil remained undisturbed under Santa Barbara's eastside residential and business sections and best beaches. Signal had invested some $20,000 in lease payments, exclusive of administrative costs.

Costs of litigating claims and suits arising from the spill will almost certainly run into millions. Administrative costs to government and industry will continue. So will additional insurance costs imposed by the spill. (Insurance underwriters declined to accept offshore pollution risks, following the channel spill and the Chevron spill off Louisiana the next spring, and operators were forced to self-insure against these risks, thus diverting tens of millions that might otherwise be productively employed.)

Total actual costs of the spill approached $100 million by mid-1971, while ahead loomed multibillion-dollar lawsuits.

LEGAL PROBLEMS

Yet to be adjudicated on July 28, 1971 as consequence of the spill, were damage suits to the amount of more than $4 billion, plus important constitutional questions such as: (1) the individual's right to an environment reasonably free from pollution and (2) applicability of the National Environmental Policy Act to continued oil operations in the Santa Barbara Channel.

In the one damage suit that had come to trial, three judges sitting as special masters for the Federal District Court ruled against thirty-four Santa Barbara pleasure-boat owners. The owners argued that loss of use was compensable and could be computed by multiplying the daily rental value of their boats by the number of days (200 days in most instances) they were deprived of the use of their craft as result of the spill. The judges agreed with oil company attorneys who argued that the case came under federal admiralty law, which did not provide for damage due to loss of use but only for physical damage. The owners contended that because no defendant vessel was involved and because admiralty law did not cover oil spills from offshore platforms, their case was governed by the Outer Continental Shelf Lands Act, which invoked state law in determining damages. They have appealed. They are asking $40,000 each, on the average, for loss of use, or a rough grand total of $1,360,000.

Attorneys for 106 other boat owners accepted $150,325.72 for physical damage without arguing for loss-of-use awards.

In other actions, Santa Barbara's plaintiffs fared no better than its boat owners. In an unusual procedure reflecting what seemed to them unreasonable delay on the part of Federal Judge Albert Lee Stephens, Jr., the city, county, and seventeen citizen plaintiffs asked the Federal Court of Appeals on February 11, 1970, to remove from Stephens' hands two cases filed the preceding August that he had not ruled on, despite the obvious urgency of the channel situation. The cases were those seeking injunctions to prevent the Interior Department from authorizing further oil development in the channel without first divulging certain technical information and holding public hearings. The petitioners asserted that Stephens had taken so long to issue a ruling that his inaction constituted a denial of the requested injunctions and was therefore appealable.

On the following day, Stephens ruled against the Santa Barbarans in both cases. He held that the injunctions would "inhibit the decision-making power" necessary to prevent another oil spill and that evidence was "insufficient to support claim" that further drilling was a threat to life or property. Stephens found there was no reason to compel the Department of Interior to reveal data or to hold hearings before oil development continued. The plaintiffs appealed.

On March 23, these appeals and a similar case against the Corps of Engineers were heard by the Circuit Court of Appeals in San Francisco. The Santa Barbarans argued that the Outer Continental Shelf Lands Act and the regulations under which the Interior Department administered offshore leases, implied that public hearings were required before oil development proceeded in the channel, and so did the regulations of the Corps of Engineers. In any event, they contended, in view of the questions involved, hearings were required by the U.S. Constitution as a civil right. Edmund B. Clark of the Department of Justice in Washington, representing the Interior Department and Corps of Engineers, contended that both agencies had the power to hold such public hearings as those requested but were not required to hold them under the circumstances.

The Appellate Court unanimously agreed with Clark. But it did not rule on the question of whether hearings were mandatory under the due process provisions of the Constitution, leaving that to the three-judge Los Angeles federal court which already was considering Santa Barbara's case challenging the constitutionality of the Outer Continental Shelf Lands Act. The plaintiffs appealed. On January 11, 1971, the Supreme Court refused to hear their case.

Meanwhile on January 13, 1970, Santa Barbara County District Attorney Minier filed criminal complaints in Municipal Court in Santa Barbara against the Platform A oil companies. Minier did this in the face of an order by Judge Stephens enjoining him not to, thus laying himself open to contempt charges.

On his part, Minier charged the Platform A consortium with polluting the waters of the Santa Barbara Channel. He alleged, as formerly, that the spill was affecting local waters, beaches, and citizens and was therefore within his jurisdiction. He openly attacked Stephens. "Any attempt by a federal judge to restrain Santa Barbara judges from proceeding further with the prosecution of the oil companies would be a shocking and indefensible abuse of judicial process." The continuing spill gave weight to Minier's remarks. But on January 28, 1970, the issue was removed from the Santa Barbara Municipal Court by the filing of a petition by the oil companies. They claimed to be leaseholders and agents of the federal government and therefore prosecutable only in federal court.

A year later Minier was fighting to have the cases returned to the local court. But no contempt charges had been filed against him.

Neither had criminal charges been filed against the Platform A consortium for violating federal regulations or statutes and causing the spill, though federal officials now admitted that such regulations and statutes had been violated.

Two years of legal effort yielded meager benefits to the Santa Barbarans. But there were significant side effects. The new willingness of the Department of the Interior to hold hearings prior to offshore leasing and to divulge information relevant to the oil spill which it had previously withheld, were almost certainly the result of the Santa Barbara cases. Embarrassed if not conscience stricken by its failure to prosecute the Platform A companies criminally, Interior had hauled Gulf Coast operators into court for causing pollution and seen them fined more than $1.5 million. The channel cases were, furthermore, adding to the steadily growing body of environmental law. When the spill began, there were estimated to be less than a dozen environmental actions before U.S. courts. Environmental law was not a recognized legal field. Two years later there were more than one hundred environmental cases in litigation, and environmental law was a recognized branch of jurisprudence.

SHIPS AND OIL RIGS

On December 4, 1969, the Matson luxury liner *Lurline*'s near-collision with the drilling rig *Blue Water II* refocused attention on the fact that more ships had been wrecked in the Santa Barbara Channel than in any other area of the U.S. Pacific Coast. It also recalled the head-on collision of the tanker *Cossatot* with the freighter *Copper State* on a foggy night in June the year before.

Following the collision of the *Cossatot* and *Copper State* about ten miles seaward from the later site of Platform A, north- and southbound traveling lanes were established for channel shipping. The lanes were a mile wide and were separated by a two-mile buffer zone. Shipping industry representatives wanted them to be at least two miles wide. The shipping people argued that large vessels often required several miles in which to come to a stop and a considerable space in which to change course. But oil industry representatives wanted the narrower lanes. When the oilmen promised to build their drilling platforms no closer than one-half mile to the proposed lanes, the special Sealanes Committee composed of Army, Navy, Air Force, Interior Department, Coast Guard, and shipping and oil industry representatives, agreed to the narrower lanes.

The committee also agreed that floating rigs could be stationed "immediately adjacent" to the lanes, that drilling platforms could be constructed in the two-mile-wide buffer zone separating the lanes, and that floating rigs could be stationed there. Anchor cables, which often radiated as much as 5,000 feet from the floating rigs, were permitted to extend into the traveling lanes provided they were at depths greater than 85 feet. Specific markings, lights, and signals were required on anchor buoys, rigs, and platforms; and oil companies were required to give the position of platforms and floating rigs to the Coast Guard in advance of construction or positioning, so that it could be plotted on maps and charts and publicized in notices to mariners. But no government agency was assigned the responsibility of checking to see if floating rigs were actually where they were supposed to be, or to see that anchor cables did not intrude into the traveling lanes at depths above 85 feet. In fact, the lanes themselves were unofficial routes. They were merely guidelines. No vessel could be compelled to follow them, because they ran through international water. The United States, which claimed the right to drill on the ocean's floor, had no right to regulate traffic on its surface—beyond three miles from shore, the extent of U.S. territorial water.

When anti-oil forces learned these facts, they protested vehemently. They claimed they had been denied their rights by not being included in the meetings of the Sealanes Committee, which had met for more than a year during the height of the pre-spill channel controversy without a member of the press, public, or concerned citizens groups present.

The anti-oil forces claimed that the new sealanes actually increased the possibility of shipping accidents by encouraging the construction of platforms and the positioning of floating rigs in close proximity to heavy traffic, and they found it incredible that the federal government should have authority to "clutter up the channel with structures and oil rigs," but no authority to regulate the movement of ships among such obstacles.

A major new issue was thus added to the oil-spill controversy.

There is general agreement as to the hazards of channel navigation, even without the presence of drilling platforms and floating rigs. Point Conception is known as the "graveyard of the Pacific." More than 37 vessels have been wrecked at or near it. John Wightman, formerly an officer with Standard of California's tanker fleet, told what the hazards were like. "About half the time in summer you never see Point Conception because of the fog. Yet there's a regular traffic jam there. Ships coming from Japan and Hawaii home in on the beacon at Conception. Then they head down the channel toward Los Angeles. Add to them the coast-wise traffic, and it's like being on a freeway. Nobody slows down. You're all alone—you and the seaman steering the ship. He can't leave the wheel. And you're doing about twelve things at once, besides interpret the radar blips. We had a close shave a time or two."

The Coast Guard reported another kind of close shave in the foggy summer of 1969 when a vessel identified as a tanker missed the Conception rocks by a scant hundred yards.

Wightman and other experienced navigators have urged the enforcement of rules of the road against tankers. "They all run at full speed. I've never known one to slow down, fog or no fog," Wightman testified.

Yet *International Rules of the Road* prescribes a "moderate speed" in foggy weather. Federal courts have interpreted "moderate speed" as "as much speed as will enable a vessel to stop within half the distance of visibility." But the rule and its interpretation are usually disregarded unless there is an accident, when they are often invoked to establish liability.

GOO has urged that the Coast Guard cite vessels that proceed through the channel breaking international rules and placing the environment under extreme hazard, but the Coast Guard replies that it has no authority to cite vessels for speeding in international water. Asked if tankers do in fact speed, the Coast Guard drily replies that most vessels meet their schedules these days. Thus about seventy-five tankers monthly continue, presumably, to speed through the channel. Their number will almost certainly increase as Alaska oil production increases and Southern California's oil deficit continues.

There is nearly unanimous agreement that a tanker wreck represents a greater threat to the channel's environment than another oil well blowout. A tanker wreck could result in a channel *Torrey Canyon* disaster—perhaps compounded by a smashed, oil-spewing drilling platform or floating rig. Were a huge new supertanker involved, the damage could be colossal.

Accordingly, anti-oil forces are stepping up their fight to ban all commercial shipping from the channel.

An international agreement might be necessary to accomplish such a ban. The United States could do it alone by extending its territorial waters to twelve miles from shore, as many nations have done, thus bringing the waters of the entire channel under federal control. But, ironically, this might cloud the federal government's title to the offshore oil it now claims. California and other states would almost certainly attempt to extend their territorial boundaries to the twelve-mile limit.

The unilateral extension of U.S. sovereignty to include the seabed of the entire continental shelf (but not of the waters over it), undertaken by President Truman in 1945 largely at the behest of the oil industry, has thus raised political and legal questions that need clarification.

23

COMMENTS IN CONCLUSION

WITHOUT THE communications media, the spill might never have become a major issue and its consequences might have been negligible.

At local level, newspapers and radio-television stations provided in-depth reporting that established the facts of the spill beyond limits given by oil company and government spokesmen and helped to define its varied impact. In both news and editorial coverage, the *News-Press* played a vital role. Its crusading leadership in the anti-oil movement crystallized the community's resistance effort. Like *Life, Time,* and *Fortune,* the *News-Press* lost oil company advertising. But it won the respect of its peers as well as of many readers. Its publisher, Stuart S. Taylor, was named 1969 "Publisher of the Year" by the California Press Association for the paper's leadership in the oil-spill controversy.

Regionally and nationally, the media made the spill the catalyst of the environmental movement. California's two leading newspapers, the *Los Angeles Times* and the *San Francisco Chronicle,* supported Santa Barbara's position against government and oil companies. Cliff Carpenter, columnist and editorial director for the Rochester, New York, *Democrat and Chronicle,* was among the first to see that the community's response to the spill might serve as a national example. Local writers helped tell the spill story in magazines of nationwide circulation: Ross Macdonald in *Sports Illustrated,* the biologist Garrett Hardin in the *Saturday Review,* the sociologist Harvey Molotch in *Ramparts.*

The critical period was June, 1969. The rebirth then of the oil-resistance movement, in response to the presidential panel's recommendation for intensified pumping and drilling at Platform A, attracted much thoughtful attention. As the community faced what appeared to be a total and unjust threat to its survival, its economic, ethnic, political, and age-group divisions all but disappeared. Something new began to happen.

Saul Pett, the veteran Associated Press feature writer, led a fresh influx of media representatives. They included Gladwin Hill of the *New York Times,* Morton Mintz of the *Washington Post,* Kemmis Hendrick of the *Christian Science Monitor,* and many more. They filed stories presenting the spill primarily as a social conflict rather than as a technical and environmental disaster.

Television was a powerful factor from the beginning. When viewers saw blue water and white sand smeared with black oil, and birds and people similarly smeared, their adrenalin began to flow. When they thought about what they had seen and heard, many of them decided to act.

Media interest peaked again with the Platform Hillhouse episode in November, when *Newsweek* maintained a writer in residence to cover the community's response to new environmental aggression.

But the catalytic summit occurred at the time of the January 28, 1970, observance of the first anniversary of the spill. *Time* devoted its issue of February 2 almost entirely to environmental matters. The February issue of *Fortune* was entirely devoted to them. Many other magazines and newspapers followed this example, or instituted regular features on the environment, and so did radio-TV broadcasters. The *Fortune* issue was prophetically titled: "The Environment: A National Mission for the Seventies."

The new national mission was nowhere more apparent than among scientists and engineers. On January 28, 1969, it was unfashionable for them to be committed as citizens to solving specific environmental problems. A year later exactly the opposite was true. By January 28, 1971, it was difficult to believe U.S. science and technology had ever been otherwise than concerned about environmental problems. Two years after the spill began, Santa Barbara's Environmental Quality Advisory Board was indicative. Established by law and furnished with a budget, it was an accepted and influential feature of community life. It dealt with such matters as pesticides, marshlands use, and liquid waste treatment, in addition to oil pollution; and citizens awaited—and debated—its recommendations on all important environmental matters.

Los Angeles and a number of other communities had established similar advisory bodies.

Science and technology—widely blamed for the spill—were in the ascendant locally and nationally in quite a new way, one much more intimately associated with individual and community needs.

Santa Barbara's scientists and engineers, Alan A. Allen, Robert Curry, Norman Sanders, Robert Sharp, Alan Eschenroeder, and their colleagues, had helped pioneer this aspect of the environmental revolution.

They and their colleagues were grappling, as the spill continued, with one of the least understood and most ominous factors of the channel controversy: earthquakes.

Dr. Stewart W. Smith of Caltech and Dr. Arthur Sylvester at U.C. Santa Barbara, leading authorities, believe that the possibilities of an earthquake causing offshore oil spills "are of overriding importance." It might damage or collapse a drilling platform, trigger a submarine landslide or ground shift that might cause an oil well or pipeline to leak, create a sea wave that could smash platforms or onshore facilities resulting in a spill. There is a possibility that drilling and withdrawal of oil might trigger an earthquake, or accentuate the effects of one, or that water injected into an oil field to replace withdrawn oil and gas (a common practice) might cause a quake. The key word is "might." Nobody knows for sure.

Sylvester and Smith are mapping the channel area's fault pattern, trying to identify active faults, the nature of the displacement along faults, and the mechanism and rate of strain release. They find that the Platform A fault is part of a major network where quakes have been centering for as long as records exist. However, a quake's epicenter, or subterranean focus, may be several miles from its surface focus, where the shock is most damaging to man. This is because the main shock travels to the surface along the fault where earth slippage occurs. If the fault is angular, the surface effects may focus at a considerable distance from the epicenter.

Platform A is situated directly over an angular fault, about four miles from the epicenter of a 3.0 Richter magnitude quake which occurred a few months before it was erected.

Union Oil engineers have been quoted as saying their platforms are designed to withstand earthquakes up to 7.1 magnitude without damage. But suppose a "giant" earthquake of 7.5 magnitude or greater centered under or near Platform A? Or suppose a "rolling" quake of lesser magnitude, which, by building up ground acceleration, did more surface damage than a "sharp" quake of giant size?

Dr. Alden Loomis, an engineering geologist and geoscientist, has testified that structures within the channel should be designed for quakes of "at least" a Richter magnitude of 7.5. Judging from what Loomis termed "inadequate data available," existing platforms are designed to withstand forces of less than half those generated by a 7.5 quake.

There is no question that the channel is in the earthquake belt, or "ring of fire," that circles the Pacific. In the days before offshore drilling, the Santa Barbara 1925 earthquake centered in the channel. It killed 20 people, did $6 million damage, and sent a sea wave several hundred feet up State Street. A 1941 quake of 6.0 magnitude also centered in the channel. It caused $100,000 damage to buildings in the downtown Santa Barbara area. The unusual "swarm" of 66 small channel quakes during the summer of 1968 damaged onshore structures at Goleta. Though it spared the channel, the rolling Los Angeles earthquake of February, 1971, magnitude 6.6, collapsed freeway overpasses, hospital buildings, and other structures, killed 65 people, caused oil to leak from ruptured pipelines, and did damage estimated at more than $500 million.

Since the Los Angeles quake, experts have revised their ideas of structural safety standards upwards. They remember that the San Francisco earthquake of 1906 was one hundred times more powerful than the recent Los Angeles shock.

Inscrutable forces may thus have the last word in the channel oil controversy. Nobody is waiting with pleasure for it to be spoken. But channel oil development continues.

Oil has never been produced in ocean depths greater than 380 feet, but Humble is proposing to develop its new field near Point Conception at the channel's western end with five platforms in depths of 500 to 700 feet. About sixty wells will be drilled from each platform. The platforms will also service submerged and bottom-situated facilities. The unitized system is designed to produce from eighteen contiguous tracts.

Though the President's Environmental Quality Council has said that the United States is three years away from being able to cope with massive offshore spills, and the President's Panel on Oil Spills has warned that at current rates of offshore production we can expect a major pollution incident somewhere every year, Humble appears confident it can proceed successfully with its "first-time-anywhere" developments, and the Department of Interior has approved its plan in principle though not in detail.

Accentuating the hazard is the fact that much of Humble's production will be at depths of 12,000 to 14,000 feet below the ocean floor, where residual pressures per square inch are three times greater than those encountered during the Platform A blowout.

Santa Barbarans have protested that the channel is once again to be used for dangerous experiments. They furthermore point out that an offshore earthquake of 7.5 magnitude centered not far west of Point Conception in 1927. It may have been located on an active fault that branches into Humble's proposed development. People on shore were thrown from their beds. A concrete highway buckled. A railroad bridge collapsed. A seismic wave resulted that was six feet high when it reached shore and was noticed by ships at sea. Also pointing to the risk of a ship-platform collision, the Santa Barbarans have asked the President's Environmental Quality Council to halt Humble's project on grounds of environmental protection and have asked the federal courts to do likewise. But their protests have been criticized as unrealistic and speculative.

Meanwhile Platforms A, B, and Hillhouse are producing some

75,000 barrels of oil a day. This production is worth about $80 million per year, the federal government taking one-sixth. In addition, the two Phillips platforms in the Carpinteria offshore field are yielding about 3.3 million barrels annually. Total production from the channel's federal leases in 1970 was 24 million barrels of oil and 12 billion cubic feet of gas. These are among the hard facts of channel life.

Politically, the fact is that after nine federal hearings, not one piece of legislation curbing or halting channel oil development has reached the floor of Congress. After nearly as many hearings, none has passed the Legislature, except one aimed at preventing further leasing in state waters, where all promising leases have long since been sold. Yet Rogers C. B. Morton, Hickel's successor as Secretary of the Interior, has indicated support for cancellation of 35 channel leases, including the 20 previously proposed by Hickel plus 13 more located north of San Miguel Island and 2 north of Anacapa. A Congress willing to deny the aerospace industry funds for ecologically hazardous supersonic transport planes might be willing to deny the oil industry rights to channel oil exploitation. But the chances are slim. The oil industry's political power is vastly greater than that of aerospace firms; and despite temporary setbacks in 1969, due largely to the spill, oil defeated attempts to curb its power in 1970. The retention intact of its oil import program was an example of this.

On the other hand, Democratic liberals have established control of the California Legislature. They may be able to muster strength to ban oil operations permanently in the state's channel waters. If the issue were submitted to California voters as a referendum measure, a ban would almost certainly result. This would put heavy pressure on Congress to do likewise. (The referendum issue became a real one when concerned citizens included an offshore drilling ban in an environmental measure scheduled for the 1972 primary election ballot.)

Legally, the U.S. Supreme Court has heard secondary issues partially obscured by technicalities and procedural protocol. In the Hillhouse case it was asked to bypass an appellate court and grant Santa Barbara's appeal directly from a trial-court ruling. Its later refusal to hear the case to enforce public hearings and compel disclosure of information was clouded by interpretations of existing regulations and statutes. Major constitutional issues may reach the court for the first time through Santa Barbara's remaining cases. The question then may clearly be: "Does the Constitution guarantee people a life reasonably free from pollution, a 'livable life'?" But the court will act boldly if it halts channel drilling. The Santa Barbarans are meanwhile contending that the National Environmental Policy Act, if enforced, gives legislative relief to their judicial complaints; but the Department of the Interior and Corps of Engineers say they are not bound by the NEPA insofar as future channel oil development is concerned.

Economically, most non-industry-aligned petroleum economists believe with Walter Mead that it would be wiser to use the channel oil at later date, to put it now into a national energy reserve that would include other major petroleum reserves, while we rely more heavily on imported oil. Dr. Howard Wilcox, a former advisor to the Defense Department and first chairman of Santa Barbara's Environmental Quality Advisory Board, argues that within a few decades world oil supplies will be so depleted that the manufacture of petroleum will become a necessity. He cites the case of oil-poor World War II Germany. By 1944, twelve German plants were using water and oxides of carbon to manufacture 200 million barrels per year of hydrocarbon products. Five hundred such plants would have produced all the petroleum products needed in the world in the 1960s. A thousand might do so in the 1970s. The carbon required could come from freshly harvested vegetation or directly from airborne carbon dioxide. Wilcox thinks we might be wiser to begin manufacturing petroleum now, while saving some natural reserves, than to use up the reserves and then turn to petroleum manufacturing.

While such concepts are in the talking stage, the oil industry claims it must find and produce 87 billion barrels of oil by 1980 to meet increasing U.S. demand. It wants to exploit the estimated 10 billion barrels conveniently located in the Santa Barbara Channel. They represent nearly one-eighth of its 1980 production goal. The industry has invested about $1 billion in the channel. It wants to realize on that investment.

Nevertheless some of the Mead-Wilcox preservation argument is contained in moratorium provisions of the newest channel legislation. Perhaps economically as well as technically it might be wiser to let the channel's oil stay where it is.

In mid-1971 a bill was introduced in Congress to stimulate U.S. oil imports and to put additional domestic oil fields in national reserves. The bill required the President to set aside federal oil-producing lands, such as those in the Santa Barbara Channel, in sufficient amount to insure against a one-year interruption of oil imports. With ninety co-sponsors from oil-consuming states that would benefit from reduced prices caused by imports, the bill was being taken seriously.

Scientifically, it seems clear that the investigation of the spill was inadequate. No systematic study was made of the oil's chemical effects on marine life. No one really knows what happened or will happen to the chemistry of the plankton, fish, shellfish, small bottom-dwelling creatures, and ocean-floor soil and plant life contaminated by the spill. But a growing body of experts believes that if the sophisticated chemical-analysis techniques (including gas chromatography and mass spectrometry) applied to the West Falmouth spill by the Woods Hole scientists had been applied systematically to the Santa Barbara spill, a much more serious picture of ecological damage would be available now. Studies of future spills will probably include chemical analytical techniques as well as the visual and statistical ones relied on at Santa Barbara. In general, more rigorous investigative standards are likely to be applied. To do otherwise may be to engage in a fatal gamble. We are evidently moving toward the principle that if a substance such as oil, or DDT, is found to be hazardous in unknown ways, we should curtail or stop its contamination of the environment until we understand its effects better. But this principle may not be applied to the Santa Barbara Channel before it is too late there.

Philosophically, there are those who believe with the historian Lynn White, Jr., that we cannot reach a solution in the channel, in the United States, or in the world, by applying more science and technology; and there are those who believe with Dr. Lee DuBridge that we can. What we may be moving toward is what James D. Carroll, a professor of political science at Ohio State, calls "participatory technology." According to Carroll, participation in the development, use, and regulation of technology is the new way by which people can increase their understanding of technological processes and of related social problems. Thus participatory technology can be a countervailing force to the technological alienation which threatens us. Santa Barbara's experience bears out Carroll's argument. It tells of a new personalism, a new enlargement of shared consciousness that may characterize the American mind of the future.

As this went to press there were these late developments. On July 30, 1971, the Department of Interior lifted its suspension of exploratory drilling on fourteen leases east and west of the Administration's proposed channel sanctuary. Exploratory drilling had been suspended since April to permit Interior to make an environmental-impact study of such drilling. Lifting of the ban seemed one more step in channel oil development, particularly since the Environmental Protection Agency had recommended against exploratory drilling and against installation of additional platforms in the Dos Cuadras field. EPA urged further consideration of risks resulting from geologic faults and pressures and a further development of plans to control oil spills. It also advised investigation of the air-quality effects of natural gas production and onshore processing plants. It warned against possible damage to marine life, and it suggested that production of oil be increased at existing platforms in the leakage area before new ones were authorized there.

In overriding EPA's objections, Interior seemed to indicate its approval of additional platforms as well as of exploratory drilling, though it deferred a final decision about platforms until a study of their environmental impact could be completed.

Meanwhile events played into the anti-oil citizens' hands. On August 24 a major oil spill polluted the beaches at the Western White House at San Clemente while the President and Mrs. Nixon were vacationing there. It came from the federal government's own Navy which had bungled an offshore ship-refueling operation. Available equipment proved wholly inadequate in controlling the spill. Beaches as far south as the Mexican border were polluted, and the President was forced to forego his usual ocean swim.

New scientific findings also strengthened the anti-oil position.

An oil-soaked murre contemplates death.
DICK SMITH PHOTO.

Dr. Dale Straughan, who conducted the controversial Western Oil and Gas Association-sponsored study of the channel spill's effects, said that Platform A oil was sinking steadily deeper into the ocean floor and that "there does appear to be a decrease in benthic bacteria due to the presence of oil." A U.S. Geological Survey spokesman, Dr. Robert M. Hamilton, said that channel oil production could cause earthquakes. A major quake was expected to strike California soon. Some experts estimated that if it centered at San Francisco, 350,000 human casualties and untold billions in property damage could result. What a giant quake might do to the channel's 100 miles of submerged oil pipelines, drilling platforms, and hundreds of wells was impossible to say.

But on September 2 the Interior Department's study of the environmental impact of the two additional drilling platforms proposed for the Dos Cuadras field was made public. The study found that the platforms would have little adverse effect on the environment and would pose no substantial risk of another spill. A cry of outrage rose throughout Southern California. Coupled with Interior's previous advocacy of the platforms, as expressed by Dr. Pecora and others, the publication of the impact study seemed tantamount to approval of platform installation, though it flew in the face of EPA's finding as well as those of other federal agencies. The Seismology Division of the Department of Commerce, for example, had advised further investigation of earthquake hazard, and the U.S. Fish and Wildlife Service said that expanded channel oil development might result in long-term damage to waterfowl and that sea-mammal rookeries would be severely threatened by spills. The National Park Service had added its weight against the platforms by finding that oil spills would sharply reduce human recreational opportunities in the channel area. Nevertheless, a formal announcement approving the two platforms was expected from Secretary of the Interior Rogers Morton within a few days.

At a meeting at GOO's Santa Barbara headquarters, anti-oil forces mapped a last-ditch fight. If they could not prevent installation of additional platforms in the Dos Cuadras field, where the long struggle had begun, all seemed lost. They planned a demonstration at the emplacement site that would dwarf the one staged against Platform Hillhouse. Once again letters, telegrams, and telephone calls poured toward Washington. The County Board of Supervisors urged the President to stop the emplacement of the platforms. City and county asked the Federal District Court in Los Angeles for an injunction against them. Congressman Teague met with Secretary Morton. Then Teague told the President that he, Nixon, might lose California in the 1972 election if he permitted the platforms to be emplaced.

Amid mounting protests, Democratic Senators Cranston and Tunney made Senate-floor speeches attacking Interior's environmental statement on the platforms and urging the President to rule against them. Senator Muskie, campaigning in California for the Democratic presidential nomination, said his Senate subcommittee would conduct hearings on "the potential threat of oil pollution due to new drilling in the Santa Barbara Channel."

On September 16 the thorny issue of platform installation was handed by Interior to the White House. On the same day, high tides uncovered deep layers of oil left on Santa Barbara beaches by the inundation of nearly three years before. Leakage at Platform A continued, and the slick there was a permanent feature of Santa Barbara's seascape.

On September 20 Morton announced a White House ruling against additional platforms in the Dos Cuadras field. Morton gave as reason "overriding environmental considerations."

Nixon said later that the decision was entirely his own. "It's good to give the secretaries a chance. They take a lot of heat. So I told Morton, 'Rog, you go out there and make the announcement.' But, I, of course, made the decision."

Nixon's decision against the proposed platforms was indeed a landmark one. It showed where the political wind was blowing. Above all, it showed that citizens who worked hard enough and long enough could influence their government decisively. Even though experienced observers cautioned that Nixon's move might be a mere ploy to embarrass the Democrats (the chances of a Democratically controlled Congress passing costly legislation to halt or eliminate channel drilling and at the same time make the President appear as the savior of the channel were not good, these critics argued) the ruling against the platforms was a clear victory for the anti-oil forces. In the tensions of the moment, the fact that one of the platforms would have drained the Carpinteria rather than the Dos Cuadras field was incidental.

Santa Barbara celebrated with a community party at GOO's headquarters. "The fight isn't over," Lois Sidenberg declared. "We've won a battle. But the war goes on." In alliance with Atlantic and Gulf Coast environmental groups and a number of senators and congressmen, GOO was submitting offshore oil planks for inclusion in both major party platforms at the 1972 elections. The planks prohibited offshore oil development in the channel and elsewhere where it posed a pollution threat. GOO was also urging radio-TV networks to include environmental questions when quizzing candidates on interview programs. Network response was enthusiastic. To pay for their own defense effort, GOO members were advocating "tithing to save the environment"—the giving of ten percent of one's income to environmental defense work. At the national level, Dr. Philip Handler, president of the National Academy of Sciences, had estimated the cost of such critically necessary environmental work at about $100 billion annually, or about one-tenth of the gross national product.

On the channel scene the next battle may be a three-way contest between: (1) those supporting the Administration's bill to cancel and buy back thirty-five leases seaward of Santa Barbara, (2) those supporting an extension of this proposal to include a five-year moratorium on oil development throughout the entire channel, and (3) those favoring unhindered channel oil development. Lending urgency is Secretary Morton's statement that unless Congress acts, before the end of its current session, to create a cross-channel sanctuary, he will throw the proposed sanctuary open to oil development. Thus 1972 became the channel's "year of decision."

A secondary battle may be between those calling for the resignation of Dr. Pecora, now Undersecretary of the Interior—and other departmental leaders who like Pecora promulgated Interior's discredited policies toward the channel and toward U.S. offshore oil resources generally—and those still wishing to continue these policies. The Interior Department has in fact been investigated by events.

Santa Barbara suffered massive pollution, but California and the nation entered the era of the environment. In many ways, the spill could not have happened at a better place, at a better time, to make this historic transition possible; and it seemed unimportant that the Platform A oil companies immediately sued to set aside the President's ruling. This time the citizens were on the government's side. Though the President's platform decision was their first clear victory, there were additional grounds for satisfaction. They had sharply curbed channel drilling, had persuaded both Democrats and Republicans to propose spending hundreds of millions to buy back channel leases, had blocked the earlier erection of Platform C (built and ready for emplacement since 1969), had probably saved the immediate offshore environment of the channel islands from despoliation (in mid-1971 a bill passed the State Legislature and was signed by Governor Reagan creating a three-mile-wide marine sanctuary around all the islands); and they had encouraged coastal protection movements in Sacramento, Washington, and throughout the country, while sparking the U.S. environmental revolution and its political coming of age.

APPENDIX

CHRONOLOGY OF THE
SANTA BARBARA OIL SPILL
AND RELATED EVENTS

1969

Jan. 28: Blowout of Well A-21. Ocean floor ruptured. Oil begins leaking into the Santa Barbara Channel.

Feb. 3: Secretary of Interior Walter J. Hickel visits Santa Barbara to inspect the oil spill.

Feb. 4: Oil inundates Santa Barbara's harbor and beaches.

Feb. 7: Senator Edmund S. Muskie visits Santa Barbara to inspect the spill. Well A-21 plugged with cement.

Feb. 12: Leakage of oil through ocean floor discovered to have resumed or continued.

Feb. 23: U.S. Senate Subcommittee on Air and Water Pollution holds hearing in Santa Barbara. New eruption of oil from under Platform A.

Mar. 19: Oil ashore on San Miguel Island threatens seals and sea lions. Oil ashore at various mainland beaches from Pismo to the Mexican border, a distance of more than 200 miles, causes further public indignation against the spill and against pollution generally.

Mar. 21: President Nixon visits Santa Barbara and inspects its polluted beaches.

Apr. 4: Congressman John V. Tunney makes 200-foot dive to ocean floor to inspect oil leak at its source.

Apr. 6: Angry Santa Barbara citizens hold rally at waterfront and march onto Stearns Wharf.

May 10: Approximately 70,000 persons, a number roughly equivalent to the population of Santa Barbara, have signed "get-oil-out-of-the-channel" petitions. Pollution of beaches continues.

June 2: Presidential panel recommends intensive pumping and drilling as best remedy for the continued leakage.

July 30: Bill to ban oil drilling in state waters of Santa Barbara Channel dies in California Legislature's Senate Finance Committee.

Aug. 11: Federal District Court refuses injunction against further drilling.

Nov. 25: While Platform Hillhouse floats upside down off Santa Barbara, the U.S. Supreme Court refuses to enjoin its emplacement.

Dec. 17: So-called "second oil spill" blackens channel beaches at Christmas time and renews public indignation against pollution.

Dec. 30: Nixon signs Tax Reform Bill reducing tax depletion allowance and eliminating "ABC loophole" for oil companies.

1970

Jan. 1: Nixon signs National Environmental Policy Act.

Jan. 28: Commemorating the first anniversary of the oil spill, the first annual Environmental Rights Day observances are held in Santa Barbara, based on the Santa Barbara Declaration of Environmental Rights.

Jan.–Apr.: The Environmental Movement sweeps across the United States and many parts of the world. Nixon and Republicans, and Muskie and Democrats, vie for political leadership in the new movement.

July 21: Hearings are held in Washington on the Nixon Administration's proposal to cancel 20 channel leases and create a cross-channel marine sanctuary.

Aug. 10: President Nixon sends historic first annual environmental report to Congress, as provided by the National Environmental Policy Act. He calls attention to the Santa Barbara spill and related issues.

Nov. 3: Environmental issues and candidates receive mixed treatment by voters in national election. But Santa Barbarans score referendum victory in land-use controversy, a spinoff of the oil-spill controversy.

Dec. 15: Dr. William T. Pecora, director of the U.S. Geological Survey, tells Santa Barbarans that "the die is cast" and they must prepare for more channel oil development.

1971

Jan. 13–14: U.S. Department of Interior conducts hearing at Santa Barbara on new platforms for channel.

Jan. 28: Second anniversary of spill. Dos Cuadras field producing 75,000 barrels of oil per day, worth about $225,000, to stop a leakage estimated at 5 to 10 barrels daily. U.S. Senators Tunney and Cranston and Congressman Teague prepare new legislation to curb and eliminate channel oil development. The new Secretary of the Interior, Rogers C. B. Morton, indicates Nixon Administration support for cancellation of at least 35 leases, representing 50 percent of the total remaining in federal water, and for creation of a cross-channel marine sanctuary.

Sept. 20: President Nixon rules against additional platforms in the Dos Cuadras field.

A LIST OF MAJOR OIL SPILLS

SOURCES: Smithsonian Institution Center for Short-Lived Phenomena, annual reports, 1968, 1969, 1970; Dillingham Corporation, *Systems Study of Oil Spill Cleanup Procedures;* U.S. Department of the Interior, Geological Survey, "Incidents in the Outer Continental Shelf Resulting in Injury and Property or Environmental Damage (1953 to 1/1/71)"; and correspondence.

EVENT	DATE	LOCATION	NATURE	AMOUNT AND TYPE OF SPILL *
Chryssi P. Goulandris Spill	1/17/67	Milford Haven, England	Tanker spilled oil in harbor	1,700–3,500 barrels crude
Torrey Canyon Spill	3/18/67	Seven Stones Reef, England	Grounded tanker broke in two	700,000 barrels Kuwait crude
R. C. Stoner Spill	9/16/67	Wake Island	Grounded tanker broke in two	143,300 barrels mixed aviation and general fuels
West Delta Area Block 73 Field Spill	10/15–27/67	Gulf of Mexico	Dragging anchor caused pipeline leak	160,639 barrels crude
Pegasos Spill	2/8/68	Off Cape Hatteras, N.C.	Tanker hull failed during storm	Undetermined amount Bunker C fuel
Tim Spill	2/18/68	Philadelphia, Pa.	Tank barge sank	Up to 7,000 barrels No. 6 fuel

* 1 barrel = 42 gallons.

EVENT	DATE	LOCATION	NATURE	AMOUNT AND TYPE OF SPILL
Ocean Eagle Spill	3/3/68	San Juan, P.R.	Grounded tanker broke in two	83,400 barrels Leona crude
General Colocotronis Spill	3/7/68	Eleuthera Island, Bahamas	Grounded tanker	21,000–37,700 barrels Venezuelan crude
South Timbalier Area Block 131 Field Spill	3/12/68	Gulf of Mexico	Dragging anchor caused pipeline leak	6,000 barrels crude
Moron Refinery Spill	3/29/68	Venezuela	Oil from refinery spilled through sewers to sea	16,000 barrels crude
Esso Essen Spill	4/29/68	Off South Africa	Tanker struck underwater object rupturing hull	30,000 barrels Arabian crude
Andron Spill	5/68	Off West Africa	Tanker sank, hull leaking oil	117,000 barrels Kuwait crude
World Glory Spill	6/14/68	Off South Africa	Tanker broke in two and sank	322,000 barrels Kuwait crude
Witwater Spill	12/13/68	Cristobal, C.Z.	Tanker broke in two	15,000 barrels mixed bunker and diesel fuel
Waterford Beach Spill	1/18/69	Waterford Beach, Conn.	Grounded oil barge	Unknown quantity No. 6 fuel
Santa Barbara Spill	1/28/69	Santa Barbara Channel	Oil well blowout	79,285 barrels *
Algol Spill	2/9/69	Long Island Sound, N.Y.	Grounded tanker	Up to 4,000 barrels No. 6 fuel
Main Pass Area Block 299 Field Spill	2/11–16/69	Gulf of Mexico	Pipeline leak	7,532 barrels
Dutch Coast Spill	2/16/69	North Sea	Source unknown	1,000 or more barrels
Cook Inlet Spill	3/4/69	Alaska	Tanker struck underwater object, rupturing hull	Unknown quantity of Alaskan crude

* First two years Alan A. Allen estimate; U.S. Geological Survey estimate for same period, 18,000 barrels.

EVENT	DATE	LOCATION	NATURE	AMOUNT AND TYPE OF SPILL
Ship Shoal Spill	3/16/69	Gulf of Mexico	Floating rig shifted in heavy seas, breaking control valve on recently completed well	2,400 barrels 40 gravity crude
Hamilton Trader Spill	4/30/69	Irish Sea	Tanker collided with another vessel	5,000 barrels heavy fuel oil
Robert L. Polling Spill	5/10/69	Portsmouth, N.H.	Tank barge struck bridge abutment	4,700 barrels fuel oil
Benedicte Spill	5/31/69	Baltic Sea	Tanker collided with another vessel	14,000 barrels crude
Weymouth Spill	6/7/69	Weymouth, Mass.	Fuel barge leaked	2,500 barrels No. 2 fuel
Alma Spill	6/16/69	Alma, Wis.	Mississippi River fuel barge ran aground and sprang a leak	950 to 9,500 barrels No. 2 fuel
West Falmouth Spill	9/16/69	West Falmouth, Mass.	Barge *Florida* ran aground	4,100 barrels No. 2 fuel
Keo Spill	11/5/69	Off New Jersey	Tanker broke in two	210,000 barrels No. 4 fuel oil
Seewarren Spill	11/19/69	Seewarren, N.J.	Storage tank collapsed	200,000 barrels crude
British Isles Seabird Mortality	12/69– 2/70	Northeast coast of England	Oil from North Sea	Unknown amount fuel and lubricating oil
Martha's Vineyard Bird Mortality	2/1970	Martha's Vineyard, Mass.	Undetermined	Amount and type unknown
Arrow Spill	2/4/70	Chedabucto Bay, Nova Scotia	Tanker ran aground	36,430 barrels Bunker C
Main Pass Block 41, OCS 0374, Chevron Oil Company Spill	2/2– 3/3/70	Gulf of Mexico	Offshore platform fire, loss of well control	30,500 barrels crude
Delian Apollon Spill	2/13/70	Tampa Bay, Fla.	Tanker ran aground	240 barrels fuel oil

EVENT	DATE	LOCATION	NATURE	AMOUNT AND TYPE OF SPILL
Kodiak Islands Oil Pollution	Feb.-Mar./ 1970	Alaska	Deliberate discharge from tankships	Unknown amount of slop oil and oily ballast
Oceanic Grandeur Spill	3/3/70	Torres Strait, Australia	Tanker struck underwater object, rupturing hull	Unknown amount Indonesian crude
Othello Spill	3/20/70	Sweden	Tankships collided	Between 420,000 and 700,000 barrels Bunker C
Tarut Bay Spill	4/20/70	Saudi Arabia	Pipeline ruptured during storm	100,000 barrels lightweight crude
Polycommander Spill	5/5/70	Western Spain	Tanker ran aground	70,000 barrels lightweight crude
Kasamatsu Maru Spill	10/16/70	Cape Irozaki, Japan	Tanker exploded and sank	8,900 barrels gasoline
Pacific Glory Spill	10/23/70	Isle of Wight, England	Tankships collided	Unknown amount of crude
Schuylkill Spill	11/13/70	Douglasville, Pa.	Retaining walls of sump failed	71,400 barrels crankcase oil
Florida Keys Oil Slick	12/1/70	Key Largo, Florida	Tanker discharge	Unknown amount Bunker C
Jacksonville Oil Slick	12/1/70	Jacksonville, Florida	U.S. Navy offshore disposal program for residue oil	12,000 to 16,000 barrels diesel oil
South Timbalier Block 26 OCS-G1870, Shell Oil Company Spill	12/1/70– 4/16/71	Gulf of Mexico	Offshore platform explosion and fire, wells blowing out of control	53,000 barrels crude

SOURCES

Following is a list of sources used in writing this book. It is not a complete bibliography of the Santa Barbara Oil Spill.*

BOOKS AND ARTICLES

"A Breathing Spell," *Science News,* Vol. LXXXXVII (April 18, 1970), p. 389.

"A California Oil Strike Nobody Wanted," *Life,* Vol. LXVI (February 14, 1969), pp. 30–31.

"A Clash of Gloomy Prophets," *Time,* Vol. LXXXXVII (January 11, 1971), p. 56.

"ACLU Suit Charges Citizens' Rights Violated by Santa Barbara Oil Leak," *Air/Water Pollution Report,* Vol. VII (July 28, 1969), p. 245.

Alexander, Herbert E., and Jones, Caroline D. (eds.). *Political Contributors of $500 or More in 1968.* Princeton: Citizens' Research Foundation, 1971.

———. *Contributions of National-Level Political Committees to Incumbents and Candidates for Public Office, 1968.* Princeton: Citizens' Research Foundation, 1971.

---

* The Oil Spill Information Center at the University of California at Santa Barbara has more than 2,000 different items dealing directly with the Santa Barbara spill and hundreds more dealing with related events.

American Petroleum Institute. "Sudden Fame for a Shy Island," *Petroleum Today*, Vol. X (Fall, 1969), pp. 2–11.

"Another Oil Slick," *Newsweek*, Vol. LXXIII (February 24, 1969), p. 37.

"API's Oil Spill Program," *Chemical and Engineering News*, Vol. XXXXVII (May 19, 1969), p. 11.

Ashkenazy, Irvin. "A Graveyard of Ships," *Westways*, Vol. LXIII (March, 1971), pp. 30–39, 54–55.

Bagnis, R., *et al.* "Problems of Toxicants in Marine Food Products," *Bulletin World Health Organization*, Vol. XXXXII (1970), pp. 69–88.

Baldwin, Malcolm F. "The Santa Barbara Oil Spill," *University of Colorado Law Review*. Vol. XXXXII (May, 1970), pp. 33–76.

———, and Page, James K., Jr. (eds.). *Law and the Environment*, New York: Walker and Co., 1970.

Battan, Louis J. "Climate and Man," *Science*, Vol. CLXVI (October 24, 1969), p. 536.

Bean, Walton. *California: An Interpretive History*. New York: McGraw-Hill Book Co., 1968.

Blumer, Max, *et al.* "A Small Oil Spill," *Environment*, Vol. XIII (March, 1971), pp. 3–12.

Boffey, Philip M. "Congress: Muskie Seeks Committee on Technological Backlash," *Science*, Vol. CLXVII (March 15, 1969), p. 1179.

Brandwein, Paul F. "Needed: An Environmental Bill of Rights," *American Forests*, Vol. LXXVI (April, 1970), pp. 28–31.

"California: The Great Blob," *Newsweek*, Vol. LXXIII (February 17, 1969), p. 31.

Carpenter, Richard A. "Information for Decisions in Environmental Policy," *Science*, Vol. CLXVIII (June 12, 1970), pp. 1316–1322.

———. "How Congress Focuses on the Environment," *Saturday Review*, Vol. LIII (August 1, 1970), p. 43.

"Carrots and Whips," *Time*, Vol. LXXXXVI (July 20, 1970), pp. 66–68.

Carroll, James D. "Participatory Technology," *Science*, Vol. CLXXI (February 19, 1971), pp. 647–653.

Carter, Luther J. "Conservation Law I: Seeking a Breakthrough in the Courts," *Science*, Vol. CLXVI (January 19, 1969), pp. 1487–1491.

———. "DDT: The Critics Attempt to Ban Its Use in Wisconsin," *ibid.*, Vol. CLXIII (February 7, 1969), pp. 548–551.

———. "Offshore Oil: Channel Blowout Points Up Information Gap," *ibid.*, Vol. CLXIV (May 2, 1969), pp. 530–532.

———. "Conservation Law II: Scientists Play a Key Role in Court Suits," *ibid.*, Vol. CLXVI (December 26, 1969), pp. 1601–1606.

————. "Environmental Policy Act: Congress Passes a Landmark Measure—Maybe," *ibid.*, Vol. CLXVII (January 2, 1970), pp. 35–36.

————. "Environmental Teach-In: University of Michigan Meeting Links Concerns about Pollution and 'Upside-Down Society,' " *ibid.*, Vol. CLXVII (March 20, 1970), pp. 1594–1595.

————. "Earth Day: a Fresh Way of Perceiving the Environment," *ibid.*, Vol. CLXVIII (May 1, 1970), pp. 558–559.

————. "The Global Environment: M.I.T. Study Looks for Danger Signs," *ibid.*, Vol. CLXIX (August 14, 1970), pp. 660–662.

————. "New Congress: Election Produces Changes in Key Committee Posts," *ibid.*, Vol. CLXX (November 13, 1970), pp. 715–716.

————. "Department of Interior: Hickel Leaves a Diminished Agency," *ibid.*, Vol. CLXX (December 4, 1970), pp. 1063–1064.

Casey, Harold D. "The Channel Islands," *Oceans*, Vol. I (March, 1969), pp. 69–77.

Chamblin, Jay. "Rumblings from the Deep," *Science News*, Vol. LXXXXVI (September 13, 1969), pp. 213–214.

"Channel Oil Slick Case Filed," *Open Forum*, Vol. XLVI (August, 1969), p. 1.

Clingan, Thomas A., Jr. "Oil Pollution, No Solution?" *United States Naval Institute Proceedings*, Vol. LXXXXV (May, 1969), pp. 63–75.

Coan, Eugene. "Oil Pollution," *Sierra Club Bulletin*, Vol. LVI (March, 1971), pp. 12–16.

Cohn, Victor. "But Who Will Pay the Piper and Will It Be in Time?" *Smithsonian*, Vol. I (May, 1970), pp. 15, 17–21.

Commoner, Barry. *Science and Survival.* New York: The Viking Press, 1966.

Cotton, Steve. "Earth Day—What Happened," *Audubon*, Vol. LXXII (July, 1970), pp. 112–115.

Cowan, Edward. "Oil on the Waters," *The Nation*, Vol. CCVIII (March 10, 1969), pp. 304–307.

Crowe, Beryl L. "The Tragedy of the Commons Revisited," *Science*, Vol. CLXVI (November 28, 1969), pp. 1103–1107.

"Crude on Troubled Waters," *Newsweek*, Vol. LXXV (April 6, 1970), pp. 77–78.

Dedera, Don. "Santa Barbara and Beyond," *Oceans*, Vol. III (May-June, 1970), pp. 18–32.

Demaree, Allan T. "Our Crazy, Costly Life with Oil Quotas," *Fortune*, Vol. LXXIX (June, 1969), pp. 105–107, 175–182.

Dubos, René. *So Human an Animal.* New York: Charles Scribner's Sons, 1968.

DuBridge, Lee A. "Science Serves Society," *Science,* Vol. CLXIV (June 6, 1969), pp. 1137–1139.

Dugger, Ronnie. "Oil and Politics," *The Atlantic,* Vol. CCXXIV (September, 1969), pp. 66–90.

Ebeling, A. W., *et al.* "Santa Barbara Oil Spill: Fishes." Unpublished paper prepared for Santa Barbara Oil Spill Symposium, University of California, Santa Barbara, December 16–18, 1970. *Passim.*

"Eco-Journalism," *Newsweek,* Vol. LXXV (February 1, 1971), pp. 43–44.

"Effects of the Santa Barbara 'Blowout'," *U.S. News and World Report,* Vol. LXX (February 8, 1971), p. 54.

Ehrlich, Paul R., and Holdren, John P. "The Energy Crisis," *Saturday Review,* Vol. LIV (August 7, 1971), pp. 50–51.

Engler, Robert. *The Politics of Oil.* Chicago: The University of Chicago Press, 1961.

"Environment: Tragedy in Oil," *Time,* Vol. LXXXXIII (February 14, 1969), pp. 23–25.

Estes, John E., and Golomb, Berl. "Monitoring Environmental Pollution," *Journal of Remote Sensing,* Vol. I (March-April, 1970), pp. 8–13.

Fisher, James, and Peterson, Roger Tory. *The World of Birds.* Garden City: Doubleday and Co., *c.* 1965.

Fortune. Vol. LXXXX (February, 1970), *passim.*

Foss, R. E. "In the Case of Santa Barbara, Part II: The Implications," *Our Sun,* Vol. XXXIV (Summer, 1969), pp. 16–17.

Frazier, Kendrick. "Earth's Cooling Climate," *Science News,* Vol. LXXXXVI (November 15, 1969), pp. 458–459.

Frome, Michael. "The Story of Conservation Stretches Back to Our Land's Early Inhabitants," *Smithsonian,* Vol. I (March, 1971), pp. 17–27.

Gidney, C. M., Crooks, Benjamin, and Sheridan, Edwin M. *History of Santa Barbara, San Luis Obispo, and Ventura Counties, California.* 2 vols. Chicago: The Lewis Publishing Co., 1917.

Gilluly, Richard. "Taking Polluters to the Courts," *Science News,* Vol. LXXXXVIII (September 26, 1970), pp. 273–274.

Gilmore, Raymond M. "The Gray Whale," *Oceans,* Vol. I (January, 1969), pp. 9–20.

"GM Gets Environmental Panel," *Science,* Vol. CLXXI (March 5, 1971), p. 880.

Goldman, Marshall I. "The Convergence of Environmental Disruption," *Science,* Vol. CLXX (October 2, 1970), pp. 37–42.

"GOO Fishes In," *Newsweek,* Vol. LXXIV (December 8, 1969), p. 100.

Good, Williamson. "Damaging Blowout," *Barron's*, Vol. XXXXIX (December 29, 1969), pp. 11–12.

Graham, Frank, Jr. *Since Silent Spring*. Boston: Houghton Mifflin Co., 1970.

Griffith, Winthrop. "The Isla Vista War—Campus Violence in a Class by Itself," *The New York Times Magazine*, (August 30, 1970), pp. 10–11, 46, 59–65.

"Growing Problem of Oil Spills—Reasons and Remedies," *U.S. News and World Report*, Vol. LXX (February 8, 1971), pp. 52–54.

"Guardian's Polycomplex Helps Mop up Oil Spill Seeping into Santa Barbara Channel," *Chemical and Engineering News*, Vol. XXXXVII (March 17, 1969), pp. 40–42.

Gustaitis, Rasa. "The Political Education of Santa Barbara," *West*, (May 10, 1970), pp. 24–29.

Hamilton, Douglas B., and Meehan, Richard L. "Ground Rupture in the Baldwin Hills," *Science*, Vol. CLXXII (April 23, 1971), pp. 333–344.

Hardin, Garrett. "Finding Lemonade in Santa Barbara's Oil," *Saturday Review*, Vol. LII (May 10, 1969), pp. 18–21.

Harris, L. M., and Ilfrey, W. T. "Drilling in 1,300 Feet of Water—Santa Barbara Channel, California," *Journal of Petroleum Technology*, Vol. XXII (January, 1970), pp. 27–37.

"Helpless Birds, Helpless Technology," *Science News*, Vol. CXXXXV (February 22, 1969), pp. 183–184.

Hickel, Walter J. *Who Owns America?* Englewood Cliffs: Prentice-Hall, Inc., 1971.

"Hickel v. Oil Polluters," *Time*, Vol. LXXXXV (April 13, 1970), p. 49.

History of Southern Santa Barbara County. Summerland: *The Advance-Courier*, 1900.

Holcomb, Robert W. "Oil in the Ecosystem," *Science*, Vol. CLXVI (October 10, 1969), pp. 204–206.

Holden, Constance. "Nixon Offers Large, Mixed Bag on Environment," *Science*, Vol. CLXXI (February 19, 1971), p. 659.

Hoult, David P. (ed). *Oil on the Sea*. New York and London: Plenum Press, 1969.

Huglin, Jinnie. "Diary of a Disaster—The Santa Barbara Oil Spill," *McCall's*, Vol. XCVII (June, 1970), pp. 58–66, 129–130.

"Issue of the Year: The Environment," *Time*, Vol. LXXXXVII (January 4, 1971), pp. 21–22.

Jackson, Henry M. "What Congress Must Now Do to Save the Environment," *Smithsonian*, Vol. I (May, 1970), pp. 14, 16.

Kelly, Frank K. "The Possibilities of Transformation," *Saturday Review*, Vol. LIII (March 7, 1970), pp. 17–19, 66–67.

Klaus, Robert L. "In the Case of Santa Barbara, Part I: The Situation," *Our Sun*, Vol. XXXIV (Summer, 1969), pp. 3–15.

Knoll, Erwin. "The Oil Lobby is Not Depleted," *The New York Times Magazine*, March 8, 1970, pp. 26–27, 103–109.

Kornberg, Warren. "The Last Refuge of Scoundrels," *Science News*, Vol. LXXXXVI (September 27, 1969), p. 261.

"Lawsuits Gush from Oil Disaster," *Business Week*, Vol. XXXIX (April 19, 1969), p. 41.

Ludwig, Harvey F., and Carter, Ralf. "Analytical Characteristics of Oil-Tar Materials on Southern California Beaches," *Journal Water Pollution Control Federation*, Vol. XXXIII (November, 1961), pp. 1123–1139.

McCaull, Julian. "The Black Tide," *Environment*, Vol. XI (November, 1969), pp. 2–16.

McCloskey, Michael. "Editorial," *Sierra Club Bulletin*, Vol. LV (June, 1970), p. 2.

McMillan, Ian I. "Disaster at Santa Barbara," *Defenders of Wildlife News*, Vol. XXXXIV (January-February-March, 1969), pp. 24–26.

———. "Another Look at the Big Slick," *ibid.*, (April-May-June, 1969), pp. 149–153.

Macdonald, Ross. "Life with the Blob," *Sports Illustrated*, Vol. XXX (April 21, 1969), pp. 50–60.

———, and Easton, Robert. "Santa Barbarans Cite an 11th Commandment: 'Thou Shalt Not Abuse the Earth'," *The New York Times Magazine* (October 12, 1969), pp. 32–33, 142–156.

Main, Jeremy. "Meanwhile, Back at the Gas Pump—a Battle for Markets," *Fortune*, Vol. LXXIX (June, 1969), pp. 109–111, 202–211.

Marx, Wesley. *The Frail Ocean*. New York: Ballantine Books, 1969.

———. "How Not to Kill the Ocean," *Audubon*, Vol. LXXI (July, 1969), pp. 27–35.

———. "Oil Spill!" *Sierra Club Bulletin*, Vol. LV (April, 1970), pp. 16–17, 21.

Maxey, David R. "Hickel Watching," *Look*, Vol. XXX (November 4, 1969), pp. 39–41.

Merritt, Vernon. "The Great Oil Slick," *Life*, Vol. LXVI (February 21, 1969), pp. 58–62B.

Meyers, Harold B. "The Fortune Directory of the 500 Largest U.S. Industrial Corporations," *Fortune*, Vol. LXXVII (June 15, 1968), pp. 186–188.

Mitchell, John G. "Good Earth?" *Newsweek*, Vol. LXXIV (July 7, 1969), pp. 57–59.

Molotch, Harvey. "Oil in the Velvet Playground," *Ramparts*, Vol. VIII (November, 1969), pp. 43–51.

Moncrief, Lewis W. "The Cultural Basis for Our Environmental Crisis," *Science*, Vol. CLXX (October 30, 1970), pp. 508–512.

Moore, Lillian. "Rachel Carson's 'Silent Spring'—Its Truth Goes Marching On," *Smithsonian*, Vol. I (July, 1970), pp. 5–9.

Munro, Dick. "Letter from the Publisher," *Sports Illustrated*, Vol. XXXII (January 2, 1970), p. 4.

Neel, James V. "Lessons from a 'Primitive' People," *Science*, Vol. CLXX (November 20, 1970), pp. 815–822.

Nelson, Gaylord, and René Dubos, Margaret Mead, Roderick A. Cameron, Henry Ford II. "Five Who Care," *Look*, Vol. XXXIV (April 21, 1970), pp. 33–41.

O'Hanlon, Thomas. "Fred Hartley and His Well-Oiled Multiplying Machine," *Fortune*, Vol. LXXXV (April, 1967), pp. 156–161, 204–208.

O'Neil, Paul. "Walter Hickel Is an Endangered Species," *Life*, Vol. LXIX (August 28, 1970), pp. 48–56.

O'Neill, Owen H. (ed.). *History of Santa Barbara County*. Santa Barbara: Harold McLean Meier, 1939.

Odum, Eugene P. "The Strategy of Ecosystem Development," *Science*, Vol. CLXIV (April 18, 1969), pp. 262–270.

Offshore, January, 1969–April, 1971, *passim*.

Oil and Gas Journal, December 2, 1968–February 1, 1971, *passim*.

"Oil: Battle Over Special Privilege," *Time*, Vol. LXXXXIII (June 13, 1969), p. 22.

Orleans, Leo A., and Suttmeier, Richard P. "The Mao Ethic and Environmental Quality," *Science*, Vol. CLXX (December 11, 1970), pp. 1173–1176.

Orr, Robert T. "The Gray Whale 'Crisis,'" *Pacific Discovery*, Vol. XXII (November–December, 1969), pp. 1–7.

Pakiser, L. C., *et al.* "Earthquake Prediction and Control," *Science*, Vol. CLXVI (December 19, 1969), pp. 1467–1474.

Pell, Claiborne, Senator. "The Oceans: Man's Last Great Resource," *Saturday Review*, Vol. LII (October 11, 1969), pp. 19–21, 62–63.

Perlman, David. "America the Beautiful?" *Look*, Vol. XXX (November 4, 1969), pp. 25–27.

Petrow, Richard. *In the Wake of the Torrey Canyon*. New York: David McKay Co., Inc., 1968.

"Pollution: Puffery or Progress?" *Newsweek*, Vol. LXXVI (December 28, 1970), pp. 49–51.

Powell, Lawrence Clark. "Upton Sinclair's *Oil!*" *Westways*, Vol. LXII (September, 1970), pp. 14–17, 58–59.

"Practical Answers to Pollution," *Nation's Business*, Vol. LIX (January, 1971), pp. 18–20.

Ritchie-Calder, Peter. "Mortgaging the Old Homestead," *Sports Illustrated*, Vol. XXXII (January 2, 1970), 45–51.

Roberts, E. F. "Plead the Ninth Amendment," *Natural History*, Vol. LXXIX (August–September, 1970), pp. 18–25.

Rogin, Gilbert. "All He Wants to Save Is the World," *Sports Illustrated*, Vol. XXX (February 3, 1969), pp. 24–29.

"Santa Barbara: Post-Spill," *Chemical Engineering*, (May 19, 1969), pp. 100–103.

Sax, Joseph L. *Defending the Environment: A Strategy for Citizen Action*. New York: Alfred A. Knopf, 1971.

Scientific American, Vol. CCXXI (September, 1969), *passim*.

Shearer, Lloyd. "The Nation's Worst Scandal," *Parade*, (March 21, 1971), pp. 4–5.

Shephard, Paul, and McKinley, Daniel (eds.). *The Subversive Science*. Boston: Houghton Mifflin Co., 1969.

Shepherd, Jack. "The Fight to Save America Starts Now," *Look*, Vol. XXXIV (April 21, 1970), pp. 23–31.

Sinclair, Upton. *Oil!* New York: Grossett & Dunlap, 1927.

Smith, J. E. (ed.). *"Torrey Canyon" Pollution and Marine Life*. Cambridge: Cambridge University Press, 1968.

Snell, David. "Iridescent Gift of Death," *Life*, Vol. LXVI (June 13, 1969), pp. 22–27.

Southwick, Thomas P. "Westinghouse's Environment School: Combining Business with Ecology," *Science*, Vol. CLXIX (July 31, 1970), pp. 453–454.

"Soviet Union: Sniffing Trouble," *Newsweek*, Vol. LXXV (May 11, 1970), pp. 62–63.

Spilhaus, Athelstan. "The Next Industrial Revolution," *Science*, Vol. CLXVII (March 27, 1970), p. 1673.

Stock, Robert W. "Saving the World the Ecologist's Way," *The New York Times Magazine*, October 5, 1969, pp. 33, 132–136.

Swift, W. H., *et al.* "Oil Spillage Prevention, Control, and Restoration —State of the Art and Research Needs," *Journal Water Pollution Control Federation*, Vol. XXXXI (March, 1969), pp. 392–411.

Sylvester, Arthur G. "Fluid Pressure Variations and Prediction of Shallow Earthquakes," *Science*, Vol. CLXIX (September 18, 1970), pp. 1231–1232.

———. Smith, Stewart W., and Scholz, C. H. "Earthquake Swarm in the Santa Barbara Channel, California, 1968," *Bulletin of the Seismological Society of America*, Vol. LX (August, 1970), pp. 1047–1060.

Taylor, Frank J., and Welty, Earl M. *Black Bonanza*. New York: McGraw-Hill Book Co., 1950.

"The Biggest Mistake Made at Santa Barbara Was Waiting," *Ocean Science News*, Vol. XI (February 7, 1969), pp. 1–2.

"The Bug as Garbage Man," *Time*, Vol. LXXXXVI (December 21, 1970), p. 36.

"The Dead Channel," *Time*, Vol. LXXXXIII (February 21, 1969), p. 21.

"The Environment: Not So Deadly," *Time*, Vol. LXXXXIII (June 13, 1969), p. 21.

"The Firing of a Fighter," *Time*, Vol. LXXXXVI (December 7, 1970), pp. 21–22.

"The GOO Story," *Newsweek*, Vol. LXIII (June 16, 1969), pp. 60–61.

"The Great Oil Hunt," *Newsweek*, Vol. LXXIV (September 22, 1969), pp. 80–90.

"The Long and Short of the Oil Spills," *Science News*, Vol. LXXXXVII (March 14, 1970), pp. 263–264.

"The Lush Era of the Tanker Tycoons," *Newsweek*, Vol. LXXVI (October 19, 1970), pp. 94–96.

"The Rhetoric of Ecology," *Life*, Vol. LXVIII (March 6, 1970), p. 36.

Tugendhat, Christopher. *Oil: The Biggest Business*. New York: G. P. Putnam's Sons, 1968.

Wagar, J. Alan. "Growth Versus the Quality of Life," *Science*, Vol. CLXVIII (June 5, 1970), pp. 1179–1184.

Walsh, John. "Pollution: The Wake of the 'Torrey Canyon,' " *Science*, Vol. CLX (April 12, 1968), pp. 167–169.

———. "Universities: Industry Links Raise Conflict of Interest Issue," *ibid.*, Vol. CLXIV (April 25, 1969), pp. 411–412.

Waugh, John. "That Was the Ooze That Was," *West*, (September 21, 1969), pp. 10–16.

"We Just Spent Five Days Slogging It Out in Santa Barbara . . ." *Ocean Science News*, Vol. XI (February 14, 1969), pp. 1–2.

Weaver, Donald W. "A Personal Perspective on the Santa Barbara Controversy," *Offshore*, Vol. XXXIII (November, 1970), pp. 30–32.

Weinberg, Alvin M. "In Defense of Science," *Science*, Vol. CLXVII (January 9, 1970), pp. 141–145.

Welty, Earl M., and Taylor, Frank J. *The 76 Bonanza*. Menlo Park: Lane Magazine and Book Co., 1966.

Wheeler, Harvey. "Bringing Science Under the Law," *The Center Magazine*, Vol. II (March, 1969), pp. 59–67.

White, Gerald T. *Formative Years in the Far West: A History of Standard Oil Company of California and Predecessors Through 1919*. New York: Appleton-Century-Crofts, 1962.

Wirin, A. L., and Levine, Marvin. "Chronology of a Cross-Country Campaign," *Open Forum*, Vol. XLVI (December, 1969), p. 3.

Young, Gordon, and Blair, James P. "Pollution: Threat to Man's Only Home," *National Geographic*, Vol. CXXXVIII (December, 1970), pp. 738–780.

Zeldin, Marvin. "Audubon Black Paper #1—Oil Pollution," *Audubon*, Vol. LXXIII (May, 1971), pp. 99–119.

DOCUMENTS

Allen, Alan A., and Schlueter, Roger S. "Estimates of Surface Pollution Resulting from Submarine Oil Seeps at Platform A and Coal Oil Point." Unpublished technical memorandum prepared for County of Santa Barbara, 1969. *Passim*.

Battelle Memorial Institute, Pacific Northwest Laboratories. *Review of the Santa Barbara Channel Oil Pollution Incident*. (Research report to Department of Interior and Department of Transportation.) Washington, D.C.: Department of the Interior, 1969.

Blumer, M. "Comments on the Report by Dr. Dale Straughan, 'Biological and Oceanographic Survey of the Santa Barbara Channel Oil Spill, 1969–1970,' Vols. 1 and 2." Unpublished letter report to Maine Environmental Improvement Commission, Woods Hole Oceanographic Institution, March 29, 1971. *Passim*.

———, et al. *The West Falmouth Oil Spill: Persistence of the Pollution Eight Months After the Accident*. Technical Report, Ref. No. 70–44. Woods Hole Oceanographic Institution, Woods Hole, Mass.: 1970.

Brown, Lieutenant George H., III. "The Santa Barbara Channel Oil Pollution Incident, January, 1969: On-Scene Commander's Report." Unpublished report, U.S. Coast Guard Group, Santa Barbara, 1969. *Passim*.

Cabinet Task Force on Oil Import Control. *The Oil Import Question*. Washington, D.C.: Government Printing Office, 1970.

California Legislature. *Santa Barbara ' Offshore Oil Problems: Joint Hearing, Senate Committee on Governmental Efficiency and Senate Committee on Natural Resources, Tuesday, February 18, 1969.* Sacramento: Senate Governmental Efficiency Committee, 1969.

City of Santa Barbara. "Report on Offshore Drilling Incident of Santa Barbara Channel." Unpublished report on Santa Barbara Oil Spill from January 29 to June 11, 1969. *Passim.*

City of Santa Barbara, Environmental Quality Advisory Board. *Panel Discussion of U.S. Geological Survey Professional Paper 679.* Santa Barbara: 1970.

——. *Report of Activities, July, 1969 Through December, 1970.* Santa Barbara: 1971. *Evaluation of the USGS Environmental Impact Statement (Draft) of February 23, 1971.* Santa Barbara: 1971.

Clyde, George H. Unpublished statement prepared for State Senate Natural Resources and Governmental Efficiency Committees, Sacramento, 1969. *Passim.*

Connell, J. H. "Submission to the Australian Royal Commission on Oil Exploitation on the Great Barrier Reef: A Review of Straughan, D., 1971. *Biological and Oceanographic Survey of the Santa Barbara Channel Oil Spill I. Biology and Bacteriology.* Allan Hancock Foundation, University of Southern California." Unpublished report, University of California at Santa Barbara, 1971. *Passim.*

County of Santa Barbara, Oil Well Inspection Department. *Offshore-Onshore Petroleum Study, Santa Barbara Channel. Phase I: Effects of Federal Leasing, Outer Continental Shelf (Preliminary Report), November 15, 1967.* Santa Maria, 1967.

Crossley Surveys, Inc. *Oil Spill Control Survey for Onshore and Offshore Facilities.* (Prepared for the Committee for Air and Water Conservation of the American Petroleum Institute.) New York: 1970.

Dillingham Corporation. *Systems Study of Oil Spill Cleanup Procedures.* 2 vols. (American Petroleum Institute Publ. No. 4024). La Jolla, Calif., 1970.

Ellrodt, A. Gray. "The Santa Barbara Oil Spill." Unpublished A.B. degree requirement paper, Princeton University, 1970. *Passim.*

Executive Office of the President, Council on Environmental Quality. *Environmental Quality: The First Annual Report of the Council on Environmental Quality, together with the President's Message to Congress.* Washington, D.C.: Government Printing Office, 1970.

Executive Office of the President, Office of Emergency Preparedness. Unpublished letter report of the participation of the O.E.P., Region 7, in the Santa Barbara oil spill, Federal Regional Center, Santa Rosa, Calif., 1969. *Passim.*

Executive Office of the President, Office of Science and Technology. *Report of Special Panel on the Future of the Union Oil Lease.* Washington, D.C.: Office of Science and Technology, 1969.

Ferry, W. H. "Statement to U.S. Senate Subcommittee on Internal Affairs, Washington, D.C., April 24, 1969." Unpublished manuscript copy, Santa Barbara, Center for the Study of Democratic Institutions, 1969. *Passim.*

Halstead, Bruce. *Toxicity of Marine Organisms Caused by Pollutants.* (Paper prepared for United Nations Technical Conference on Marine Pollution and Its Effects on Living Resources and Fishing, Rome, Italy, December 9–18, 1970.) Colton, California: World Life Research Institute, 1970.

Kolpack, Ronald L. (ed.). *Biological and Oceanographical Survey of the Santa Barbara Channel Oil Spill, 1969–1970: Volume II, Physical, Chemical and Geological Studies.* Los Angeles: Allan Hancock Foundation, University of Southern California, 1971.

Library of Congress, Legislative Reference Service. *Blowout in Santa Barbara Channel: Background and Chronology.* Washington, D.C.: Library of Congress, 1970.

———. *Oil Pollution: Selected References, July 1969–1970.* (Revised Sept. 8, 1970.) Washington, D.C.: Library of Congress, 1970.

———. *The Economy, Energy, and the Environment: A Background Study Prepared for the Joint Economic Committee, Congress of the United States.* Washington, D.C.: Government Printing Office, 1970.

McKee, Jack Edward. *Report on Oily Substances and Their Effects on the Beneficial Uses of Water.* Publication No. 16. Sacramento: State Water Pollution Control Board, 1956.

Mead, Walter J., and Sorensen, Philip E. "The Principal External Costs and Benefits of Marine Mineral Recovery." Unpublished paper prepared for the Offshore Technology Conference, Houston, Texas, April 23, 1970. *Passim.*

———."A National Defense Petroleum Reserve Alternative to Oil Import Quotas." Unpublished paper prepared for the Western Economic Association Annual Meeting, Davis, California, August 27–28, 1970. *Passim.*

———. "The Economic Cost of the Santa Barbara Oil Spill." Unpublished paper prepared for the Santa Barbara Oil Symposium, University of California, Santa Barbara, December 16–18, 1970. *Passim.*

Miller, Alan S., and Farnham, Phil. *The Ecology and Politics Manual.* San Francisco: Bay Area Radical Education Project, 1970.

National Oil and Hazardous Materials Pollution Contingency Plan. Washington, D.C.: Council on Environmental Quality, 1970.

Neushul, Michael. *Santa Barbara Oil Pollution, 1969: Final Report Dealing with the Early Stages of the Santa Barbara Oil Spill.* Washington, D.C.: The Federal Water Pollution Control Administration, 1970.

Peterson, R. S., and Le Boeuf, B. J. "Report of an Expedition to San Miguel Island, 25–28 March, 1969." Unpublished report, University of California, Santa Cruz, 1969. *Passim.*

Reinhart, Philip W. *Oil Seepage Potentialities of Dos Cuadras Oil Field.* Santa Barbara: City of Santa Barbara, 1970.

Report of the Santa Barbara Citizens Commission on Civil Disorders. Santa Barbara: 1970.

Santa Barbara Channel Oil Advisory Committee. Unpublished minutes and reference material, City of Santa Barbara, 1968.

Santa Barbara Oil Spill Panel. *The Oil Spill Problem.* (First Report of the President's Panel on Oil Spills.) Washington, D.C.: Government Printing Office, 1969.

———. *Offshore Mineral Resources: A Challenge and an Opportunity* (Second Report of the President's Panel on Oil Spills.) Washington, D.C.: Government Printing Office. 1969.

State of California, California Disaster Office. Unpublished letter stating "Chronology of pertinent Disaster Office actions," Sacramento, 1969. *Passim.*

State of California, Central Coast Regional Water Quality Control Board. "Role of Regional Board and Staff in Santa Barbara Oil Spill and Comments Regarding the Operations." Unpublished letter, Sacramento, 1969. *Passim.*

State of California, Department of Conservation. "Oil Pollution Incident, Santa Barbara Channel: Summary of Department Activities." Unpublished Summary, Sacramento, 1969. *Passim.*

State of California, Department of Fish and Game. *Progress Report on Wildlife Affected by the Santa Barbara Channel Oil Spill, January 28–March 31, 1969.* Sacramento: Department of Fish and Game, 1969.

———. *Santa Barbara Oil Leak: Interim Report.* Sacramento: Department of Fish and Game, 1969.

———. *Second Progress Report on Wildlife Affected by the Santa Barbara Channel Oil Spill, April 1–May 31, 1969.* Sacramento: Department of Fish and Game, 1969.

———. Unpublished summary of the "Department of Fish and Game's participation in the recent oil spill incident in the Santa Barbara Channel," Sacramento, 1969. *Passim.*

State of California, Resources Agency. *Joint Report of the Resources Agency and State Lands Commission.* (Requested in House Resolution 77 of the 1969 Regular Session, California Legislature.) Sacramento: Resources Agency, 1969.

———. *Report of the Ad Hoc Committee, State Regulations and Practices, Oil and Gas Operations and Oil Pollution, June 18, 1969.* (Includes proposed California Oil Spill Disaster Contingency Plan.) Sacramento: Resources Agency, 1969.

Straughan, Dale (comp.). *Biological and Oceanographical Survey of the Santa Barbara Channel Oil Spill, 1969–1970: Volume I, Biology and Bacteriology.* Los Angeles: Allan Hancock Foundation, University of Southern California, 1971.

The Committee of Scientists on the Scientific and Technological Aspects of the Torrey Canyon Disaster. *The Torrey Canyon.* London: Her Majesty's Stationery Office, 1967.

The Environmental Law Digest. Washington, D.C.: The Environmental Law Institute, 1970.

The Santa Barbara Declaration of Environmental Rights. Santa Barbara: The January 28 Committee, 1970.

Turner, Charles H., Carlisle, John G., Jr., and Ebert, Earl E. *Offshore Oil Drilling: Its Effects Upon the Marine Environment.* Sacramento: California Department of Fish and Game, 1962.

Union Oil Company of California. Special and quarterly reports to stockholders and employees, 1969–1971. *Passim.*

———. "Santa Barbara Is Alive and Well in California!" *Seventy-Six.* Vol. XIII (July-August, 1969), pp. 10–16.

———. "A Visit to San Miguel Island," *ibid.,* pp. 18–23.

———. "Halting the Oil Seepage," *ibid.,* pp. 24–25.

———. *1970 Annual Report.* Los Angeles: 1971.

University of Southern California Sanitary Engineering Research Laboratory, and United States Public Health Service Robert A. Taft Sanitary Engineering Center. *Determination of the Quantity of Oily Substances on Beaches and in Nearshore Waters and Characterization of Coastal Oil Pollution by Submarine Seeps.* Publication No. 21. Sacramento: State Water Pollution Control Board, 1959.

U.S. Coast Guard. *Local Notice to Mariners.* Long Beach: Eleventh Coast Guard District. November 19, 1969.

———. *Local Notice to Mariners.* Long Beach: Eleventh Coast Guard District, January 4, 1971.

U.S. Comptroller General. *Investigation of the Handling and Control of Petroleum Products in Southeast Asia.* Washington, D.C.: General Accounting Office, 1970.

U.S. Congress. *Governmental Intervention in the Market Mechanism: Hearing Before the Subcommittee on Antitrust and Monopoly of the Committee on the Judiciary, United States Senate, Ninety-First Congress, First Session (S. Res. 40) The Petroleum Industry, Part I, Economists' Views, March 11, 12, 24–26, and April 1 and 2, 1969.* Washington, D.C.: Government Printing Office, 1969.

——. *Interior Nomination: Hearings Before the Committee on Interior and Insular Affairs, United States Senate, Ninety-First Congress, First Session, on the Nomination of Governor Walter J. Hickel of Alaska to be Secretary of the Interior, Part 1: January 15, 16, 17, and 18, 1969; Part 2: January 18 and 20, 1969.* Washington, D.C.: Government Printing Office, 1969.

——. *National Environmental Policy. Hearing before the Committee on Interior and Insular Affairs, United States Senate, Ninety-First Congress, First Session, on . . . Bills to Authorize the Secretary of the Interior to Conduct Investigations, Studies, Surveys, and Research Relating to the Nation's Ecological Systems, Natural Resources, and Environmental Quality, and to Establish a Council on Environmental Quality, April 16, 1969.* Washington, D.C.: Government Printing Office, 1969.

——. *National Environmental Policy Act of 1969.* Washington, D.C.: Government Printing Office, 1970.

——. *Oil Pollution: Hearings Before the Committee on Merchant Marine and Fisheries, House of Representatives, Ninety-First Congress, First Session, on . . . Bills to Amend the Oil Pollution Act of 1924 . . . and for Other Purposes, February 25, 27, March 11–13, 18, 26–28, April 1, 1969.* Serial No. 91-4. Washington, D.C.: Government Printing Office, 1969.

——. *Oil Spillage—Santa Barbara, Calif.: Hearing Before the Subcommittee on Flood Control and Subcommittee on Rivers and Harbors of the Committee on Public Works, House of Representatives, Ninety-First Congress, First Session, February 14, 1969.* Washington, D.C.: Government Printing Office, 1969.

——. *Santa Barbara Channel Leases, California: Hearings Before the Subcommittee on Mines and Mining of the Committee on Interior and Insular Affairs, House of Representatives, Ninety-First Congress, Second Session, on . . . Bills to Terminate . . . Certain Leases . . . and for Other Purposes . . . September 14–15, 1970.* Serial No. 91-34. Washington, D.C.: Government Printing Office, 1970.

———. *Santa Barbara Oil Pollution: Hearings Before the Subcommittee on Minerals, Materials, and Fuels of the Committee on Interior and Insular Affairs, United States Senate, Ninety-First Congress, Second Session, on Santa Barbara Offshore Oil. Leasing Bills and Creating Marine Sanctuaries, March 13 and 14, 1970, Santa Barbara, Calif.* Washington, D.C.: Government Printing Office, 1970.

———. *Santa Barbara Oil Pollution: Hearings Before the Subcommittee on Minerals, Materials, and Fuels of the Committee on Interior and Insular Affairs, United States Senate, Ninety-First Congress, Second Session, on Santa Barbara Offshore Oil Leasing Bills and Creating Marine Sanctuaries, July 21–22, 1970, Part 2.* Washington, D.C.: Government Printing Office, 1970.

———. *Small Business Act.* Washington, D.C.: Government Printing Office, 1970.

———. *The Santa Barbara Oil Spill: Hearings Before the Subcommittee on Minerals, Materials, and Fuels of the Committee on Interior and Insular Affairs, United States Senate, Ninety-First Congress, First Session, on a Bill to Direct the Secretary of the Interior to Take Certain Actions . . . with Respect to Drilling and Oil Production . . . Under Leases Issued Pursuant to the Outer Continental Shelf Lands Act, May 19–20, 1969.* Washington, D.C.: Government Printing Office, 1969.

———. *Water Pollution—1969 (Part 2): Hearings Before the Subcommittee on Air and Water Pollution of the Committee on Public Works, United States Senate, Ninety-First Congress, First Session, on Bills to Amend the Federal Water Pollution Control Act . . . and Related Matters Pertaining to the Prevention and Control of Water Pollution, February 5 and 6, 1969, Washington, D.C.* Serial No. 91–2. Washington, D.C.: Government Printing Office, 1969.

———. *Water Pollution—1969 (Part 3): Hearings Before the Subcommittee on Air and Water Pollution of the Committee on Public Works, United States Senate, Ninety-First Congress, First Session, on Bills to Amend the Federal Water Pollution Control Act . . . and Related Matters Pertaining to the Prevention and Control of Water Pollution, February 24 and 25, 1969, Santa Barbara, Calif.* Serial No. 91–2. Washington, D.C.: Government Printing Office, 1969.

———. *Water Pollution—1969 (Part 4): Hearings Before the Subcommittee on Air and Water Pollution of the Committee on Public Works, United States Senate, Ninety-First Congress, First Session, on . . . Bills to Amend the Federal Water Pollution Control Act . . . and Related Matter Pertaining to . . . Control of Water Pollution,*

February 27–28, March 3, 10, May 20, 23, June 4, 1969. Serial No. 91–2. Washington, D.C.: Government Printing Office, 1969.

———. *Water Quality Improvement Act of 1970,* Washington, D.C.: Government Printing Office, 1970.

U.S. Department of the Army, Los Angeles District, Corps of Engineers. "Summary—Corps of Engineers." Unpublished summary of Corps of Engineers' activities related to the Santa Barbara Oil Spill, Los Angeles, 1969. *Passim.*

U.S. Department of Commerce, Environmental Science Service Administration, Weather Bureau. "Santa Barbara Oil Spill Incident." Unpublished report, Weather Bureau Forecasting Office, Los Angeles, 1969. *Passim.*

U.S. Department of the Interior. "Hearing Conducted in Santa Barbara, California, January 13–14, 1971, in Regard to Platform C [and Platform Henry] . . ." 2 vols. Unpublished hearing record, Oil Spill Information Center, University of California at Santa Barbara, 1971. *Passim.*

———. *National Multiagency Oil and Hazardous Materials Contingency Plan.* Washington, D.C.: Department of the Interior, 1968.

———. News Releases, February, 1969–July, 1970. *Passim.*

———. *Notices to Lessees and Operators of Federal Oil and Gas Leases in the Outer Continental Shelf, Pacific Region.* (OCS Order Nos. 1 through 10, Pacific Coast), Washington, D.C.: Department of the Interior, 1970.

———. "Permanent Effects of the Santa Barbara Oil Spill." News release, August 17, 1970.

———. *San Miguel Island: Marine Mammals as Related to Oil Spill in Santa Barbara Channel.* Washington, D.C.: Department of the Interior, 1969.

———. *United States Petroleum Through 1980.* Washington, D.C.: Department of the Interior, 1968.

U.S. Department of the Interior, Bureau of Sport Fisheries and Wildlife. "Special Report, Santa Barbara Channel Oil Pollution Incident, January 28, 1969–April 1, 1969." Unpublished letter report dated May 9, 1969.

U.S. Department of the Interior, Fish and Wildlife Service. "Cruise Report: R/V David Starr Jordan, Cruise 33." Unpublished report dated February 14, 1969. Fishery-Oceanography Center, La Jolla, California, 1969. *Passim.*

U.S. Department of the Interior, Geological Survey. *Final Environmental Statement, Exploratory Drilling Operations on Federal Oil and Gas Leases Issued Under the Outer Continental Shelf Lands*

Act, Santa Barbara Channel Area. Washington, D.C.: Department of the Interior, 1971.

———. *Final Environmental Statement, Proposed Installation of Platforms C and Henry on Federal Oil and Gas Leases OCS-P 0241 and 0240 Issued under the Outer Continental Shelf Lands Act, Santa Barbara Channel Area.* Washington, D.C.: Department of the Interior, 1971.

———. "First Field Report on Union Oil Co., Lease OCS-P 0241, Platform A, Well No. 21." Unpublished report dated February 4, 1969. Geological Survey, Los Angeles, 1969. *Passim.*

———. "Second Field Report on Union Oil Co., Lease OCS-P 0241, Platform A, Well No. 21." Unpublished report dated February 9, 1969. Geological Survey, Los Angeles, 1969. *Passim.*

U.S. Department of the Navy, Naval Air Station, Point Mugu. "Chronological Report of Santa Barbara Oil Pollution Incident." Unpublished letter report, Point Mugu, Calif., 1969. *Passim.*

U.S. Environmental Protection Agency. "Comments on Draft Statement on Exploratory Drilling Operations, Santa Barbara Channel." Unpublished letter report dated June 25, 1971. Environmental Protection Agency, Washington, 1971. *Passim.*

———. *EPA Suggests Revisions in Santa Barbara Impact Statement.* News release, July 23, 1971. Washington, D.C.: Environmental Protection Agency, 1971.

U.S. Naval Construction Battalion Center. "CBC, Port Hueneme, Chronology of Participation in Oil Pollution Incident, Santa Barbara Channel." Unpublished letter report, Port Hueneme, California, 1969. *Passim.*

U.S. Secretary of the Interior, and U.S. Secretary of Transportation. *A Report on Pollution of the Nation's Waters by Oil and Other Hazardous Substances.* Washington, D.C.: Government Printing Office, 1968.

Vedder, J. G., *et al. Geology, Petroleum Development, and Seismicity of the Santa Barbara Channel Region, California.* (Geological Survey Professional Paper 679.) Washington, D.C.: Government Printing Office, 1969.

Ventura Port District. "Detailed Chronological Summary of the Events and Actions Occurring on Scene of the Ventura Marina Oil Pollution Incident." Unpublished report, Ventura, California, 1969. *Passim.*

Walmsley, David J. "Oil Pollution Problems Arising out of Exploitation of the Continental Shelf: The Santa Barbara Disaster." Unpublished study, Harvard Law School, 1969. *Passim.*

Western Oil and Gas Association. "Rules and Procedures of the Santa

Barbara Oil Control Coordination Committee." Unpublished draft of new rules and procedures, Los Angeles, 1969. *Passim.*

Wilcox, Howard A. "The Impact of the Santa Barbara Oil Blowout of January, 1969: Some Fundamental Aspects of the Struggle for a High-Quality Environment." Unpublished paper prepared for the Santa Barbara Oil Spill Symposium, University of California at Santa Barbara, December 16–18, 1970. *Passim.*

NEWSPAPERS

Baltimore Sun, Christian Science Monitor, Los Angeles Times, National Observer, New York Times, San Francisco Chronicle, San Francisco Examiner, Santa Barbara Independent, Santa Barbara News-Press, Summerland Advance-Courier, Ventura Star-Free Press, Wall Street Journal, Washington Post.

PERSONAL CORRESPONDENCE AND/OR INTERVIEWS
(between the author and the following except as noted)

Alan A. Allen; American Association for the Advancement of Science; G. Ray Arnett; J. A. Baker; Helen Delich Bentley; Harold Beveridge; James Bottoms; William Botwright; George H. Brown, III; John C. Calhoun, Jr.; California Institute of Technology; Joe J. Callahan; Clark T. Cameron; George Castagnola; Pearl Chase; Gary Clark; George Clyde; Joseph H. Connell; Richard Crane; Alan Cranston; Robert R. Curry; Lee A. DuBridge; Leon Durden; A. W. Ebeling; Frederick Eissler; Enjay Chemical Company; Executive Office of the President, Council on Environmental Quality; Executive Office of the President, Office of Science and Technology; Federal Water Pollution Control Administration; Gerald S. Firestone; Fishermen's Cooperative Association of San Pedro, California; Daniel G. Grant; Guardian Chemical Corporation; Bruce Halstead; Murray F. Hawkins, Jr.; Christian A. Herter, Jr.; Walter J. Hickel; Dennis Hogle; Robert W. Holmes; Humble Oil and Refining Company; Henry M. Jackson; Hamilton M. Johnson; Tom Kleveland; Robert J. Lagomarsino; B.J. Le Boeuf; Marvin Levine; N. B. Livermore, Jr.; William Lorman; W. Don MacGillivray; Ross A. McClintock; Clifford Matthews; D. W. May; Walter J. Mead; George Murphy; Edmund S. Muskie; National Academy of Engineering; National Academy of Sciences; National Research Council; National Science Foundation; Gaylord Nelson; Michael Neushul; Charles A. O'Brien; James J. Oppen; Robert T. Orr; Joy Parkinson; Pauley Petroleum,

Inc.; Charles Paulsen; Peter Bawden Drilling, Inc.; Victor Peacock; W. T. Pecora; C. G. Petrie; Larry Pidgeon; William Proxmire; Radio Station KIST; Radio Station KDB; Red Adair, Inc.; Philip W. Reinhart; William R. ("Bill") Robinson (pseud.); Santa Barbara Chamber of Commerce; Donald R. Sathre; Carl H. Savit; Robert C. Sharp; Shell Oil Company; Lois Sidenberg; Richard J. Smith; D. W. Solanas; Robert H. Sollen; Standard Oil Company of New Jersey; State of California, Department of Fish and Game; State of California, Department of Justice; State of California, State Lands Commission; Marvin Stuart; Dale Straughan; Arthur G. Sylvester; Stuart S. Taylor; Charles M. Teague; Television Station KEYT; Vern W. Tenney; The Conservation Foundation; Stanley T. Tomlinson; John V. Tunney; John V. Tunney to Wayne Aspinall, April 21, 1969 (letter); Union Oil Company of California; University of California; University of Southern California; U. S. Coast Guard Eleventh District Headquarters; U.S. Department of the Interior; U.S. Department of State, Bureau of International Scientific and Technological Affairs; U.S. Department of the Navy, Pacific Missile Range, Point Mugu, California; Paul Veblen; Clarence Waage; Russell G. Wayland (also Wayland to W. T. Pecora, Dec. 31, 1969, letter); Donald W. Weaver; Alvin C. Weingand; Western Oil and Gas Association; Richard S. Whitehead; John Wightman; A. L. Wirin; Henry W. Wright; Claude E. ZoBell.

AUTHOR'S ACKNOWLEDGMENTS

MANY INDIVIDUALS and organizations have helped in the writing of this book. I thank all of them. I am particularly grateful to Lieutenant George H. Brown, III, of the U.S. Coast Guard, on-scene commander under the National Contingency Plan during the Santa Barbara Oil Spill, and to Fred Hearth, director of the Oil Spill Information Center at the University of California at Santa Barbara, and to the staff members of the Information Center.

I am also particularly grateful to Paul Veblen, executive editor of the *Santa Barbara News-Press,* and to its staff writers, Robert H. Sollen, Larry Pidgeon, Charles Ireland, Steve Sullivan, Walker A. Tompkins, Walter L. Healy, and Barclay Brantingham, and to staff librarian Georga Scheftic. I also wish to acknowledge the work of *Los Angeles Times* writers Philip Fradkin, Robert A. Rosenblatt, Murray Seeger, Robert L. Jackson, Bryce Nelson, Earl W. Foell, Ken Reich, Dial Torgerson, and Leonard Greenwood; also the Associated Press and United Press reports of the Santa Barbara Oil Spill and related events. Santa Barbara radio station KDB and KIST reports and those of television station KEYT were important aids as were those of the national radio-television networks.

A. D. Willard of the California Lands Commission was particularly helpful, as was Henry W. Wright of the Western Oil and Gas Association. W. L. Fillippini, secretary of the Santa Barbara Building and Construction Trades Council, provided much useful information, as did "William R. Robinson." Robinson's name has been fictionalized to protect his privacy. Pearl Chase, for fifty years a leader in Santa Barbara's environmental battles, provided valuable material from her files and recollections, as did Richard S. Whitehead, former Santa Barbara County Planning Director.

Santa Barbara County Supervisors George Clyde and Daniel G. Grant, Santa Barbara Mayor Gerald S. Firestone, City Administrator C. G. Petrie, and Public Works Director R. D. Hogle gave generously of their time and recollections. California State authorities were generously cooperative, as were those at the University of California, at the California Institute of Technology, and at Eleventh Coast Guard District Headquarters, Long Beach, California.

I regret that the Union Oil Company and Peter Bawden Drilling Incorporated declined to be interviewed concerning the spill, citing pending lawsuits as their reason. The same objection was made by the U.S. Geological Survey Oil and Gas Division's Los Angeles Office, which nevertheless provided much useful data in correspondence, as did the Department of the Interior in Washington. Peter M. Flanigan, the White House aide, declined to discuss his involvement in the *Sansenina* affair and in Barracuda Corporation, but the White House Office of Science and Technology was fully cooperative.

The San Francisco regional office of the Federal Water Pollution Control Administration provided much useful information through its public relations director, Vern Tenney.

For unusual aspects of California's oil history, I am indebted to Lawrence Clark Powell's article in the September, 1970, *Westways*, titled "Upton Sinclair's *Oil!*" —and to Sinclair himself, for his important novel, *Oil!*

For unusual aspects of U.S. oil history, Robert Engler's *The Politics of Oil* was valuable. Senator Lee Metcalf's analysis of the ownership of oil stocks by universities has also been helpful.

In addition I wish to acknowledge the many persons—their names listed herein under "Sources"—who gave me information during our interviews. I also thank those who have wished to remain anonymous.

MTA, producers of musical records, and Glaser Publications, Inc., copyright owners, kindly permitted use of the quotation from "Santa Barbara Gold" which appears on page 149.

Alice Kladnik helped prepare the manuscript for publication; and I am grateful to Marvin Levine, Robert Sharp, Norman Sanders,

Gregory W. Brumfiel, Walter J. Mead, Alan A. Allen, Michael Neushul, Joseph Connell, and Kenneth Millar for critical comments. Dick Smith's help with illustrations was invaluable, and the editorial help of Manon Tingue has been similarly essential.

My wife, Jane Faust Easton, contributed ideas, read proof, and was patiently tolerant during nearly three years of work.

R.E.

INDEX

oil industry and, 209-10
report on blowout by, 201-6
responsibilities of, 11, 25, 101
See also Pecora, William T.; Solanas, Donald W.
Germany, 280
Get Oil Out!; *see* GOO
Godfrey, Arthur, 149, 172
Goldberg, Arthur, 242
Goldsmith, Dr. John R., 245
Goleta, 4, 75
GOO (Get Oil Out!), 56, 146, 187, 233, 286
ban on drilling and, 71
Bottoms and, 32, 36, 45, 191
Coast Guard and, 272
disruption opposed by, 144
Feb. 8 rally of, 110-11
guerrilla theater of, 132-33
Hickel and, 50, 223
membership of, 222
Nixon and, 190-91, 223
origin of, 32, 36, 45-46
petition circulated by, 46, 77, 81, 133, 190-91, 223
Platform Hillhouse controversy and, 177-80
representativeness of, 78-79
resumption of drilling and, 159
scientists and, 166, 192
See also Sidenberg, Lois; Weingand, Alvin
GOO TWO, 222
Grant, Daniel G., 18, 20, 79-80, 153
Brown and, 28
channel leases and, 95, 96
delay in notification of, 12
Grant, William E., 104
Gravel, Mike, 65
Grunsky, Donald, 162
Guerrilla theater, 132-33
Gulf of Mexico, spills in, 15, 248
Gulf Oil Corporation, 5, 52, 77, 249

Haider, Michael L., 188
Hall, Gene, 58, 77, 255
Halstead, Bruce, 260
Hamilton, Robert M., 284
Handler, Philip, 286
Hansen, Clifford P., 155
Hardin, Garrett, 275
Harding, Warren G., 132
Harlan, John M., 180
Harris, Ellen Stern, 73-74, 196
Hartley, Fred, 79-80, 122, 138, 149-50, 192, 211, 212

at Air and Water Pollution Subcommittee, 67-69, 73
appearance and personality of, 67-68
leakage control plan of, 155
Hastings, Keith, 128
Hawe, Jack, 55
Hawkins, Murray, Jr., 212
Health, Education, and Welfare, U.S. Department of, 236-37
Healy, Walter, 18
Hellfighters (film), 37
Hemphill, Jack, 264
Hendrick, Kemmis, 275
Herter, Christian A., Jr., 233
Hickel, Walter J., 21, 68, 75, 143, 162, 240
at Air and Water Pollution Subcommittee, 125-26
changes in the policy of, 125-26, 192-93, 234
controversy over nomination of, 48, 108
dismissed by Nixon, 243-44
GOO and, 50, 223
marine sanctuary by, 193
Muskie on, 126
off-shore drilling and
ban on, 50-52, 76, 137, 146
resumption of, 66, 72, 137, 142, 158, 159, 164, 171, 175
off-shore leases suspended by, 119, 234, 279
oil industry and, 108, 137, 213
regulations on leases and drilling issued by, 119, 136, 146, 173
rift between Nixon and, 236, 237
Santa Barbara visit of, 48
team of experts sent by, 35, 42, 44-45
Hill, Gladwin, 275
Hitch, Charles J., 139
Holmes, Robert W., 260
Hood, Daniel E., 60-62
Hoods, plastic, 165
Hoover, Herbert, Jr., 91-92, 127, 210
Hortig, Francis J., 123, 161-62
Hot water, pressurized, 114, 253
House of Representatives, U.S., *see specific committees and congressmen*
HOWCO pumps, 81-82
Huber Corporation, J. M., 146
Humane Society, Santa Barbara, 41
Humble Oil and Refining Company, 52, 93, 106, 166